There was a concerte
street. When Carlisle
instantly r

The Four Horsemen
hundred feet high, we
War, Famine, Pestilence, and Death, armor
gleaming, spear raised, scythe swinging. They
seemed to be galloping full tilt for the Hudson, New
Jersey, and the rest of America. Fire burned from
their horses' nostrils and sparks flew from their
giant hooves.

The sight took Harry's breath away. It was
magnificent.

MICK FARREN

Armageddon Crazy

ORBIT

AN ORBIT BOOK

First published in the USA by Ballantine Books
First published in Great Britain by Sphere Books Ltd 1990

Reproduced, printed and bound in Great Britain by
Cox & Wyman Ltd, Reading

ISBN 0 7474 0470 4

Orbit Books
A Division of
Macdonald & Co (Publishers) Ltd
Orbit House, 1 New Fetter Lane,
London EC4A 1AR
A member of Maxwell Macmillan Pergamon Publishing Corporation

ONE

Mansard

"**N**O ECONOMY CAN SUPPORT AN INSTITUTIONALIZED RE-ligion of this size. It's a matter of simple arithmetic."

Mansard was drunk and he didn't give a damn. Over the last few months, his downtime drinking had been getting worse and worse, but when anyone summoned the courage to say something to him, he simply shrugged and asked them what they expected. In a world that had patently gone crazy, the sane man surely had a moral obligation to shut out as much of the lunacy as possible. He looked slowly around the bar. O'Ryan's was a cheesy joint, but that went for every bar in the city, and probably for every bar in the whole sorry country. He ought to be thankful that there was any kind of bar at all for him in which to lose himself. The return of prohibition had been a major plank in the Faithful/Wrench platform. When they had ridden the landslide into power, however, the idea had been quietly dropped. Someone had whispered in Faithful's ear that, judging from the last time around, the net result of a new Volstead act would be to give an astronomical amount of money to organized crime. Larry Faithful might claim a direct line to God, but in day-to-day practice he was nothing if not the pragmatist. The last thing that he and any of the people around him wanted was to give astronomical amounts of money to anyone outside their circle.

Still, Faithful and his gang had done what they could to discourage the social drinker. The friendly tavern had been reduced to a place of shame. Gone was the warmth and comfort that

Mansard remembered from his youth. All that remained was a flyblown red-and-blue Budweiser sign with a third of its tubes burned out, a rack of bad generic booze on electronic measure, and a line of barstools so patched with gaffer tape that scarcely any of their original fabric remained. The walls were dominated by the legally mandated display signs that reminded patrons of the manifold evils of demon drink. The sound system oozed one after another of the mawkish saccharine neobilly ballads that dominated the top forty. The deacons and even the miserable, vindictive children of the Young Crusaders came through at least twice a night, checking IDs and generally intimidating the customers.

Mansard signaled for another shot.

"It's like the poor goddamned Tibetans," he said to no one in particular. "The whole sad-ass country, which was an uphill struggle at the best of times, fell apart in the mid-twentieth century under the strain of supporting a system in which 60 percent of able-bodied men were engaged in full-time religion. The country starved because its main industry was Buddhism. This country is going the self-same route because our major industry has become Jes-*us*."

The sneering singsong stress on the final word was a clear parody of the Faithful whine. Most of the other people in the bar were avoiding looking at him, trying to pretend that he did not exist. Eddy the bartender was beginning to give him the hard eyeball. Eddy generally tolerated his mouthing off. Mansard did, after all, piss away the bulk of his salary in O'Ryan's and places like it. Only when people got nervous enough to start leaving would Eddy move firmly to shut him down.

That moment was getting very close. A shabby middle-aged couple with furtive faces who, from the look of them, subsisted on the dingy fringe of the black market, were already gathering up their change.

Mansard snarled at them. "What's the matter with you? Am I driving you out?"

The man took the woman's arm protectively as they stood up. They refused even to glance in Mansard's direction. Mansard swayed ominously, half off his stool.

"I'm talking to you."

The man raised a frightened, defensive hand. "Listen, mister, we don't want no trouble. We've got troubles of our own."

" 'Fraid of the thought police? Is that it?"

The couple were edging toward the door. Mansard finished his shot. He doubted that Eddy would give him another.

"You don't have to worry about me. They can't touch me. Charlie Mansard can blaspheme all he wants and there ain't a damn thing the deacons can do about it. You want to know why?"

He received no response, but he went on anyway.

"They can't touch me because they need me too bad. I'm an artist, goddamn it, and they can't do without my art. I make their stinking miracles for them."

Eddy was moving down the bar. The boom was about to be lowered on Charlie Mansard's evening.

Carlisle

The call had come just twenty minutes earlier: There was a bomb in the prayer parlor at the corner of Broadway and Eighth. The caller had identified herself as a Lefthand Path. She had used the antihoax code that was the terrorsect's only compromise with the authorities, so it was close to certain that the call was the real thing. The LPs inevitably meant business and rarely screwed around with false alarms. The data had flashed on the T7 screens as an emergency interrupt; it would have simultaneously been routed to the deacons and the bomb squad. T7, the NYPD's lower Manhattan antiterror task force, worked out of the brand-new Combined Crime Control complex on Astor Place, and there was no excuse for them not being among the first on the scene.

By the time Lt. Harry Carlisle had reached the corner, uniforms had already closed off the streets for three blocks in every direction. Union Square was probably already gridlocked, the traffic beginning to back up all the way to midtown. Carlisle took a deep breath of the crisp autumn air. It was a tense situation, but at least it was real. He was out of the Astor Place complex and temporarily beyond the reach of its internal politics, its paranoia, and its induced religious mania. He had joined the police department to chase criminals, not to absorb a lot of crap about the wrath of God and the punishment to come. Of course, back in the days when he had been a rookie patrolman, life in general had seemed a whole lot simpler. Religion had been a thing that was there on a Sunday morning for those who wanted it. It had not been a virus that infected the whole damned country.

A heavily armored blue-and-white bomb-squad truck with black-and-yellow warning bars on its rear doors was pulling up beside the prayer parlor in a flurry of lights and sirens. Reeves and Donahue, also from T7, were already there. They were standing well back, keeping a healthy distance between themselves and any possible explosion. It was the members of the bomb squad who were paid to risk their lives. T7 sifted for clues once the danger was over.

The bomb squad, in full blast armor, was off-loading its ATCO J40 search robot. The prayer parlor was one of the Good Shepherd chain, the biggest franchise east of the Mississippi. In Harry Carlisle's estimation, the prayer parlor was one of the rinkiest of dinky ideas in an ultimately rinky dink epoch. If a person wanted to talk to God, all he had to do was to plastic in, duck into a pod, and wait while his credit was checked out. If his plastic was good, the opaque cover closed and he was free, in seeming privacy, to mutter his specific needs, hidden fears, or darkest confessions into the nativity-blue microphone that was supposed to lead directly to the ear of the Almighty. The sense of privacy was illusory. The microphone also led to the deacons' central records complex in Virginia Beach. Each individual's desires, fantasies, and shameful little sins were collated, analyzed, and data-shaped. If no other action was taken, they would finally be downloaded into the memory banks by which the Good Lord, with the help of his everpresent secret police force, kept his flock on the straight and narrow. According to the deacons, God could never get enough data.

Of course, the deacons paid through the nose for their tap into the heavenly hotline. It was supposed to be a closely guarded secret, but anyone in the know was well aware that annual user fees garnered by Good Shepherd Inc. alone ran into the hundreds of millions. The deacon hierarchy would have been overjoyed to cut out the middleman and run the prayer parlors itself, but not even the deacons could walk over the fundamental principles of Christian free enterprise. Government and even religion were supposed to stay off the back of business. Thus the deacons had to lease their access to the data matrix from the franchise owners.

The robot swayed down the ramp that led out of the back of the bomb-squad truck. There were wisps of blue smoke coming from the small rotary engine set between its two sets of treads. That did not bode well. Harry Carlisle scowled. The deacons got everything they wanted while the regular cops, who in his estimation did the dirty, day-to-day work of law enforcement, had to operate with hardware that was little more than obsolete garbage. There was hardly anything in the department that was not held together with epoxy and duct tape.

The deacons themselves had arrived on the scene. Two of their big black Lincoln Continentals were nosing through the police barriers to stop on the corner of Tenth Street. They, too, were keeping their distance. The doors opened, and eight deacons climbed out of the two cars. They were the standard issue: cold-faced young men in dark suits so alike that they were virtually a uniform. Although he could not see from where he was standing, Carlisle knew that they were wearing the tiny gold crucifix insignia in their lapels. He reached the spot where Reeves and Donahue were standing and nodded to the two detectives.

Reeves grimaced. "That J40 looks about to burn out."

"So what else is new?"

Carlisle checked his tracy. When it finally came on line, the small wrist screen showed a robot-eye view of the entrance to the Good Shepherd. The robot lumbered forward. Carlisle flicked the channel changer with the nail of his index finger. The image changed to a closeup of the bomb-squad officer who was monitoring the operation from inside the truck.

The man glanced impatiently into the screen. "What do you want, Lieutenant? I kind of got my hands full here."

The man's name was Vargas. One of the last holdout Catholics on the force, he would probably never make it past sergeant. The two men were not friends, but they knew each other by sight, and there was a certain mutual respect.

"Is that robot of yours going to hold up?" Carlisle asked.

"How the hell should I know?"

"Shouldn't talk like that with deacons around."

"Believe me. I've got more shit to worry about than petty blasphemy."

"We could really use a bomb that was defused and intact— anything that could give us a lead."

"I'm doing the best I can."

Vargas cut the connection, and Carlisle's screen once again showed the view from the robot. It was inside the prayer parlor, running on its redscope and moving slowly along the row of pods. The Good Shepherd was a big joint as prayer parlors went—a full two dozen pods. There was the heat image of a human figure inside the pod at the very end of the line.

"What the hell is that? I thought the place had been cleared."

Vargas' voice boomed and crackled from the robot's speakers. "Come out of there right now with your hands in plain sight!"

The reply was picked up by the robot. It was a man's voice, weakly amplified.

"Jesus won't let me be harmed."

"Christ, we got a nut in there. How did you morons manage to miss him?" Vargas was back on the wrist screen again. "We'll have to get some uniforms in there to drag him out. Goddamn lunatic."

A uniformed officer whom Carlisle did not know was on the screen. "My men can't go in there. They don't have any armor."

Vargas was cursing in Spanish as he sent in his own men. The deacons remained aloof and silent throughout the entire exchange. There was a confusion of heat images on the tracy. The nut was screaming about sacrilege and damnation, and then abruptly he stopped. One of the bomb squad must have chopped him out with armored gloves that could quiet just about anyone. The robot was on the move again, sniffers going. Within seconds, the bomb location symbol was flashing. Then the screen snowed. The J40 had malfunctioned.

"Now we're screwed," Vargas said.

"How long to detonation?" Carlisle asked.

"Six minutes, if the warning call was on the money." Vargas was shaking his head. "I can't send in any of my men."

One of the bomb squad cut in. "It's Massey, chief. I'm still inside, and I'm on the device."

"Get out of there."

"I think I can drop the sucker."

"Don't try it. There's no time."

"It looks like a couple of keys of juiced plastique with a simple d-style timer. It's in a supermarket bag. A&P."

"Timer got a readout?"

"Yeah."

"How long to go?"

"Four forty-two and counting."

"So get out of there."

"I tell you I can down it."

"Forget it!"

"I can do it, Sarge."

"Give me the bomb location."

"It's under the seat in one of the booths."

"Which one?"

"Hang on, I can't read the numbers . . . It's seven. Booth number seven."

"Just look in the bag. Don't touch a thing."

"I'm looking."

"And?"

"There's no sign of a trembler. I'm going to try to get it out of the bag."

The explosion left Carlisle deaf for thirty seconds. Flying glass had cut his cheek. Reeves had been hurled to the ground. The glass was like a carpet of fresh, glittering hail that stretched for a block and a half in every direction. Windows were gone from buildings all around the intersection. The deacons were sheltering behind their Lincolns. Flames were licking inside the ruined shell of the prayer parlor. Debris showered down. There was no longer a link with Vargas in the truck. Carlisle started running. The back doors of the truck burst open, and Vargas staggered out, pulling off his protective helmet and shaking his head. It would turn out that his hearing was permanently impaired.

Speedboat

Speedboat waited until well after dark before he decided to leave the apartment on Avenue C. The girl was out cold on the bare mattress. She had been packing away bootleg doomers all the previous night and was in a world of her own. A tiny trail of spittle ran from the corner of her mouth. He could hardly believe that just eighteen hours earlier he had figured her to be the hottest thing on spikes. For an hour he had sat on the rusting fire escape and watched the bloodred sun going down over the buildings. There had been an explosion earlier that had sounded like a bomb. Probably some cult bombing—if there really were cults. Sometimes he wondered if the deacons didn't plant the bombs themselves to give them the excuse for more purges.

He found the apartment altogether too oppressive. It was just too witchy. The broad was full doombeam, and had all the spooky crap that those people felt they had to surround themselves with. The broken dolls; the ropes of beads hanging from rusty nails; the fans and feathers; the tattered, one-eyed stuffed owl; the crumbling building itself—all added up to a particularly defeated strain of spiritual decay that Speedboat was willing to skirt in the course of business but in which he never wanted to become completely immersed. Her violently disturbing collages, made of plates ripped from medical textbooks juxtaposed against mutilated images from twentieth-century girlie books, were more than enough to convince him. If the dekes ever kicked their way in there, they would have a field day with her artwork. She would probably wind up in Joshua.

Winding up in Joshua was something he, above all, wanted to avoid. One could die in the camps. That was why he waited for the cover of big-city darkness. It was not just simple paranoia either. When he left the place, he would be carrying more than enough contraband to make him dead meat if he was picked up by a prowler. Behind the strip of false baseboard, he had stashed a small fortune in pornosoft and a dozen proscribed audio discs from the '80s and '90s. The latter included a couple of Billy Idols and a mint Motorhead. The old packrat Metal Monster on Third Street would pay premium for those, while Manny on St. Marks would give him a good price for the hardsoft in-out. All in all, he should realize some seven hundred on the evening's running. That, in turn, would be enough to get him a hundred Haitian spansules from Jook Aroun, which he could straightaway peddle in the rat traps for twenty a pop. Escape to Canada was nearing reality, but as it did, anxiety made quantum leaps. Nothing must go wrong.

The sun had gone, and the block beyond the airshaft was a black silhouette against a deep red sky. Speedboat did not turn on the light but just sat in the gathering gloom, staring at the shape of the girl on the mattress. She had told him that she had been a phone whore for nine months. That was probably enough to have flipped her over all on its own, sitting there and listening night after night while the holy bastards with the jobs and the plastic spewed out the sump poison of their God-fearing psyches. He could imagine them crouching in dark rooms, muttering their equally dark fantasies to a girl at the end of an anonymous phone. It was a world where everything had to be hidden from the light. Speedboat had stopped getting angry about it a long time ago. He was getting out.

He realized that he himself was crouching in a dark room. It was time to go to work. He carefully closed the drapes before he turned on the light. The single unshaded bulb made him blink. The girl muttered something and turned over, but she did not wake. Speedboat watched her for a moment, then stooped down and removed his contraband from its hiding place. He had to distribute it around his body—carrying any kind of a bag was asking for trouble. The diskettes of pornosoft were no problem. They would fit into any of the dozen or so secret pockets of his old, stained military parka. The audio discs were a bit more of a problem. The only place where they would fit was in the large pocket just below his shoulder blades. Even then, they were sufficiently bulky that there was a risk they might produce a telltale outline, even in the deliberately voluminous olive drab. He would have to chance it and try to walk with his shoulders back instead of up around his ears as he normally did.

He started down the stairs on silent Reeboks that had cost him an entire bag of yellow octagonals down on Delancey Street. He paused for a moment in front of the street door. He opened it a crack. Nothing on the street looked out of place. The box people were setting up their homes, and a couple of fires had been lit. That was usually a good sign that there was no law about. A couple of the streetlights were out. He ran a hand through his close-cropped suedecut and slipped out into the dark.

Winters

Deacon Winters put down the phone with a sigh. The sweep of the crime scene had given the lab boys exactly nothing. It was the third LP bomb in a month and it had gone off right on the corner of Broadway and Eighth, within walking distance of the Astor Place CCC complex where he was based. Three of the bomb squad were dead, and no one was even a fraction closer to identifying the terrorcult. There was bound to be another internal inquiry, and as one of the investigative team assigned to the case he would find himself being asked a lot of questions to which he had no answers.

He wanted to slam his fist into the desk, and it was only with the greatest of effort that he restrained himself. Any such display of temper would be picked up by the surveillance cameras and go down on his record. It would indicate that the Peace of the Lord was definitely not upon him. Being suspected of having a potential low-stress quotient was a black mark that he could do without. He had enough problems already. The very last thing he needed was to slip any farther down the ladder of departmental grace. Not even the long hours of visible public prayer at the Deacon Tabernacle on Seventy-third Street seemed to help. After all the kneetime for the cameras, it still had been a nightmare of a week, and it was only Wednesday. The efficiency ratings and devotion assessments had been released on Monday morning, and he had showed up well down in the pack.

When he had transferred from Cleveland to New York City, he had had the reputation of being a bright and promising young man with an equally bright future. The New York deacons had a policy of recruiting their young officers from the heartland, where youths supposedly were untainted by the Babylonian evils of the metropolis. Once they were in the city, though, they were expected to shine. Winters was not shining. In fact, he was floundering. The inquiry after this latest bombing might actually turn that floundering into a state of full-scale drowning. He could not even see a way that he could pass some of the buck onto the NYPD task force. He had played that card twice already.

Back in Ohio, he had woven small-town, TV dreams about high-city law enforcement. While he had chased minor-league pornographers and teenagers fooling around with petty Satanism, he had played with romantic images. He pictured himself kicking down doors with a machine pistol clutched in his fist, smiting the ungodly, bringing the terrorists and heretics to justice, and generally making the world a safe place for decent, God-fearing people. Those comic-book scenarios had been destroyed in the first flaming crash of his innocence. In the eleven months that Winters had been in New York, he had not kicked down a single door. He had not even so much as drawn an automatic weapon from the armory. He had been buried in an avalanche of cross-referential data. He tracked and matched minor details and ran patterns looking for possible anomalies. The most drama that ever came his way was provided by the spying and backbiting of internal politics. It was a long way from the heady excitement of swashbuckling, more akin to the constant numbing fear of walking the edge of a razor or swimming in a tank of man-eating sharks.

The phone rang. It was Carlisle from the NYPD team. The debris from the explosion had gone to the deacons' lab, and he wanted to access the results. No doubt he was also looking for a clue to what, if anything, Winters or the other deacons might be planning to pull when the reports went in. Winters did not trust Carlisle. The way the man played the world-weary street cop only barely concealed a deep-seated contempt for the established religion. Winters inwardly toyed with an image of Carlisle in the pit. On the phone, he adopted a closed and neutral tone.

"They've come up with nothing so far," he told the cop.

On the other end of the phone, Carlisle sounded as if he did not believe him. Winters gave just a fraction. Carlisle was probably a closet heretic, but Winters had to do business with him.

"Of course, I'll let you know immediately if they do find anything."

Carlisle grunted and hung up. Winters silently vowed that one day he would get the NYPD officer. Making empty, unheard threats, though, did not help too much. He was still in a vise and he had no way that he could see to stop it from closing on him. He stared across the large open-plan squad room with its beige walls and bright panel lights that made it look like an aquarium. Orderly lines of dark-suited figures hunched over blue-gray computer terminals. Overhead, the small, black watch cameras with their glowing red LEDs swiveled from side to side, scanning the people below like inquisitive birds. The watch cameras were the electronic eyes of the Lord. All was seen and all was noted. Winters picked up a pencil, trying to give the appearance of doing something. Unfortunately, there was nothing that he could do except wait and pray for a break in the case. If that break failed to materialize, the case would undoubtedly break him.

Cynthia Kline walked by his desk carrying a sheaf of print-outs. In her mid to late twenties, she kept her chestnut hair swept back into a tight bun and wore little or no makeup; her only jewelry was a pair of discreet gold earrings. Yet even in the severe and unflattering tailoring of her clerical auxiliary uniform, there was something about the way she moved, the way she carried her slim, athletic figure, that caused Winters to observe her covertly whenever she was in the junior deacons' squad room. She had never smiled at him or even given him any indication that she was aware of his existence. There was no way he could think that she was somehow encouraging him in the lusts of the flesh. The problem was that his interest was not

limited to simple observation. Despite all his efforts, he could
not stop his imagination, could not stop the dark thoughts and
images that crept into his inner mind. The most vivid picture
was straight out of a proscribed magazine: Cynthia Kline
stripped down to scanty silk lingerie, standing on tiptoe, arms
stretched above her head, wrists secured by leather thongs. He
shook his head as if trying physically to dislodge the vision. He
found that his palms were sweating. Get behind me, Satan.
He realized that if anyone could read his thoughts, his career
would be over.

After the first couple of times he had seen Cynthia Kline, he
had accessed her departmental records. All he had gotten were
prints and a picture and a few short paragraphs of background.
He had attempted to go further, to get through to her personal
file, home address, and recruitment investigation report, but he
had run into a privacy block. The computer had demanded an
AC-19 clearance and details of how the required data applied to
an ongoing investigation. Not wanting to draw attention to himself, Winters had garbaged the request. Unfortunately the images of Cynthia Kline had not gone away. If anything, they had
become more intense. If they did not go away soon, he would
be forced to go to see one of those women on Fifteenth Street
again.

Kline

Cynthia Kline walked quickly out of the junior deacons' squad
room and headed for the elevators. She needed a cup of coffee
and maybe an illicit cigarette in the women's rest room. She was
certain that little bastard Bernie Winters had been staring at her
again. There was something creepy about those large pale-blue
eyes under the blond brushcut. He was so typical of the repressed, small-town kid who enlisted in the deacons. On one
level, they believed that they were the wrath of God, but deeper
down they were constantly at war with themselves, so constantly
on the run from their perfectly normal impulses that they ended
up being twisted out of shape by the conflict and the shame.
There was probably nothing more sinister to Winters' stares
than the usual banked-up horniness, but he still made her nervous. She kept reminding herself that she had encountered more
than enough of it in the four months since the organization had

planted her as a sleeper in the clerical auxiliary of the deacons. Her nervousness could probably be chalked up to the fact that Winters was part of the team that was actually hunting the Left-hand Path. The team appeared to be getting nowhere, but if it ever did get lucky and blow the organization apart, she would be one of the first to be arrested. If they did not hang her out-right, she would certainly die slowly in Joshua or one of the other camps.

In the third-floor women's rest room, a burly, masculine di-rectoress was inspecting her eyebrows in the mirror over the line of sinks. As Cynthia entered, the woman turned and gave her an unmistakably appraising look. She treated Cynthia to a half smile. "Praise the Lord, my dear."

Cynthia nodded absently and avoided the woman's eyes. "Yes . . . praise the Lord."

It was damn lucky that paranoia and prudery looked so much alike. The women in the female branch of the deacons seemed a good deal less repressed than their male counterparts.

The door closed behind the directoress, and Cynthia Kline allowed herself a silent sigh of relief. She let herself into a stall, dumped the pile of printouts that she was taking up to the twenty-third floor on the cistern, and rummaged for her pack of ciga-rettes. The twenty-third floor could wait. Policy frowned on the idea of deacons, directoresses, or even the clerical auxiliary smoking or drinking, but an official blind eye was turned to the odd smoke in the bathroom. No one could be perfect all the time.

When she was through, she dropped the butt in the toilet bowl and flushed, then emerged from the stall to find a senior clerical assistant sniffing the air with a disapproving expression.

"Your body is a temple of the Lord, my dear. It's a shame to pollute it with nicotine."

Cynthia nodded. "I know, but it's been a rough day."

"Some days are like that. I'd pray about it if I was you." The woman started to vigorously wash her hands.

Cynthia wondered how much more she could take. It was very tempting to just give it all up and run for Canada. In the beginning, what she was doing had seemed like a noble mis-sion—to actually go undercover, right into the very heart of the enemy, even maybe to turn key deacons. She had felt like a modern Mata Hari fighting for the return to sanity. The reality had turned out be something very different. She was on assignment at the heart of the disease. She was starting to believe that if she stayed around those people much longer she would finish up as crazy as they were.

There was commotion outside in the corridor. Uniformed NYPD in full riot gear were milling in front of the elevators waiting for a descending car. Another clerical auxiliary was standing back against the wall letting them go by. Cynthia did the same thing.

"What's the panic?" she asked.

"Bread riot at a supermarket."

"Where?"

"A&P at Twentieth and Eighth."

"Deliveries didn't happen?"

"Something like that."

Cynthia Kline cursed under her breath. It was uncomfortably close to where she lived on Ninth Avenue. She might well have problems getting home. Suddenly she caught herself. Something was happening to her attitude. There had been a time when she would have been overjoyed at a bombing and a riot in the same day. It would have been proof that the regime was really coming unglued. But events like this had become mere nuisances. She needed to watch herself.

1346408 Stone

1346408 Stone lay motionless on the hard plastic mattress and stared at the underside of the bunk above. Every fifteen seconds it was illuminated by the glare of the searchlight on the south gun tower. His body ached all over, and his stomach was cramping again. After the bosses had found the radio, the rations had been cut for everyone in D block. The evening meal was down to half a cup of the pink goop and three slices of Wonder Bread. 4321921 Gotti, who had actually had the radio hidden in his mattress, had been dragged off to the bunker for three weeks' intensified. There was a great deal of speculation as to whether he would make it back. Since the radio had gone, a deep gloom had settled over the block. The radio, on which Gotti had picked up the news out of Canada, had been more than just a lifeline to the world beyond the wire of the Joshua Redemption Center. It was also more than just an antidote to the pap of game shows and preachers and the constant claptrap about Jesus, punishment, and repentance that blared from the TV from the moment the working parties returned to the barrack block clear through until lights-out sounded. It was a small but defiant symbol of the fact that the system had not totally broken them. It was hard to accept that their symbol was gone.

Stone's mind felt numb. He was convinced that they were putting hexapan in the food again. He wriggled in a vain attempt to get comfortable on the mattress and immediately let out a groan. His ribs were bruised on the left side where Boss Carter had lashed out with his billy club. Stone had not even been doing anything wrong. Everyone knew that Carter was a psycho who got his jollies inflicting pain. There was a scream from over in the women's section. Someone else was getting their kicks. The women suffered more at the hands of the guards than the men did. For a penal system that put such emphasis on morality, it harbored an extraordinary number of deviants.

Despite the fact that he was exhausted, sleep would not come. A few bunks away, someone was muttering in the throes of a bad dream. Someone else was coughing. That was probably 8368728 Katz. The general opinion was that Katz did not have much longer to go. After fourteen days in the bunker, he had come back with damaged lungs that had been getting progressively worse.

Stone closed his eyes. He could feel the anger building inside of him. It was the anger that had sustained him through the nineteen months that he had been in Joshua. During that time, he had learned that anger was something that could not just be squandered. If a person let it run loose as an unchecked rage, it either slowly consumed him or built up until he exploded in some suicidal outburst, until he attacked a guard or walked into the electrified wire. Anger was a thing that had to be conserved. It could not be allowed to blaze bright; but, on the other hand, if the spark went out, then one was nothing but an obedient zombie. Above all anger had to be focused and directed. It was fatally easy just to hate the immediate instruments of oppression, to center a bitter loathing on the guards or the deacons, or to silently rail against big generalities. It was too simple to hate the Fundamentalists or a figurehead like Faithful, or to damn all Christians and their bloody religion.

Hating Christianity was an easy trap to fall into. It even defied logic. The number of Christians shut up in Joshua, the stubborn, passive resisters who had been among the first to challenge

Faithful and his tyranny, were more than ample proof that the whole philosophy could not be held responsible for the few that used its trappings to cloak their evil. It made no more sense than cursing all Moslems for the acts of the few fanatics who had touched off the Gulf War. The second trap to avoid was the urge to hate oneself. In this one did not have much help from logic. It was easy for Stone to demonstrate to himself that, without his own unbelieving complacency and that of those like him, Faithful and his gang would never have been able to do what they did. He was one of the ones who had been too busy congratulating themselves for their sanity and liberalism to notice what was going on, the ones who had made the mistake of assuming that, whatever happened, things would remain within the limits of civilized behavior. By the time they had discovered their error, it was far too late.

It had all started with the collapse of '98. The banks had run the economy to the edge in the hope that a threat of global currency panic would finally unseat the Democrats and kill off the Second Chance once and for all. Unfortunately, Rilker and his cronies, backed up by a generation of ex-Reagan yuppies panicked by early middle age, overestimated both their own strength and the monstrous inertia of the world's money system. They had managed to push the economy to the edge because that was easy—it had been drifting in that direction for half a century. When it got there, no power on Earth was capable of stopping it, and it plunged over. The crash of '98 was followed by the wide-eyed panic of '99, and the economic chaos became coupled with the superstitious upheavals that tended to erupt at the turn of any century. The country was paralyzed by fears, both real and imagined, and ready to follow anyone who offered a way out. Faithful did not even have to claim a vision with which he would lead them to the promised land. All he had to promise was to get Jesus to intervene and stop the rot. The election of the year 2000 was a landslide.

At first it had looked like business as usual. The quality of television had dropped markedly, but most of the smart set had put that down to the movement of the public into one of its infantile phases. Van Der Kamp had just had the big, summer, nonfiction bestseller with *Cycle/Social*. The TV evangelists had been shucking and jiving all over the place, but that was also easy to dismiss. Everyone assumed that if they were allowed to run, they would eventually make themselves ridiculous just as they had before. The censorship battles that flared up on a number of fronts were so scattered and protracted that nobody was really able to focus on them as a single campaign. It was hard to equate *Wet Bimbo Magazine* with *The Catcher in the Rye*. When the antiabortion amendment was pushed through a totally intimidated Congress, protesters took to the streets, but their efforts were largely negated by a total media blank. When the more militant pressed their point, the marches and sitdowns were broken up by police with clubs, tear gas, and water cannons. Many of them became a part of the first mass jailings.

It was over a year before the situation touched Stone personally. *Reality*, the magazine for which he wrote, was closed down, and the editors were charged with sedition. After that, no other publication seemed willing to hire a left-of-center columnist with his kind of track record. He went to work as a copywriter for Mandell, Jenkins, and Howard, the advertising agency. The money was okay, better in fact than he had been making at *Reality*. He kept his head down and tried to pretend that everyone would eventually come to their senses. Things were going okay, if one did not count his inability to sleep well, until they landed the TLC account. As the biggest of the booming evangelical conglomerates, TLC was able to swing a lot of muscle. All employees of the agency were expected to sign something called the "Six Minimal Articles of Faith." When Stone started muttering about McCarthyism, he was immediately fired. He wound up flipping burgers and working with a small group that put out a Xeroxed samzat. Then the Young Crusaders had come around and smashed their copying equipment.

The mask had come off during the summer of 2004, "The Summer of the Three Crises." In those three months of manufactured panic, Faithful and his gang had made their moves. A terrified Congress had suspended the Constitution and then dissolved itself. With nothing to stop them, the administration had started rewriting the rules. The Heresy and Blasphemy Laws were enacted, and the deacons were formed. The redemption centers, concentration camps by any other name, were under construction. By the fall, the country was as fully fledged a religious police state as Iran had been under the Ayatollahs. It had taken Hitler some five years to change the face of Germany. Faithful had done it to America in just three. Of course, he had had some heavy hitters helping him. The Orange County Ring had been behind him from the start and the multinationals had at least used him as natural cover while they transferred their U.S. operations to Brazil or Australia. Stone often wondered if those passive, corporate collaborators should not have been the real targets for his hate and anger.

After the start of 2005, there was no pretending. All over, people were leaving for Canada and Europe. Stone had applied for a passport, but he had been turned down. His record at Mandell, Jenkins, and Howard was given as the reason. Even then, he thought that he could make it through the system. Instead of going on the run, he filed an appeal. The major waves of mass arrests did not start until the spring of that year. Whole neighborhoods were sealed as accused heretics were dragged to the black windowless deacon buses. When Shea Stadium was full they had started taking the detainees across the river to the Meadowlands. There were horror stories on the streets about beatings and summary executions. Finally Stone did run, heading for Canada. He did quite well for an amateur. He made it to Buffalo before they caught him. After two and a half months on Rikers Island, he was shipped to Joshua. He had never had a trial, and his sentence was indeterminate. He wore the green patch of a second-degree heretic on his striped uniform.

The light from the south gun tower was starting to hypnotize him. It was getting difficult to think. They had to have started putting hexapan in the food again. A dull and far from comforting insulation was wrapping itself around the hunger, the aches, and the anger. He felt himself slipping. He only hoped that the drug would suppress the nightmares.

Carlisle

Harry Carlisle came out of the elevator on the rear ground floor and ran straight into the riot squad. They were moving out in force, loading onto the armored trucks. The Pharaohs were already lumbering up from the underground motorpool, belching diesel smoke. The uniforms were loaded for bear with body armor, full helmets, gas masks, and squat black riot guns, over and under, Remington Controllers, with the new forearm clamp that made it possible to use the weapon with one hand. One in every five had been issued with a pepper fog generator. A water cannon came up the ramp between the Pharaohs.

Carlisle grabbed the nearest patrolman. "What the hell is all this? World War III?"

The armored patrolman, anonymous behind his visor, glanced briefly at the lieutenant. "Big 9-79 up on Twentieth."

"It don't rain but it pours."

"Don't it just."

The patrolman was gone, scrambling into the dark interior of a Pharaoh. Harry Carlisle was on the rear ground floor only because that was where one had to change elevators to get to subbasement four, the restricted-access area where the deacons conducted their depth interrogations. Normally, Carlisle would not have gone anywhere near subbasement four. The deacons' idea of depth was more than enough to turn his stomach. Nevertheless, despite his stomach, he had hurried on down after hearing that the headcase—the one who had been dragged from the prayer parlor shouting for Jesus just before the bomb exploded—had been taken down there. Carlisle wanted to talk to him before they beat him stupid. There was always a chance that he had seen the bomber.

Carlisle eased his way through the milling riot squad, making for the single elevator door that would take him down to Sb4. Their excitement was infectious. He could feel their adrenaline rising. They were working themselves up to bust heads. A food riot inevitably turned ugly.

The elevator was guarded by a junior deacon in black combat fatigues. He carried an Uzi slung under his right arm, and his face wore an expression of blank, all-encompassing hostility. "There's no admission."

Carlisle was not going to stand for that attitude. "There is for me, sonny boy."

"You think so?"

Harry took out his ID plate. "Run by this."

The deacon took the card, making clear his obvious contempt for the ordinary police department ID. He stuck it into the slot. The green light immediately came on. The deacon shrugged. "It looks like you can go on in."

Harry Carlisle gave the young man a hard look. "You should watch those manners of yours, kid. I seriously outrank you."

The deacon came to approximation of attention. "I'm sorry, sir. It's hard to tell."

Carlisle shot him a bleak look as the elevator door opened. At the bottom of the shaft there was another guard.

"Can I help you?"

"The man they brought in after the Eighth Street bombing, where have they got him?"

"ID?"

Carlisle handed over his card for a second ID check. The deacons were very particular about whom they let into their torture chamber. Again the light flashed green. The card was handed back.

"Interrogation room five. Along to your right. You can't miss it."

The headcase was doubled over with his arms pulled up hard behind him. His manacled wrists were secured to an overhead pipe by a short length of chain. Blood was dripping from the tip of his nose, creating a spattered puddle on the floor. The walls, floor, and ceiling of the interrogation room were covered with hard, washable plastic, so the place could be hosed down after use. The prisoner was surrounded by three deacons in gray sweatsuits that were also spattered with blood. The word "Zealots," along with a clenched-fist symbol, was silkscreened across the back of each sweat top. The Zealots were the New York deacons football team. They had won the interdepartmental championship for four years running. They also turned football into a bloodsport.

One of the interrogators lifted the prisoner's head by the hair so he could look into his face. "Shall we try that again?"

The headcase spluttered. Blood ran down his chin. "The Devil was in me. The Devil was in this body."

"And how did you recognize the Devil?"

A second interrogator joined in. "Confess it all and save your soul."

Carlisle looked on in disgust. "What exactly do you three expect to achieve by torturing a loony?" he asked.

"This is none of your concern, Carlisle. This is a devotional matter. It's moved from the temporal to the spiritual."

"Yeah, sure. That old-time religion."

The loony's head was allowed to drop. The three interrogators turned to face Carlisle. He knew all three of them. Baum, Bickerton, and Kinney. The trio had a reputation throughout the CCC for extreme brutality. Although they all held the same rating, Bickerton was the apparent leader of the holy trio. He was also the Zealots' quarterback.

"You just stepped out onto very thin ice, Carlisle."

Baum joined in. The linebacker, he tended to be the blunt one. "Your own state of grace could be investigated."

Kinney brought up the rear. He played tight end. "What do you want here, Carlisle?"

"I was hoping that I could question this witness about the bombing. There was just a chance he might have seen something." Carlisle looked around coldly. "I can see that I'm wasting my time. You've made him altogether too spiritual."

"I'm glad you recognize you're wasting your time."

Baum was holding a short, leather-covered billy. He prodded the prisoner with it and grinned. "A soul that has become so complex in its sin requires a great deal of saving."

Carlisle shook his head. "I hope you manage it."

"All it takes is a comprehensive confession and an acceptance of Jesus."

The loony's bloody mouth was moving slackly. "Jesus . . . Jesus . . ."

Harry Carlisle turned on his heel and left. The guard at the bottom of the elevator shaft called after him as he passed.

"See enough, did you, Lieutenant?"

Carlisle had to contain his fury until he was in the privacy of his own office. The bastards thought what they were doing was amusing. They tortured a harmless mental case and thought that they were funny. When he reached his cubicle on the tenth floor, he roared in like an express train, slamming the door as hard as he could. There was a pint of Wild Turkey with an inch left in it in the bottom drawer of his desk. He swallowed the bourbon in three angry gulps and then hurled the bottle into the wastebasket with enough force to shatter it. Then he stood and glared up into the watching lens of the surveillance camera.

It was only when his anger had subsided a little that he realized what he had missed. And then he was mad at himself.

He opened the door and yelled. "McNeil, I want the bombsquad audio from this afternoon. The last dialogue between Vargas and Massey, immediately before the bomb went off."

Winters

Winters's phone startled him. He grabbed for it as if it were dangerous. "Winters," he said abruptly.

"This is Lieutenant Carlisle. Will you come up to ten, please, Winters? I think I may have found something."

"Perhaps you could tell me over the phone."

"Just get your ass up here."

Winters swallowed. He wanted to tell the flatfoot to take a jump, but once again he reminded himself that, in his position, he could not afford a conflict with the PD. Carlisle could easily make him look bad at a progress inquiry. He hung up the phone and logged himself out to the tenth floor. When he arrived at Carlisle's office, the lieutenant had a small audioplayer on the desk in front of him.

Carlisle hit the PLAY button. "I want you to listen to this."

His voice was soft, but there was a certain built-in menace. Winters noted that the PD had not invited him to sit down. The tape was from earlier in the afternoon. Vargas, the bomb-squad coordinator, was talking on the radio with one of his men, Massey, the one who had blown himself up trying to down the bomb.

"Give me the bomb location."

"It's under the seat in one of the booths."

"Which one?"

"Hang on, I can't read the number . . . it's seven. Booth number seven."

"Just look in the bag. Don't touch a thing."

"I'm looking."

Carlisle cut it off. "Notice anything?"

"What am I supposed to be looking for?"

"The bomb was in booth number seven."

"Right."

"So what does that tell us?"

Winters was aware that he was being tested, but he could not imagine what Carlisle was driving at. The detective had hard, tired blue eyes with lines fanning out from the corners as if he had spent too much of his time squinting at things that did not please him. They were eyes that could produce the illusion that they were looking directly into his soul. Winters had heard that there was some kind of scandal in Carlisle's past, but he had never been able to access the details. Sweet Jesus, if only he could prove that the man was an agent of Satan.

"I don't know. What does it tell us?"

"That the bomber must have activated the booth in order to get into it and plant the bomb. He would have had to act like any other confessee."

Carlisle's tone indicated that he believed he was talking to a simpleton. Winters again reminded himself that one day he would get the man. "So?"

"So the bomber must have used either cash or plastic to get into the booth, and there's an outside chance that he may have said something while he was in there. Every prayer booth in the country is wired into deacon central. There must be a record of it somewhere in the Virginia Beach facility, and I want you to access it."

"I don't know."

Carlisle looked at him coldly. "What don't you know?"

"I'd need an AC-19."

"So get one. There's the terminal."

Access to the Virginia Beach data banks was one of the deacons' most jealously guarded secrets. The Virginia Beach computers contained the files of God. With great reluctance, he sat down in front of the lieutenant's terminal. He did not have to be told that this tenuous lead was all they had, but it still went against the grain to have to access into Virginia Beach for a mere PD. He menued up an AC-19 application and started to respond to the lengthy questionnaire. When it was complete, the computer considered it for about fifteen seconds and then let him in. While Carlisle watched him, Winters went after the data. Finally he had it. It was less than enlightening.

He slowly shook his head. "Booth seven could be cash activated."

"Go further. He or she must have been the last person to use the booth before the explosion."

"You think it might be a woman?"

"It's a fifty–fifty chance. There's plenty of broads with no cause to love the regime."

"How do you know the bomber was the last one to use the booth?"

"He would have had to have been. He couldn't risk anyone finding the bomb. The placing of it must have been coordinated with the phone call and an intelligent guess at our response time."

"Or he just listened for the sirens."

"Maybe. It's still a pretty slick setup."

"You think so?"

"This ain't no bunch of pinhead Satanists. These people are

classic terrorists. If they weren't pretty slick, we'd know something about them by now.''

''They do keep themselves well hidden.''

''What we want to do now is to get the tape of the last session in the booth. If it was a cash payment our bomber would still have at least to enter some kind of name. Can you do that?''

''Sure.''

Winters went further in.

''I've got it,'' he said a short time later. ''I'll run it on audio.''

There was the sound of the booth cover closing. Then there was a voice. It was that of a robot.

Carlisle and Winters looked at each other.

''He's talking through one of those kid's toys,'' Winters said. ''They completely distort the voice print.''

''Shut up and listen.''

''. . . and by the time you hear this, you'll know all about why we were here. We are the Lefthand Path and we will not cease our actions until the Faithful tyranny is overthrown. You're probably wondering where we will strike next. I can't exactly tell you that but keep watching the skies.''

Carlisle was half smiling. ''Definitely slick.''

Winters looked carefully at the lieutenant. It was almost as if Carlisle admired those sinners.

TWO

Mansard

CHARLIE MANSARD HAD A KILLER HANGOVER. THE CIGArette was all but burning his fingers, and he was on his third cup of coffee. He glowered at his secretary. "I've got to have some speed. I can't do Arlen Proverb at the Garden without speed."

Rita Webb shook her head. "I told you after the last time. I don't get drugs for you anymore."

"I could fire you."

"You won't fire me. I'm the only one who'll tolerate you."

"Damn it, woman, I'm dying here. I need medication."

"The last thing you need is an amphetamine. It turns you into a psychotic, and you're quite likely to have a heart attack."

"How am I supposed to work when everyone is against me?"

"Just go to work. You always feel better once you get started, and anyway, Jimmy Gadd is waiting to talk to you. Proverb's people have sent over a preliminary script, and he wants to go through it with you."

"What did you tell him?"

"I told him you'd be ready for him once you'd stopped groaning about your hangover."

"Thanks for covering for me."

"Jimmy knows you as well as I do. What do I need to lie to him for?"

"Seems like everybody knows about me."

"You adhere to a pretty repetitive pattern."

25

Mansard regarded his secretary with bleary venom. "You don't take any prisoners, do you?"

"Shall I tell Jimmy to come on in?"

"Charlie Mansard sighed. "Yeah, wheel him in. Don't worry about my pain."

Jimmy Gadd was Mansard's strong right arm and, along with Rita, he bore the brunt of his boss's erratic and generally self-destructive behavior. In the old days, he had worked for a major rock-and-roll act. Indeed, most of the older technical staff at Miraco Productions had come out of rock and roll. They had the experience of arena special effects, and since rock and roll had been replaced by pop acts that sang about Jesus in stupid chipmunk voices, the technicians had to find work wherever they could. Jimmy Gadd was a short, wiry man with a full beard and unfashionably long hair. The worn blue jeans and nylon bomber jacker were something straight out of the '70s or '80s. He had a bulky, bound printout under his arm.

Mansard raised a weary eyebrow. "So what do we have there? The usual hellfire and blood?"

"The boy seems to be going for broke."

"Oh, yeah?"

"He wants a skywalker."

"Does he, by God?"

"A hundred-foot hologram figure on top of the Garden."

"No shit. What does he want? A figure of himself?"

Jimmy Gadd shook his head. "Uh-uh."

"Not another Jesus?"

"Nope."

"I'm not in any condition to play guessing games."

"He wants us to do the Four Horsemen of the Apocalypse charging the Empire State Building."

Mansard whistled. His hangover was temporarily forgotten. "Does Proverb have any idea what something like that is going to cost?"

Gadd nodded. "I checked with Jason, his controller. They seem prepared to go the distance as far as the money is concerned. Proverb seems to have something to prove."

Mansard started making calculations on a pad. "Can we put up an image that big?"

Gadd ran a hand through his hair. "In theory we can, if we get something of an overcast and rent every fog generator in town. The real problem is the multiple imaging. We've only done single figures. This is four horsemen. Count them. Four. Four horsemen and four horses. For all practical purposes, it's eight figures. Nobody's ever attempted anything close to it. Not even Visioninc.''

Despite himself, Mansard grinned. "It'd be an all-time coup. Can we do it?''

"If we get the hardware that we need.''

"So what would we need?''

"With those new DL-70s from Sony, it'd be a breeze, but we don't have the DL-70s yet.''

"I thought that it was all arranged. Didn't we have the tithe barriers beaten?'' Mansard asked.

"On paper we did. We had the stuff ordered through a Chilean purchasing agent. It's the usual way of getting around the Japanese embargo. Everyone does it.''

"So where are they?''

"Last I heard they were still sitting in a warehouse at Santiago airport. You know what the Chileans are like.''

"Can we get them in time?''

"I sure as hell hope so. Marty's on the phone right now.''

Mansard started flipping through the script. "The interior effects seem well within our capabilities.''

Gadd nodded. "No problem. Although Proverb does seem to be going for the edge.''

Mansard continued to examine the script. "He does, doesn't he? But, then again, Arlen Proverb has never been your run-of-the-mill preacher.''

Arlen Proverb had never been anything like a run-of-the-mill preacher. In the tight power frame of the theocracy, Arlen Proverb was the rebel, the perennial thorn. Although, for public consumption, it was all brothers in the Lord, there was a deep and hostile gulf between Faithful and his cronies and the flamboyant Proverb. He simply had too big a following for them to off him. Where Faithful and his circle radiated a scrubbed corporate wholesomeness, Proverb ranted and roared and dressed in Nashville spangles. He was a wild man, a throwback to the tent shows and the snake handling of the raging Bible belt, a hunched and brooding figure in a white jumpsuit that could suddenly lash out with an Old Testament fury. He was a throwback, though, who performed in front of a battery of state-of-the-art special effects of such intensity that they were close to psychedelic. He was adored by the unemployed, the blue collar, the marginal, the brought down, and just about anyone who had a head of anger that he wanted to blow off. In that, he was the closest thing the country had to an aboveground political opposition. Unlike Faithful, who expected passive acceptance from his devotees, Proverb encouraged his followers to be an integral part of the show. They stomped and clapped. They had visions and talked in tongues. They even writhed on the floor in convulsive spasms of ecstasy. In fact, ecstasy was what set Proverb apart from the others. He delivered an old-time, holy roller good time, and that made him dangerous.

Mansard stopped at a page in the script. "He's actually going to use 'Love Me Tender'?"

Gadd shrugged. "That's what it says."

"He's sailing kind of close to the wind, isn't he?"

"He's always attracted Elvi in his crowds."

"But he's never pandered to them before."

The followers of Elvis Presley were another problem that the Faithful orthodoxy had with Arlen Proverb. The Elvi flocked to his shows in droves, out in the open in their scarves and badges, sideburns and sunglasses. There was no doubt that the Elvis cult was a non-Christian belief, and on a number of occasions plans had been hatched at a high level to suppress it. Somehow, though, they had never been acted upon. Elvis was so deep in the psyche of poor white America that even the Fundamentalists were scared to mess with his memory. They seemed to suspect instinctively that they might be dealing with a sleeping giant who, if roused by oppression, might become quite uncontrollable. For Proverb actually to go out of his way to court them was something else entirely, and it would undoubtedly widen the gulf between him and the hierarchy.

Mansard grinned. "Proverb's up to something."

Jimmy Gadd was not smiling. "Do you really think we should be getting involved with him?"

"We've always done Proverb."

"If he's planning on tweaking Faithful's tail by playing up to the Elvi it could be the start of a whole holy nasty. We don't want any of that nastiness to rebound on the company."

"Nothing nasty can rebound on us. We're just the hired whores. Next month we'll be working for Swan. Sublime to ridiculous. We take no sides. They know they need us more than we need them. In the meantime, we'll give Proverb his four horsemen. Maybe they'll all want monster skywalkers after that.

We can get rich and go put on rock-and-roll spectaculars in Australia.''

Gadd grinned wryly. "That'll be the day."

Mansard became professional. "Let's get to it."

"Should I start Manny on the visualization?"

Mansard nodded. "Yeah. The sooner we get the master drawings, the sooner we can start on the rig design."

Kline

Cynthia Kline came out of the heavily protected street entrance to the CCC Astor Place complex and discovered that the combination of the bread riot and the bombing and the official response to both had turned the streets to total chaos. The only traffic that seemed to be moving belonged to law enforcement. Police Pharaohs and prowlers, the deacons' Continentals and their sinister buses with the blind windows and cargoes of unfortunate prisoners, came and went at high speed with sirens screaming and lights flashing. Cynthia had originally intended to take a cab home, but that was clearly impossible. The subway offered no better prospects. It was well past the rush hour, and there were still lines of people waiting to get into the Astor Place station, casting nervous glances at all the police activity. A number of uptown lines had failed, and a lot of commuters seemed resigned to the prospect of spending the night on the platforms. The buses were equally bad. The insides were packed, and still more people clung to the sides and the backrails even though they did not seem to be going anywhere.

Cynthia got a tight grip on her shoulder bag and started out in the direction of Third Avenue. Her clerical auxiliary uniform helped to get her through the knots of officers who filled the sidewalk in front of the building. They all seemed so tightly wrapped, so dangerously primed for violence, and she wanted to get out of there as quickly as possible. After all her training and even after operating under cover for so long, the proximity of so much armed authority still made her nervous. She would never forget the horrors of '04 and '05 when so many of her friends had vanished.

Things were no better on the corner of Third. Civilian traffic had been waved over to the curb, and even the pedestrians who usually crowded the corners of Third and St. Marks had melted away. She had no more chance of getting a cab than she had of flying in the air. She had to face the fact that she was walking home. As she started north up Third, she wondered how many streets in the twenties would be closed off because of the riot.

"Want a ride, baby?"

Cynthia swung around, ready to tell whomever it was to take a jump. But it was a regular police cruiser that had pulled up at the curb. Two young patrolmen were grinning at her from behind the steel grill, their expressions suggesting that their intentions were less than honorable. They were out to have a little fun.

"Going our way?"

Her instinct was to tell them what they could do with their ride, but at the thought of the long walk to her apartment, she put on an idiotic smile and pushed her voice up half an octave. Experience had taught her that cops were easier to handle if they thought they were dealing with Betty Boop.

"I need to get to Thirty-eighth and Ninth."

"No problem."

"You want to squeeze in the front here with us?"

Cynthia regarded the helmets and riot guns racked and ready between the front seats. Fitting her in was an obvious physical impossibility.

"Too tight a squeeze," she said.

The nearest cop's grin broadened. "You could sit on my lap."

"I think I'll get in the back."

He pretended to be horrified. "A nice girl like you can't sit in there. That's where we put the prisoners."

His partner joined in. "You know? Sinners?"

"We've had all kind of scumbags back there."

"Probably diseased."

Cynthia reached for the rear door handle. "I'll manage."

"Suit yourself."

The lock popped. Cynthia opened the door and climbed inside. There actually were some unpleasant-looking stains on the plastic seat cover.

"You asked for it."

"I'll live with it."

"Hold tight."

"I'm holding."

The cruiser took off in a squeal of laid rubber, the scream of its siren, and a blaze of flashing lights. The boys were showing off. They had those plain, scrubbed, unlined faces that seemed to have become so common in the last few years, as if they were manufactured somewhere out in the Midwest, complete with crewcuts, emotionless eyes, and mouths that seemed designed only to leer and sneer. They roared up Third Avenue at high speed. At Fifteenth Street they all but plowed into a bus.

"Goddamn it."

"Had to be on Fifteenth Street."

As they got underway again, the cop riding shotgun swiveled in his seat. "You know about Fifteenth Street?" His leer was back.

The driver sniggered. "Sure she does. I heard some of these clerical auxiliaries even moonlight back there."

Cynthia Kline did not, in fact, know anything about Fifteenth Street and made the appropriate noises. She was certain that the grinning assholes in the front seat couldn't wait to tell her. She was immediately proved right.

"The dekes have a house on that block. A regular sink of iniquity. It's where they go to have a bit of illicit fun."

"When the strain of being righteous gets too much for them."

The driver laughed. Cynthia found the sound instantly irritating.

"Maybe you shouldn't talk like that in front of the lady. I mean, she's practically one of them."

Shotgun put his face close to the grille that separated the back of the car from the front. "You wouldn't get us into trouble, would you, gorgeous?"

Cynthia shook her head. "I always do my best to avoid trouble."

She was storing away the tidbit of information about Fifteenth Street in the back of her mind. There was no knowing when something like that might come in handy. She might be a damn sight more use moonlighting in a deacon whorehouse than shuffling data on Astor Place. Or maybe not. She could imagine what those repressed bastards might want to have done to them.

The cruiser was still screaming up Third as if it were on its way to an emergency. The two cops kept up a running commentary on individuals on the sidewalk. All of it was abusive and a good percentage was homicidal.

"Look at that big fat bastard. Imagine pumping a hollow point into his fat gut."

There seemed to be nobody that they did not hate. But, Cynthia reflected, it was actually understandable that the younger cops should behave like an occupying army. That was virtually what they were. After the takeover, working on the principle of divide and rule, the NYPD had adopted the same recruiting policy that the deacons used. They went out and hired country boys from the depressed Midwest. The new rookies came as strangers to a town they disliked and distrusted, and they quickly developed a relationship of mutual loathing with its inhabitants.

They hung a tire-wrenching left on Twenty-third Street and started heading west. Cynthia realized that they were driving directly into the riot area.

"Are you going to drop me off, or what?" she asked.

"Thought we'd take a look around first. You want to see what's happening, don't you?"

"I . . ." She trailed off as she realized that there was no point in answering. She was going to get a tour of the riot scene whether she wanted one or not. She had seen riots before, more than enough, but she was not about to admit that. It hardly fitted with her current identity.

There was a police barricade across Eighth Avenue. A crowd had gathered on the north side of Twenty-third Street. Quiet and sullen, the rubbernecks kept a cautious distance from the line of heavily armed police. There was a smell of gasoline and burned plastic in the air, as well as the bite of lingering tear gas. Gunships circled overhead with their rotors slapping and their spotlights probing the area. As the cruiser nosed up to the barricade, two patrolmen in full riot gear, visors locked down, pulled a pair of sawhorses aside to let them pass. The cruiser had to give way, though, as a paramedic unit came through. The two cops put on their helmets and downlocked their Remingtons. They were noticeably more tense now that they were in the battle line.

"There's been a lot of casualties. St. Vincent's is having quite a problem coping," the driver said.

Shotgun grunted. "Bastards should be left in the street to bleed."

"A lot of them were."

Cynthia wanted nothing more than to be out of there.

Beyond that barrier, the power was out and the streetlamps dark. The only lights came from flickering fires, the searchlights of the slowly turning gunships, and the rotating red and blue of the dozens of police and fire department vehicles. The center of everything was the supermarket at the corner of Twentieth. It had been reduced to nothing but a burned-out skeleton of blackened girders. To the north and east, the lights on the Empire State Building shone bright and clear. Farther north, the Trump Grand Tower gleamed in the night.

"The firemen couldn't get to the blaze until about an hour ago. There were snipers on the rooftops."

"Can't take the guns away from the people." Shotgun sounded bitter. It was one of the major paradoxes of the Faithful regime that although pornography and rock music had been outlawed, it was easier than ever to get a gun. During the campaign of 2000, Larry Faithful had gotten himself so far into hock with the gun lobby that there was no way he could ever institute gun controls. In a situation of almost complete repression, the American people had the inalienable right to arm themselves to the teeth.

They passed a long line of chained and handcuffed people, covered by riot guns while waiting for transport to the lockup. Other huddled shapes draped in black plastic sheeting were obviously bodies. The car crunched over a continuous carpet of broken window glass. There were still flames inside a building across the street from the supermarket. Cynthia peered through the rear window of the cruiser. Despite all that she had seen, part of her still found it hard to believe that such chaos could result from what was really only a minor distribution screwup in the Daily Bread program. She remembered the words of Tom Weber, her political science instructor back at the camp in the woods outside Vancouver. "It's far easier to run an inefficient welfare program that fouls up all the time than just end welfare altogether. You have the advantage of appearing to do something while, at the same time, you are equipped with an ideal tool to manipulate the underclass. Faithful's Daily Bread program is the perfect example. By substituting a crude handout for every other kind of more sophisticated safety-net program, it reduced the recipients to the most degradedly dependent level. Whenever glitches occur in the system, they spark riots. If you start instigating these glitches according to a planned pattern, you are able to use them as an excuse to raze neighborhoods and relocate unwanted populations."

The cops were guffawing.

"Daily Bread."

"Sounds like a newspaper."

"So let the scum eat newspaper."

The neighborhood looked as if it were well on the way to being razed. Cynthia doubted that the A&P would ever be rebuilt. The cardboard box people would be setting up homes in the ruin inside of a week. The police stood around in tight, watchful knots, weapons at the ready, scanning the rooftops. They obviously had the area secured but were still nervous about random sniper fire. House clearing had already started. A brown-skinned teenager was being dragged from a doorway. Two cops were holding his arms, and a third had him by the hair. There was blood on his face, and his eyes were wide with terror. He put up a certain minimal struggle, and immediately the three uniforms laid into him with their nightsticks. The cops in the front of the cruiser shouted encouragement.

"Yeah! Trash that piece of garbage!"

"Beat some manners into the little bastard!"

Cynthia had had quite enough. "I'd really like to get home now."

"Don't worry, gorgeous. We'll get you home."

"It's been a long day and I'm kind of beat."

"Where were you going to? Thirty-fourth and Tenth?"

"Thirty-eighth and Ninth."

"Whatever. We'll take you up there as soon as we take a look around the side streets."

The two young cops exchanged a look that Cynthia did not like at all.

"Don't you have to call in?" she asked.

The driver shrugged. "There's no point. It's chaos back on Astor Place. Ground control's completely jammed."

He switched on the radio to prove his point. There was a babble of unrelated voices. It seemed impossible that Astor Place communication center was so inefficient. The cop had to be doing something with the radio. Cynthia was now quite convinced that they were up to no good. She wanted to get out right there, but she was not about to walk through the aftermath of a riot. The cruiser was rolling slowly through the darkness of Nineteenth Street. Shotgun was squinting into the shadows, looking as though he had been reared on old Clint Eastwood movies. Midpoint on the block they passed two flattened, burned-out buildings that were the legacy of a previous disturbance or isolated arson. Shotgun thought he saw something. He hit a switch, and a spotlight cut in.

"Goddamn deacons get to have heatseekers in their cars."

At first there was nothing—just heaps of blackened brick and broken spars that were already being swallowed up by drifts of garbage. Suddenly four figures cut and ran in among the piles of rubble. Shotgun whooped.

"There they go! They're rabbiting! Let's go get 'em!"

The driver spun the car in a screaming turn. Even though there was a makeshift trail bulldozed through the debris, the car bounced like a bucking horse, and Cynthia's head made painful contact with the roof. Shotgun was hanging half out the window, letting rip with his Remington. One of the runners went down. The cruiser screamed past the others, the driver spinning it again in a sliding 180-degree turn. The fugitives turned and ran back the way they had come.

Cynthia could no longer suppress her outrage. "They're unarmed!"

"They're scum!"

Shotgun took out another runner. The driver slammed on the brakes. Shotgun was out and running, firing as he went. The driver went after him, leaving Cynthia alone in the flashing police car. Bursts of static barked from the radio. She unlocked the rear door and slowly climbed out. There were more shots in the distance and then silence. She was tempted to walk quietly away. Unfortunately, her escape would not be quiet: she would have to do a lot of explaining before she would be allowed out of the sealed riot zone. She realized that she would have to stick with the cops for a while longer.

It was a full minute before they came back into view, breathing hard and carrying their weapons and helmets loosely at their sides. They seemed exceedingly pleased with themselves. The driver had stopped to inspect one of the bodies, but Shotgun was moving straight toward Cynthia. There was nothing at all pleasant about his grin. He seemed to be intoxicated by the violence.

"So you got out to watch the fun, did you?"

Cynthia didn't say anything. He was very close to her. She could smell his breath. He had been chewing gum or eating mints.

"Maybe we can have a little fun of our own?"

"I'm not interested. I just want to get home."

"We're interested." He was reaching for her. "Come on, baby. Nobody's going to hurt you."

"I'll report you."

"You won't report anyone, bitch. You know the score. You'd never survive the scandal. Besides, it'd only be your word against the two of us."

His hands were on the front of her uniform jacket. The driver had finished looking at the body and was coming toward them. He, too, was grinning. Something snapped in Cynthia. It was part revulsion, part anger, and part the conditioned reflexes of her training. Her hands and knee came up as one in a move that she had practiced a hundred times. As Shotgun doubled over in pain, she half turned and flipped him over. He was lying in the dirt with an expression of pure, ugly fury. His hand was creeping toward the pistol on his belt. Already she was down on one knee, scooping up the Remington that Shotgun had dropped. Behind her, the driver was laughing. The gun roared. Shotgun was blown backward. His face was a bloody pulp. The driver's laugh froze in openmouthed horror. He was fumbling with his own gun. The Remington in Cynthia's hands roared again. The driver spun and fell. She lowered the gun, trying hard to control her breathing. Every instinct screamed at her to run. Somebody was bound to be on their way to investigate the gunfire. She fought down the impulse to flee. What had they always told her? Do not react. Think. She leaned into the driver's seat of the cruiser and detached the mike from the radio.

"This is an emergency. Two officers are down."

"Who is this?"

There was no longer chaos on the airwaves. She identified herself and gave her position. It was scarcely a minute before the gunship was overhead and had her in its light. She placed the Remington on top of the police car and raised her hands.

Carlisle

Harry Carlisle let himself into the apartment. It was over a year since Gail had been arrested, but the place still had the air of gaping emptiness each time he walked into it. Gail had been a damned fool. It was not as though her woman's group had actually been doing anything. They had not been planting bombs or robbing banks. They had been little more than a leftover from the abortion protests with a few proscribed books and magazines, a meeting place, and some minimal contacts with the underground railroad and refugee organizations. It was having a regular meeting place that had been their downfall. They had been labeled a coven. At the show trial, there had been talk of Satanic rituals, animal sacrifice, and orgies, but he knew there had been nothing like that. The deacons had wanted something to throw to the media. The public had been getting bored with the dopey kids from the suburbs who dropped belladonna, burned black candles, and collected Led Zeppelin records, and were being hyped as the menace of Satan. A cult of radical lesbian devil worshipers was something that they could finally get their teeth into.

Carlisle had been lucky that he had not been arrested along with them. Gail had always maintained a nominally separate apartment of her own, and that single fact had saved him from cohabitation and consorting charges. As it was, his record had been terminally tarnished. There would be no more promotions. After the trial was over, he had been severely tempted to quit the police department. Friends had advised him against it. There was little future for an ex-cop under a cloud. The deacons would eventually find a way to get him.

When Gail had been in Joshua, he had managed to visit her quite regularly. Seeing her in that place tore him up every time. The drab uniforms, the electric fences, and the obvious brutality filled him with a cold, sick anger, but he knew that she needed the lifeline, and he persevered. After four months she had been transferred to Solomon, the new supercamp outside St. Louis. Her letters had grown fewer and fewer and then stopped altogether. He had used his position to make sure that she was still alive, but all other contact had been lost.

Carlisle checked his answer unit. No one had called. He realized that he was turning into a recluse, but he seemed to have no inclination to do anything about it. He poured himself a stiff drink and dropped into the old leather armchair. It had been a long depressing day. He was weary of the continual madness and worn out by a world that was run by bigoted thugs. There was a frozen dinner in the icebox and dirty dishes in the sink. He also had no inclination to do anything about them. He flicked on the TV. It would be a suitable background to his internal gloom. There was a deacon show on the screen. Handsome, dedicated young dekes kicked down the door of a Hollywood mansion and stormed into the dark interior. There were pentagrams on the purple walls, and the cult that was getting busted consisted, in the main, of well-developed young women in skimpy leather nun habits that showed off a lot of thigh. It was the usual propaganda nonsense that passed for action adventure. Carlisle could remember when detectives had been the heroes of TV fantasy. He sighed and flipped the channel. He needed a girlfriend, but that was yet another thing about which he seemed unable to do anything. Next up was Roone Nelson.

". . . so let's us ask ourselves, my friends: Do we want to see a return to those heathen days when our popular entertainment was provided by drug addicts and sexual deviants and our children aped Godless barbarians? Jesus has time and again demonstrated . . ."

Carlisle quickly flipped again. He did not give a rap what Jesus had time and again demonstrated. He was sick of goddamn preachers. He hit the *Ten O'Clock Good News*. A family of heretics had been killed by the Border Patrol. A Fort Worth woman's sight had been restored by the direct intervention of God and Larry Faithful. There was some local coverage of the riot on Eighth Avenue. Most of it was patently phony footage of steadfast riot police holding the line against ravening mobs of hideous and diseased inner city subpeople from the depths of some suburban nightmare. He flipped on. Disgust was becoming a way of life. An antique rerun of *Little House on the Prairie* got short shrift, as did the quiz show *Catch It and Keep It*. TBS was running an Audie Murphy festival, and he settled on that. The green and magenta of decaying technicolor added a tint of unreality to the TV twilight.

He wanted off this damn case. It was a pain in the ass to have to work so closely with the deacons. He needed to get back to real crime. He would take the robbery detail. Hell, he would even go back on vice. Busting hookers and pillrollers was preferable to the current nonsense. There was too much weirdness attached to terrorism. There was the constantly looming threat of politics, and that brought him right back to the deacons again. Not that anyone was going to let him go anywhere. The hunt for the Lefthand Path was going so badly that it was starting to feel like an albatross he was doomed to carry around his neck for the rest of time. There was something a little spooky about the case itself. Carlisle distrusted the way that this latest bunch of terrorists had come right out of nowhere. There should have been some kind of whisper somewhere, an informant, something. They were efficient and apparently well funded. He was not the kind who immediately jumped to the conclusion that all evils were hatched in the dark Satanic mills of Moscow, Damascus, or, at the very least, Montreal, but it did seem that they might be controlled by a foreign power. Even the name bothered him. Most terrorists went for initials, or else the people's this or the revolutionary that. There was a mystic ring to the name "Lefthand Path" that smacked of a slick, twenty-first-century magic. It was as though they had given considerable thought to hitting the Fundamentalists right where they lived. It had to be assumed that more of such thinking would come into play if the campaign continued. The official fear was that they would escalate from bombing to political assassination. Privately, he would not have minded that at all. At least cops would not be getting blown up. It might not be a bad idea if politicians and preachers got shot up. It would certainly introduce a measure of reality into their lives.

He got up to pour himself another shot. He spent a moment looking out of the window. A thick fog was descending on the city, smothering the lights and blanketing all life out there in a cloud of gray invisibility. The fog was very fitting to his mood. It was also probably a health hazard. People who believed that Jesus would be along at any minute to put everything to rights did not spend either time or money in protecting the environment. With Judgment Day and the Rapture just around the corner, such heavy industry as still remained was free to pollute to its heart's content. Acid rain had been one of the very first issues that had pushed Canada toward the waiting arms of the Russians. Carlisle shook his head. Was the country never going to wake up to these religious maniacs and put a stop to their antics?

He knew he ought to go to bed. There was no reason to assume that tomorrow would be anything but another bitch of a day. The trouble was that he was in that state of wide-awake exhaustion that made sleep impossible. His shoulder holster was sticking into his ribs. He unhooked the harness and took it off. He paused and looked at the holstered pistol. More than one cop had taken that way out when it had all seemed too much. He half smiled and hung the rig over the back of one of the straight-backed chairs in the dinette. He was not that far gone yet. Maybe after another couple of shots and another half hour of Audie Murphy, he might be ready to doze.

Winters regarded the phone as if it were a venomous snake. He had only been at his desk for a matter of seconds before it rang. Someone must have been watching the monitors, waiting for him to come in. He nervously picked it up.

"Winters."

"I want you for an internal investigation."

It was Sommerville, his immediate superior. The words made Winters's stomach turn to ice.

"I beg your pardon."

Sommerville laughed. He had the knack of making a laugh sound cold and threatening. "It's not you that's being investigated. Not yet. I want you to help conduct one. This morning. It won't take very long. You'll be able to go back to doing nothing about the Lefthand Path after lunch."

Winters made his voice absolutely neutral. "I understand. Who's the subject of the investigation?"

"A CA called Cynthia Kline. She was apparently riding in a police car last night when it was attacked by rioters. The two officers were killed, but she survived. She claims that she blew away one of the rioters with an officer's guns. I figure she's on the level, but I want you to run her through her story."

Winters could scarcely believe it. He was going to get to interrogate Cynthia Kline. "Am I to conduct this interview on my own?"

"Of course not. Rogers and Thomas will be with you. She's on ice in interview room F. I suggest you access the statement that she gave to the PD last night. Read it and then go talk to her. There's to be no rough stuff. You understand?"

"I understand."

When Winters looked over the statement, he found it to be much as Sommerville had described. Reading between the lines, he guessed that the dead cops had been a couple of damned fools who had gone on a kill spree that had blown up in their faces. The one in the passenger seat had gotten out of the car to chase down some riot suspects. They had jumped him, taken his riot gun, and killed him. They had killed the driver as he got out of the car to help. Kline, who was also out of the car, had managed to grab the driver's shotgun and blast one of them. After that, she had radioed for help. Winters wondered if they had all been d.inking.

Rogers and Thomas were waiting for him outside the interview room. Rogers was a fast-track junior deacon who did nothing to conceal the fact that he was on the make. Thomas was older and no high flier. He plodded but rarely stumbled.

Rogers seemed determined to take the point. "So I figure the woman's basically on the up and up, although I very much doubt that they got out of the car the way she tells it."

Winters made an effort to hold his own. "I was wondering if they'd been drinking."

Rogers regarded him coldly. "It's possible, but there were an awful lot of other officers in the area. They'd have to be pretty stupid."

"It's hardly an act of intelligence to get blown away with your own gun." Winters realized that without really intending to he had opened hostilities.

Thomas ignored what was going on between the other two. "Do we have the crime scene report?"

Rogers was way ahead of Winters. "I got it from the PD. Needless to say, they fouled it up. In the excitement, the bodies were moved before the whole thing was put on tape, so there's no hard evidence to either support or break down her story. Two cops are dead, four rioters are dead, and she's alive."

"So what do we do, sweat her on the details and hope she cracks?"

Rogers picked an invisible piece of lint from his suit. "I think we'd be wise to look at the big picture. We can turn up the heat initially, but unless she cracks and confesses that she went to the vacant lot to gang-bang the two officers, I figure we give her a clean bill of health and turn her over to the PR people to make her into a heroine. Jesus knows we could use one."

"Do the media have this yet?"

"There's a freeze on it until we come up with our findings."

Winters wondered if Rogers was laying some kind of elaborate trap. "You're saying that if we don't find something obviously wrong, we make her a media star and all look good in the bargain."

Rogers smiled. "You have something against looking good?"

"Not in the least."

"Then shall we go in and talk to her?"

Cynthia Kline was sitting in an upright wooden chair. She looked a little nervous but was otherwise calm and collected. Her fair hair was twisted back into a tight bun, and her uniform was pressed and neat. She looked more like a job applicant on an interview than a traumatized victim. There were three chairs facing her, already set up for the three deacons. They seated themselves. Thomas started the interrogation.

"We are here to ask you a few questions."

"I realize that."

"If you've been telling the truth up to now you have nothing to worry about."

"I've been telling the truth."

Winters caught himself staring. She was really something. She was like one of those late-show movie idols. He tried to put a name to the face. Did she remind him of Grace Kelly? There was something more earthy about her than Grace Kelly. Kathleen Turner? Of course, Kathleen Turner's earlier films had been proscribed. She had even worked with the heretic Russell. Winters found that he was drifting to the dark fantasies. His mind scrabbled for a question, any question. It came out as a blurt.

"Had you been drinking?"

Rogers and Thompson both looked sharply at Winters. He immediately realized that the question was quite inappropriate. He was behaving like an idiot.

Kline shook her head. "I was on my way home."

Rogers moved in to put things back on course. "Perhaps you'd like to tell the story in your own words."

Nobody interrupted as Kline, slowly and carefully, told her story. It matched exactly with the recorded statement. That bothered Winters. She should not have been that calm. The cornerstone of the official philosophy was that women were to be protected. Kline seemed in no need of any protection whatsoever. His Midwest deacon instinct smelled heresy. He could not however, work out why. He framed his next question more carefully.

"Please go into a little more detail as to how you came to get into a police car when you were on the way home from work."

"As I already said, mass transit was halted because of the emergency. I'd resigned myself to walking when the two officers pulled over and offered me a ride."

"Fuchs and Burger?"

"I didn't know their names until afterward."

"Do you often take rides with PD officers, Auxiliary Kline?"

"This was the first time."

"But you did get into a car with two strange men?"

"It was better than walking nearly forty blocks. It had been a bad day, what with the riot on top of the bombing."

"You didn't feel that you were in any danger?"

"These were peace officers in an armored cruiser. It was a lot safer than being out on the street, on foot, in a riot."

"You trust PD officers?"

"If you can't trust the guardians of a Christian society, who can you trust?"

"We ask the questions here, Kline." The by-the-book innocence just did not fit.

Rogers picked up the ball. "But after you accepted the ride, you decided that it might be fun to see the riot area from the back of a PD cruiser."

"Quite the reverse. I was very tired and wanted to be home as soon as possible. It was the officers who insisted on giving me the tour."

"Why should they do that?"

She hesitated. "I think they were trying to show off their . . . virility."

"And on this tour you ran into the fatal incident."

"That's right."

Thomas started on a very different course. "You seem to have had alarmingly fast reactions during this incident."

"I don't know. When I saw the two officers go down, I thought they were going to kill me next. I didn't want to die."

"Even in the sure and certain knowledge of the resurrection?"

"I didn't want to die."

"Clerical auxiliaries aren't trained in the use of the Remington Controller, are they?"

"We only train with handguns. Strictly for our own protection."

"How did you manage to fire the officer's riot gun so swiftly if you had never handled one?"

"I had two brothers who were both hunters. They taught me to fire most kinds of weapons."

Rogers was actually smiling. He was clearly imagining her talking about her hunting, shooting brothers on TV. His face fell at Thomas' next question.

"Your brothers owned state-of-the-art riot guns?"

"No, but when I grabbed the gun, I found that it fired just like any autoload."

Thomas leaned back in his chair. "There are other places that teach people how to fire weapons, sophisticated weapons they'd normally have no reason to know about."

For the first time, Cynthia Kline looked less than confident. She said nothing.

Thomas leaned forward. "Perhaps in a terrorist training camp?"

Kline looked frightened. That response was, however, understandable. The word "terrorist" could strike fear into the totally blameless. Rogers was looking at Thomas as if he had gone mad. At that moment, the phone on the wall rang. Rogers grabbed for it. He listened for almost a minute with an expression of increasing shock. Finally he nodded and hung up. Winters and Thomas looked at him expectantly. Rogers shook his head.

"Three deacons have just been killed. Right out in broad daylight. Bickerton, Baum, and Kinney."

"From the Zealots?"

"Bickerton, Baum, and Kinney. From the Zealots. We're instructed to term this interview and join our respective teams. It's a redline flap."

"Where did it happen?"

"On First Avenue. Between Fourteenth and Fifteenth. They were taken out with a burst of heatseekers, probably fired from a point-six-oh Mossberg."

"We're the only ones who're supposed to have smart ammunition."

"That's the weird part."

Thomas sighed. "If they were on Fifteenth and First, we know where they'd been. Probably all night."

Rogers quickly motioned to Kline, indicating that no more should be said in front of her. Winters glanced at him.

"What do we do with her?"

Kline

What were they going to do with her? she wondered.

"There's a CA escort coming down for her."

Cynthia Kline's mind was in turmoil. She had been a damned fool. She despised the deacons so intensely that she had allowed herself to underestimate them. The older, slow one had only been shooting in the dark, but he had come close enough to the truth to rattle her. Even a dummy like Winters had been plainly disturbed by her attitude. She had talked down to them and made them uncomfortable when she should have come on like a helpless little waif and had them eating out of her hand. It still remained to be seen if her pride was going to hang her. The phone call had temporarily saved her, but it had also brought a new set of questions.

Three deacons shot dead, presumably on their way from their private bordello on Fifteenth, was a major incident. Who was behind it, and was it going to affect her situation? The abrupt removal of her three interrogators had to be cause for some kind of optimism. They couldn't be thinking of her as a dangerous terrorist, if they were prepared to rush off like that.

Her new escort arrived in the form of two burly CA matrons. Cynthia far from liked the look of them, but to her complete surprise, they seemed quite well disposed toward her.

"Here you greased a couple of the scumsuckers for us. How did you manage that?"

"I was scared out my head, to tell the truth."

Now, after the fact, she was playing it the right way. The nearest matron all but patted her on the head.

"You got 'em though."

"I guess I did."

"You want to watch out, though, getting into a car with those PD bastards. They got just one thing in mind."

"So what happens to me now?"

"We're going to take you up to Directoress Lumet. I figure they've got your case all figured out."

Cynthia did not have to fake the fear. The matrons laughed.

"Don't look so worried. They going to make you a sainted hero, honey."

They took her quickly to the directoress's office on the nineteenth floor. Cynthia was taking it one minute at a time. She was just relieved that they were not taking her to a subbasement—she had heard too much about what those sadists did to female suspects.

The directoress fancied herself as voluptuous and was fighting a stubborn rearguard action against the ravages of middle age. She wore her hair in the high platinum bouffant of a big-time country singer. Her makeup was thick, her eyelashes were false, her nails were bloodred, and her uniform skirt was cut a little too tightly across her ample hips. She was lounging back in a large leather swivel chair behind an L-shaped combined desk and workstation. The two matrons withdrew and left Cynthia standing in front of the directoress's inspecting gaze.

"So you're our little Dirty Harriet?"

"I think that's putting it a little strongly, ma'am."

"You'll have to get used to it."

"I'm sorry."

"And you can cut out the phony humility. I monitored your interview. You're a tough cookie."

Cynthia stiffened. "Yes, ma'am."

Directoress Lumet stood up and came out from behind the desk. She walked slowly around Cynthia. "I suppose you look the part."

"Yes, ma'am."

"You want to get on in the service?"

"Yes, ma'am."

"Well, you could make it big if you don't foul up on this next assignment we've got for you."

"Yes, ma'am."

"There is no more important backup for an agency like this than a good public image. We are the constant targets of lying Satanist propaganda, and we badly need to show the public the part we play in protecting society from its enemies. A story like yours is just what we need at the moment."

Cynthia blinked. "It is?" What the hell were they up to?

"It's been decided to second you to the PR section. You will report to Deacon Longstreet for initial grooming. As soon as you are ready, you will be subjected to saturation TV coverage. You'll be on every talk show in the eastern area and the covers of all the magazines. You're going to be a nine-hour wonder, Kline. 'Heroic CA slays scum.' "

Cynthia was bewildered. She had never bargained for anything like this. Could she safely go so public? She had to talk to her control, but it seemed as if she was not going to be given the chance. "I don't know what to say."

"Don't screw up. Cooperate with the PR people even if they are a bunch of fags and, above all, don't let it go to your head. We're not making you into a movie star. It's just another facet of law enforcement."

As Lumet finished her speech, another CA stuck her head around the door.

"Lefthand Path just claimed the killings."

Lumet looked up sharply. "Are you sure?"

"Anderson just took the call."

When the other woman was gone, Lumet glanced at Cynthia. "You didn't hear that, right?"

"Right."

"It'll be all over the building soon enough, but I don't want it coming from here first."

"I understand."

"So go to the thirty-fifth floor and report to Longstreet."

"Yes, ma'am."

Anslinger

Maud Anslinger turned off the TV. She could not watch any longer. Satan seemed so close. All but one of the local channels had preempted their regular programming to run live coverage of the terrible murders on First Avenue. Channel 9 was still showing *Treasure in Heaven*, but she couldn't watch a soap when the presence of Evil was all around. She turned on the Jesus Wave and knelt beside the bed. The lights warmed to a comforting glow, and she clasped her hands.

"Sweet Lord Jesus, please do not forsake us in this time of our testing."

She really felt that God was testing her—her and all the good Christian people in the country. That was the only explanation for all the awful things that were happening. Looking into the lights of the Jesus Wave made her feel a little better, but even with its soothing hypnotic pulse she could not shake the feeling that the storm clouds were gathering all around. It was just as President Faithful had told them last week on *Fireside Sunday Night*. "Let us pray for America in what may prove to be our finest hour. Dear Jesus, we are a country under siege. A beleaguered enclave of decency in a dark world of pain and iniquity. To the north, we are menaced by the Godless Red Canadians and the Evil Empire of their Soviet slave masters. At the same time, beyond our southern defenses, the brown hordes from the jungles of South America are massing to descend on our pastures like a plague of locusts. Dear Jesus, bless this Fortress America, dedicated in thy name, and strengthen us lest we despair. Let us not forget that thy banner, though torn, is still flying. Make us strong, sweet Jesus. Make us strong.''

The text of the prayer had been published in the *Post* on Monday morning. Maude had cut it out and taped it to the mirror, beside the postcard that her sister Eva had sent her from Holyworld.

Theodore the cat was watching her balefully. She had gone to the store early, but for the second day running there had been no milk delivery. There had been no chicken bits in a week. The cat had been forced to settle for the new generic Petfood with the white label on the can and the funny smell.

Suddenly there were tears running down her face. God had to be testing her.

''Make us strong, sweet Jesus. Make us strong.''

Carlisle

Harry Carlisle put on his sunglasses and climbed the steps to the front door of the brownstone. It was a house without a face, the windows having all been replaced by steel sheets. There was a watch camera mounted over the door but, surprisingly, it did not swivel to look at him as he mounted the steps.

He motioned to Reeves. ''Get ready for a show of force here.''

Reeves and Donahue braced their legs and raised their Remingtons. They were dressed for *The Untouchables* in long overcoats and fedoras. Behind them were six of the riot squad's meanest with helmets and armor and leveled M-40s. Carlisle was very much aware that what was about to happen had a lot more to do with theater than with law enforcement. He had given himself the Eliot Ness role. He could not help grinning as he extended an assertive, black-gloved finger to the old-fashioned, polished brass bellpush and pressed. There were a lot of paybacks about to be exacted. In his other hand he clutched a lovingly maintained, long-barreled .375 Magnum that he brought out only on special occasions. After the first ring, nothing happened.

Reeves glanced at Carlisle. ''Kick it down?''

Carlisle looked up at the black front door with its discreet gold lettering. 555 East Fifteenth Street. He shook his head. ''They're probably a little confused in there right now.''

He pressed the bell again, leaning on it. After about twenty seconds, the door was opened by a junior deacon. He was wearing his dress grays, but his tunic was unbuttoned and his T-shirt was hanging out of his pants. He looked bleary and hung over. "What the hell do you want?"

Carlisle had to give him full marks for blind pig arrogance.

"T7 taskforce. We're here to ask a few questions before the whitewash gets spread too thick."

"Are you crazy?"

Carlisle smiled. "Maybe, but at least I've got my pants buttoned."

"You can't come in here."

"You ready to buck a Suspicion of Terrorism warrant?"

"Where did you get that from?"

"Judge Sawyer signed it just a half hour ago."

"That old fool?"

"A judge is a judge is a judge."

"Forget it."

"We're coming in."

Carlisle moved quickly forward. The others were right behind him. The junior deacon took a fraction of second to realize that an attempt to block Carlisle would be an unwise course. Instead, he turned on his heel and hurried into the building, yelling at the top of his voice.

"It's the PD! The idiots think that they can come in here on an S of T!"

The decor was classic whorehouse, burgundy velvet and dark crystal. Even though Carlisle and his men stormed in like heroes, there was no way to resist a moment of awe. Goddamn deacons really took care of themselves. The main parlor was an impressive, high-ceilinged space with the inevitable staircase running up one wall. A half-dozen, half-dressed deacons had already gathered there. They looked shocked and not a little anxious. They were obviously meeting in response to the news that three of their more notorious coworkers had walked out of the pleasure dome to die in a hail of heatseekers. Seven or eight girls in lingerie or less sat on the couches looking thoroughly frightened. Carlisle went straight for the high ground.

"Nobody move! Don't breathe! Don't even think! This is the real thing, and you are all in a lot of trouble."

Five deacons instinctively froze. The sixth started forward, working up to bluster. But one of the riot squad was right there, and the flashguard of an M-40 was jammed under his chin.

"The lieutenant said freeze, blowhard."

Carlisle raised his tracy to his mouth. "We're secured in here. Send in the investigation team."

More uniforms streamed through the open front door. One squad charged up the stairs. Others fanned out in the parlor. Detectives followed, some carrying electronic search equipment. They were the shake and scan crew. By the time they finished, there wouldn't be anything in and about the house that they wouldn't know. Another particularly hard-faced group would conduct the individual interrogations. Carlisle had picked his team with some care.

There was shouting from the head of the stairs.

"What's the meaning of this? The whole bunch of you are going to end up in a camp!"

A red-faced senior deacon dressed only in longjohns was struggling with the uniforms at the head of the stairs. Carlisle knew him by sight: Booth, a big deal in the midtown CCC. Carlisle, waiting at the foot of the stairs, signaled that Booth should be allowed through.

"I'm executing a lawful S of T warrant."

"Are you out of your minds? You know what this place is."

Booth had obviously only just crawled out of bed. Carlisle realized that the deacon had not yet heard the news.

"Three of your men have just been murdered by the Lefthand Path as they left this building."

Booth looked sharply at the younger deacons. "Is this true?"

They nodded. Carlisle pressed on.

"It is possible that they may have been fingered by someone in here. Accordingly, the place is now sealed and everyone here will be questioned."

"What were the names of the victims?"

"Bickerton, Baum, and Kinney."

"My God."

Booth quickly recovered. He rounded on the nearest women.

"You're right, Lieutenant, and we'll start with the whores. I don't think we need to be too gentle."

Carlisle's reply was soft and cold. Early in his career he had learned the trick of talking quietly and forcing people to listen. "You won't start with anything, Deacon Booth. You're a suspect yourself for the time being. If one of the girls hasn't been passing information to the terrorists, the possibility has to be considered that the deacons have been infiltrated. As of now, this is a T7 case.''

''I have to call someone about this.''

Carlisle shook his head. Someone in the phone company who owed him a favor had ensured that all communications were cut off to and from the house. ''This place is sealed.''

Booth looked as if he were going to burst a blood vessel. Carlisle savored the moment. The raid had been his own brainwave. The plan had come to him fully formed immediately after he had heard about the killings, and it had taken him only a matter of minutes to sell the idea to a devilishly gleeful Captain Parnell. Of course, Parnell had protected himself. When the shit finally came down, it would fall directly on Carlisle, but right at that moment, Harry Carlisle was not thinking too much about long-term consequences. He was taking too much delight in sticking it to the deacons. Besides, what could they really do to him? The entire episode was too high profile for them simply to disappear him. The cloud that already hung over him would darken, but that hardly worried him. He was marked already.

Carlisle's team went to work like a well-oiled machine. The deacons' protests were ignored as their IDs, along with those of the women, were verified and individuals were taken into separate rooms for questioning. In fact, it all was running so smoothly that Carlisle found himself standing in the ornate parlor with nothing to do.

Reeves leaned over the bannister at the top of the stairs. ''You ought to take a look at this place. They've got it all.''

Reeves was not exaggerating. Before the Fundamentalists had taken over, Carlisle had taken Gail to a couple of love motels in New Jersey, but those had not been anywhere near as elaborate as the upper floors of the deacons' private fantasyland. He followed Reeves through the series of sexual playrooms. He saw silk sheets, circular beds, and fur rugs. He looked up at himself in mirrored ceilings and peered through one-way mirrors at hastily vacated love nests. There were no less than three fully equipped dungeons, each with its complement of chrome chains, leather restraints, slings, and pulleys, and its racks of whips, masks, canes, and paddles—and a few devices that Harry did not recognize. Even in their leisure time, the deacons seemed obsessed by the idea of pain and punishment.

''No expense spared.''

''You're not kidding.''

There was a certain twisted logic to the deacons maintaining their own closed whorehouse. Indeed, it was the same logic of applied hypocrisy that operated on every level of the Faithful regime. They used their thought police to enforce public morality, but at the same time they had to recognize that, among their gestapo, some of the boys would definitely be boys. This recreation facility and, Carlisle assumed, many others across the country, had been provided so that God's strong right arms could sexually unwind with only a minimal risk of scandal. Carlisle was quite proud that he, with a single stroke, had considerably upped the ante on that risk.

"The place is lousy with cameras. They must record everyone's every stroke," Reeves said.

Carlisle sniffed. "It's a system of interlocking blackmail. I know your sins, but you know mine."

"God can never have enough data."

Loud voices floated up from the parlor. The tour was cut short as Carlisle and Reeves hurried to the head of the stairs.

"What's going on down there?"

A new squad of deacons had arrived. They were being held at gunpoint in the parlor by the boys from the riot squad. Their leader was a tall man with a black leather coat draped over his shoulders. His hair was close to white blond and very long for a deacon. His eyes were hidden behind black Raybans.

Reeves whistled under his breath. "Christ, now you're in for it."

Carlisle nodded. "Dreisler. I didn't expect him so soon."

Matthew Dreisler was the head of Deacon Internal Affairs and, as the deacons' chief headhunter, possibly the most feared man in all of New York.

Carlisle hurried down the stairs, angrily demanding answers from the riot squad. "I thought I told you to seal this place!"

"We did."

"So how did these people get in?"

"They brought their own warrants."

Cold black sunglasses were regarding him. When Dreisler spoke, it was a patrician drawl that seemed almost decadent. "You must be Carlisle."

Harry nodded. "I'm Carlisle."

"And you're the one with the theory. You think someone here is in cahoots with the LPs."

"I find it a little too much of a coincidence that a triple assassination should happen just a stone's throw from this establishment.''

''You suspect a direct connection.''

''I thought it merited investigation.''

Dreisler removed his sunglasses. ''Or did you just see a chance for the PD to humiliate the deacons?''

Carlisle did not answer.

Dreisler shrugged. ''As it happens, I agree with you. With the first part, that is. That's why I'm taking over this investigation as of now.''

Carlisle folded his arms across his chest. ''I don't think I can go along with that.''

Dreisler's pale eyebrows shot up. ''You don't?''

''I'm the officer on the scene here and I've got the authority to keep anyone out if I decide they might compromise the investigation.''

Dreisler had a white silk evening scarf draped around his neck. He was slowly twisting one end of it between the fingers of his left hand. ''Go on.''

''There's the possibility that a deacon has been turned by the terrorists, or that you have an infiltrator among you.''

''If anyone fingered those boys, it was more likely one of the girls.''

''Sure it is, but until I'm satisfied that it wasn't a deacon, I'm not letting any one of you near this.''

Dreisler was smiling as if he admired Carlisle's gall. ''Are you always so gung ho on procedure?''

Harry shook his head. ''Not usually, but now and then it comes in handy.''

''Do you know who I am?''

Carlisle nodded. That was the warning shot that he had been waiting for. ''I know who you are, Deacon Dreisler.''

''Either you have a lot of balls, or you're plain stupid.''

''I'm a New York cop, Deacon Dreisler. Everything that might imply.''

Dreisler laughed as if he were conceding the point. ''You have forgotten one thing, though.''

Carlisle was instantly on his guard. ''What's that?''

''There's been no crime committed here. You're not the officer on the scene because there is no scene.''

Carlisle looked bemused. ''We're standing in the middle of a functioning brothel.''

"In that case you should have brought a vice warrant. We've been talking terrorism, and I don't see a single terrorist on the premises."

"I figure that this is close enough to the shooting to qualify as a secondary investigation point, and I've secured the premises accordingly."

Dreisler sighed as if he were getting weary of all this sparring. He held out the tracy on his wrist. "Do you know how long it would take me to get a ruling in my favor on this?"

Carlisle raised his hand. Enough was enough. "I know you can run me out of here at any time, but if you do, I'll be back with the first camera crew I come across. There's media all over the neighborhood. They were tipped and they went live with the killings before the censors could get in and blanket it. They'll love this."

Dreisler looked Carlisle up and down as if really seeing him for the first time. "Well, well, you don't give up too easily, do you, Carlisle?"

"Just doing my job."

Dreisler smiled. "The classic Nuremberg answer. I tell you what, Lieutenant Carlisle. While your men are doing their work, why don't you and I go somewhere on our own and talk about terrorism?"

THREE

Mansard

THERE WAS A CHILL WIND BLOWING OFF THE RIVER AND across the landfill. Charlie Mansard huddled his shoulders deeper into the bulk of his sheepskin coat. Behind him, the lights of the city had taken on their nighttime unreality. Mansard glanced back at them. All his life he had worked with lights, but they never lost their essential magic. It was ironic that light and illusion should have become his stable reality. He fished in his coat pocket for his other stable reality, pulled out the silver hip flask, and took a quick nip of scotch.

"Is there any coffee?"

Rita poured steaming coffee from a vacuum flask and held out the Styrofoam cup to him.

"You want to call a break so we can all get warm?"

Mansard shook his head. "Absolutely not. I want to get on with it."

Mansard had never transcended the elemental fear that the device would simply refuse to work. In the last minutes before the field test of the scale model, the tension was unbearable. If anything went wrong at this point, it would be a long way back to the drawing board. He turned to the nearest production assistant and pointed to the communicator on his belt. "Give me that."

He all but barked into the radio. "Are we ready yet?"

The unruffled voice of Jimmy Gadd came back to him through the tiny speaker. "Not quite, boss. Just a couple more minutes."

55

Mansard impatiently stamped his feet as he handed back the communicator.

Rita was as calm as Gadd. "Do you want an Equital?"

"No, I don't. I don't want any pills." In fact, he had taken two uppers on the way down to the landfill.

Rita sniffed. "If you don't calm down, you'll burst a blood vessel."

"I'm perfectly calm."

"Sure you are."

Mansard turned and faced the towering cityscape. "They could have blacked out the twin towers for us."

"They threw a shitfit. Said they couldn't do it, just for the test of a model."

Mansard turned back on the offending skyscrapers and faced the river. "Screw them."

The PA had his communicator to his ear. "It's Gadd, Mr. Mansard. He's ready to go."

Charlie Mansard held out his hand for the unit. "How is it, Jimmy? You can roll it?"

"Everything on line, boss. Zero on the fault deck."

"Okay, then, let's get to it."

Bono, the chief engineer, was already punching buttons on the portable masterboard. Rita handed Mansard a bullhorn. Mansard took a final look around.

"Okay, ladies and gentlemen, here we go. Fog up."

A dozen or more pillars of vapor rose straight up into the night sky from a point some fifty yards away. At first they were thin individual strands, but quickly they thickened and solidified into a single cohesive column.

"Fog running ten of ninety on the board, boss."

Mansard nodded. "Put up the reference points."

A complex constellation of bright green stars appeared in the column of mist.

"Image up to one-third."

In the mist ghostly figures were shaping themselves around the green stars. They were too faint, however, for Mansard to make out any details.

"So far so good. Bring in the base structure nice and slow. We don't want any overload this early in the game."

The ghostly figures began to solidify until they were static sculptures of white light. Now it was possible to see exactly what they were. The four mounted figures of horror on their equally terrible steeds stood motioness in the mist: War, Famine, Pestilence, and Death, each over fifteen feet tall and perfect in every detail—the cowl of Death, the ornate armor and plumed helmet of War, the outstretched arm and rotting flesh of Pestilence, and the hollow skull eyes and sunken cheeks of Famine. Mansard rubbed his hands together. The design was holding together very well. About the only blemish was the tip of the spear that War brandished aloft. If flickered and wavered. The image came and went.

Mansard spoke urgently into the communicator. "Jimmy, what's the story on that spear?"

"It's too long. It's projecting beyond the effective apex of the fog generators."

"Will we have the same problem on the full-size version?"

"If anything, it'll be worse. We can't expect the same fog apex on the real thing."

"Damn."

"Do you want us to rerig it?"

"No. We can fix it on this end by simply lowering the figure's arm."

Mansard walked over to Bono at the masterboard. After a short discussion, the engineer put up a schematic on the main function monitor and nursed a simple joystick. In a perfectly natural movement, War dipped his lance until the tip came into sharp focus.

"That's good. Let's color the matrix."

It was like the dawn of some medieval hallucination. As the color came up, the Four Horsemen of the Apocalypse took on a ghastly solidity. The colors vibrated into the night.

Jimmy Gadd whooped through the communicator. "How's that, boss? Right on the master drawing or what?"

Mansard grinned. "Close enough for rock and roll."

The colors were, in fact, perfect: the graveyard, damp earth brown of Death's robes, the glowing red coals that were his horse's eyes, the sheen of orange fire on War's blue-black armor—it was all there, just as Mansard had dreamed it, and it was awesome.

"Okay, here comes the big test. Run the animation up to fifty percent speed."

Bono nodded. "Running them nice and easy."

The Four Horsemen slowly started to move. The horses raised one foot and then another. Their heads nodded ponderously, their nostrils flared, and their manes fanned out behind them. It was as if they were attempting to gallop through some thick heavy liquid.

"How's the power load holding up?"

"Everything's in the green."

"Let's ease it up toward normal. Pull back immediately if anything starts to redline."

"Stop sweating it, boss. It's all going fine."

Mansard knew that Bono was right, but he would never admit it. "Just watch out for an overload."

The Four Horsemen began to gather speed. Mansard was transfixed. When those images were scaled up to nearly a hundred feet tall, they would blow the city away. There had really been nothing like it before.

"Up to normal motion."

The horses' hooves pounded the empty air in eerie silence. Their necks stretched and strained; their glowing eyes bulged from skull sockets. Death swung his scythe, and the outstretched arm of Pestilence broadcast contagion across the Earth.

Mansard rubbed his hands together. "How's it holding up?"

"It's holding. Quit worrying."

Mansard started to walk toward the shining images. He glanced back at the lighted apartment windows of the Tribeck Tower. What the hell would they think of this apparition on the landfill? Not that he particularly cared. The general population had become so goddamn weird that they deserved all they got. He stepped carefully over the snaking cables that connected the laser banks and the massed fog generators. Jimmy Gadd and his crew crouched beside the bulky equipment, watching tensely. Gadd straightened, weary but grinning, as Mansard approached.

"I think we got it."

"It does look like it."

"Now all we have to do is build the big one."

Mansard made a dismissive gesture. "Just a detail."

Gadd sniffed. "Tell me that on the day."

Winters

"Have you heard about the subbasement?"

The suspect from Fifteenth Street had stopped being truculent and was becoming genuinely frightened. She inspected her fin-gernails. They were bloodred and as long as claws. She was avoiding his eyes.

"I've heard about it. There's a few of your buddies who just can't stop talking about it."

"We have our own dungeon down there."

"I said I heard about it."

"It's not one of your fantasy games. It's the real thing down there."

"I said I heard."

"I have the power to send you down there."

The woman looked frantically at the clerical auxiliary who was chaperoning the interrogation. The CA remained stone-faced. The suspect turned back to Winters. "You can't do that to me."

In fact he could not. The instruction had been very simple. The deacons assigned to each of the women brought in from Fifteenth Street were to scare the hell out of them, but there was to be absolutely nothing physical. "If you so much as breathe hard on one of those whores, you're dead. You got that?" Those assigned to the job were all junior deacons. Too many of the senior officers had been regular customers at the house. Dreisler and his headhunters were all over the building. The working girls from the house were rapidly becoming an embarrassment. Even though Dreisler had managed to keep away the media, the matter of the house on Fifteenth Street was still a loose cannon in the department. A cover might have been put on it if the PD had not burst in there first, but, as it was, the thing was so close to being public that the hookers had to be handled with kid gloves. Carlisle was walking around like a man who had the world by the balls, and without a doubt, if the women simply disappeared, he would blow the story to the more hostile ele-ments in the press. The deacons had reacted by falling into a holding pattern. Junior deacons like Winters would keep the women in a state of shock, off balance, and malleable, until some upper echelon decided what to do with them.

"I can do pretty much anything I want with you."

The woman was looking at her nails again. "I want a law-yer."

"This is nothing to do with the law. We aren't policemen. We're the spiritual guardians of society. What happens here is a matter between you, me, and God."

The woman's face twisted. "God?"

"Don't add blasphemy to the rest of your crimes."

Winters was starting to enjoy himself. The woman was small, with black hair, green eyes, and spectacular breasts. Although she had been in the Astor Place complex for close to half a day, she had not been allowed to change out of her working clothes. She was still half-naked in a leather twopiece, black latex stockings, and alarmingly high heels. It was extremely exciting to have even illusionary total power over a creature who, in almost any other context, would have completely intimidated him. In the interrogation room, the costume put her at a positive disadvantage. She kept shifting around in the hard, high-backed chair as if trying to hide or protect her considerable expanses of bare flesh. A bluebird was tattooed on the outside of her left thigh. She caught Winters looking at it and covered it with her hand.

"I don't understand why you're doing this. I haven't done anything. I haven't committed any crimes."

"You're a first-degree common harlot. That, on its own, would be worth a year in Joshua."

"This is ridiculous. We were working for the goddamn deacons. We had a deal and we kept up our end of it."

"You had a deal until three of us were murdered coming out of that place."

"That was nothing to do with any of the girls."

"We don't know that. It's quite possible that any of you could have been working with the terrorists."

"That's impossible. The place was bugged from top to bottom. You couldn't get away with anything. I already told the PDs and now I'm telling you. Me and the rest of the girls were there for one purpose and one purpose only."

"The unclean lusts of the flesh?"

"Money. We were making money and keeping out of trouble."

"I suppose you have some suitably pathetic sob story about how you first became a fallen flower."

"You don't need a sob story when unemployment's at thirty percent. I come from Bangor, Maine, Mr. Deacon. You know what they get up to up there? Those bastards passed a city ordinance that prescribed branding for fornicators."

"Some areas are more zealous than others when it comes to the Lord's work."

Winters was staring at the suspect's breasts and thinking about fornication and branding. The woman went on talking.

"So I get down to New York and I find that there ain't any more jobs down here. My second night, I get picked up on Tenth Avenue and instead of getting busted, I get recruited."

"You saying that society made you a slut?"

"What gives you the right to judge me?"

"Just doing my job."

Anger was taking over from the woman's fear. "You're really enjoying this, aren't you?"

Winters was, but he could not admit it. It was as if the woman knew all about his sexual stirrings. She was leaning forward in her seat.

"You can call me what you like, but you'd better remember how well I know you guys. I'm an expert in all your dirty little urges." She half smiled. "You're getting hot right now, aren't you?"

Winters avoided her eyes. The more she talked, the worse the images in his head became. He wanted to grab her there and then. If it had not been for the chaperone, he might have. She leaned back slowly, spreading her legs and stroking the insides of her thighs.

"You'd just love to feel these around you, wouldn't you?"

The chaperone looked at her sharply. "That'll be quite enough of that."

"Someone else just doing their job?"

Kline

Cynthia nervously lit a cigarette. She was scared. It was a kind of fear that she had never experienced before. She knew the breathless fear of life-threatening situations, but this was completely different. It was her first time on television. Her mind grabbed at the obvious details. Would someone out there in the huge TV audience recognize her from the old days? The plastic surgery she had undergone in Montreal before she had been planted in the deacons had not been particularly drastic. She knew it was a risk, but she had been given no instructions to cover such an event. Nobody had suspected that the deacons would decide to make her into a media star. She had sent out the emergency signals that she wanted to talk to her control, but no one had contacted her. She was on her own.

Beneath the details, there was the less complicated fear of the lights, the cameras, and the millions of pairs of invisible eyes watching her through their TV sets. She had been given a four-hour crash course in TV technique. It had not helped too much. She knew what she was supposed to do, but she still wondered if she could do it. Nothing that she had been taught in the PR section on the thirty-fifth floor stopped her legs from feeling like jelly or a sense of nausea from gathering in her stomach. Deacon Longstreet, a somewhat effeminate officer who handled his duties from a position of total cynicism, had tutored her on her public image and the official story that she was a simple country girl who had discovered, quite to her own surprise, that she could handle herself in a tight spot. Even he could not convince her that her mind would not become a complete blank when the camera was pointed at her.

This first ordeal was taking place live on the *Vern and Emily* show. They were broadcast locally on Channel 9 and distributed by satellite to the rest of the country. Vern and Emily Burnette ran a traditional Christian talk show. They were aggressively downhome, and Jesus played a continuous personal role in their public lives. Emily dispensed recipes, makeup tips, home hints, and advice on pet care. When she and Vern felt the need to leaven the relentlessly cute and folksy with some slightly harder content, they ran exposés of the evils of lust and promiscuity or the demon drink. Vern had a definite mean streak. He would dare prominent sinners to come on the show and, when they did, he would sweat them without mercy. Vern and Emily were the third-rated show of their kind, following Harry Hollister's *Happy Talk* and *The Ingram Family Hour* in the national ratings.

Cynthia had been through makeup and was in the green room waiting for her turn. Everybody seemed to be ignoring her. A researcher had talked her through the interview but then left her to her own devices. She had yet to meet either Vern or Emily. There was coffee and Danish on a side table, but Cynthia was too nervous to eat. What she really wanted was a drink. She mentioned that to a passing production assistant and received a look that was part pity and part contempt.

"Vern and Emily don't like any of their guests going on the air with alcohol on their breath. They're very particular about that."

"I don't want to get drunk; I'm just very nervous. This is my first time."

"I'm sorry, it's one of the rules of the show."

Cynthia made a mental note. Before the next show she did, she would hide a hip flask in her bag.

She was scheduled to go on right after Emily had finished conducting a wedding between a pair of miniature poodles. Their owner did not want the dogs mating without benefit of the Lord's blessing. As Cynthia watched it on the green-room monitor, she was once again convinced that the lunatics really had taken over the asylum. Once the wedding was over, the commercials rolled. After that, Vern would go on and do a solo pitch for their personalized, mail-order Jesus Wave units. When he was through, it would be Cynthia's turn.

Emily bustled into the green room followed by the dogs' owner, a makeup girl who was attempting to powder her off, and a gofer carrying the two poodles. The dogs seemed to have become completely hysterical and were busily trying to bite the kid.

"So you must be little Cynthia."

Cynthia did not quite know how to react to being called little by someone who scarcely made five one in four-inch heels. The chubby hand that was extended in greeting was weighed down by no less than four huge diamond rings. Any one of them was probably worth enough to keep the average family for a couple of years.

"I heard that you're pretty handy with a gun."

Cynthia did her best to look shy and awkward. It was not hard. "I just did what I had to do."

"There's only one way to treat criminals, honey."

Emily Burnette was a fat cherub losing the fight against flab. The worst bulges were concealed by the folds of a loose-fitting blue dress that was cut like a surplice. Her makeup was layered on with a trowel, and her false eyelashes were so long that Cynthia could not see how they did not impair vision. She bid the poodle owner a gushing farewell and then turned her attention back to Cynthia.

"Now don't you worry about a thing, my dear. Just ignore the cameras and all the folks out there. You and me are just going to sit ourselves down and have a nice friendly chat."

Emily took Cynthia firmly by the hand and towed her out of the green room, down a corridor, and through the double doors that led into the dark, cavernous hangar space that was the studio. Apart from the single camera that was pointed at Vern, everything was concentrated on the sitting room set where Emily conducted what she liked to call her little chats. When they were both seated and micromikes had been attached to their clothes, the cameras moved in. Cynthia knew that she was going to be rendered mute. The floor manager was counting them in.

"Three, two, one, and—"

Emily Burnette's face formed itself into its famous on-screen smile. Her voice also changed to the high, chipmunk squeak that was her public trademark.

"We have a little lady with us today who did something that most Americans only see on TV. Let's have a big Vern and Emily welcome for Deacon Clerical Auxiliary Cynthia Kline."

The applause light flashed, and there was a wild yell from the studio audience seated in a half circle of banked bleachers. One whole section was given over to an entire troop of red-and-white uniformed Young Crusaders. The remainder of the crowd was liberally sprinkled with the regular teenage yahoos who provided a noisy rooting section when Vern launched into one of his political diatribes. They were waving the stars and stripes and crucifix banners and howling their approval. Cynthia found them scary. Emily gave them a few seconds to blow off steam and then silenced the crowd with a single gesture.

"Cynthia here is a brave little girl. She's attached to the crime control unit here in New York City and, a few days ago, as part of her normal duties, she was riding in the back of a police cruiser when the car was called to a violent street disturbance in one of the less pleasant sections of the city. A large gang of third world thugs attacked the car, and although the two officers fought bravely, they both died defending the car and themselves."

There were angry boos and catcalls from the bleachers. The yahoos were shaking their fists. Emily held up an acknowledging hand.

"Believe me, I now how you good people feel, and I just hope those brave officers are resting in the bosom of the Lord."

There were shouts of amen. Emily moved quickly along.

"Now, I know that if anything so terrible happened to me I would have been hiding under the seat. Not Cynthia, though. She must be one of the pluckiest little gals around. She just snatched up one of the fallen officers' guns and started blasting.

She drove off the subhuman mob, killing a few in the process. Now how about that?''

The yahoos were roaring. Emily let them rip for a while and then turned to Cynthia.

"So weren't you scared out of your wits, my dear? I know I would have been.''

Cynthia was amazed at how easily she found her voice. "Oh, I was plenty scared, but when I saw the two officers go down, I just did what I had to do. I guess you could say it was like the old-time pioneers who first opened up this great country. In the normal run of things, it was the menfolk who did the fighting but, if something happened to the menfolk, then the women picked up the guns.''

"So you think that you've inherited the spirit of our pioneer women?''

Cynthia did her best to look helpless. "I really don't know. It all happened so fast, I didn't have time to think about anything. Like I said, I just did what I had to do.''

"And were you hurt at all?''

Cynthia shook her head. "No, I was in shock afterward, but nobody laid a finger on me. I must have been too fast for them.''

"Well, praise the Lord for that.''

There were more shouts of amen.

"One thing that I don't understand, honey, is how come you got to be so good with a gun. I mean if, the Good Lord forbid, but if I got myself into a situation like you did, I wouldn't have had a clue what to do. Put a gun in my hand and I wouldn't have the first idea what to do with it.''

Cynthia did not believe a word of it. Emily Burnette could probably smile while she killed. Cynthia, however, continued to go with the program.

"Well, Emily, I grew up a country girl with a bunch of brothers, and they taught me to shoot when I was a little girl.''

"Maybe the Lord knew what was coming up in your life.''

"Maybe. We never know, do we?''

Cynthia was over her stagefright and starting to feel a little queasy. Talking to Emily was like sucking saccharine. For a few more minutes they went on, Emily asking all the prearranged questions and Cynthia coming out with the bullshit as laid down by Deacon Longstreet. Finally the floor manager signaled to Emily, and she wrapped it up.

"Well, honey, I'm real pleased that you stopped by to chat

with us. I know it must have been a terrible ordeal for you and I know that everyone watching will be praying, not only for you, but also for the dear departed souls of those brave officers."

Vern was walking toward them, clapping as he walked. He faced the studio audience.

"Let's have a big Christian hand for this brave little girl. I don't know about you, but I think that she struck a real blow for all of us who are sick of getting pushed around by dopehead atheists and communists and agents of Satan and all the other scum that need to be cleared out of our cities."

The studio audience went berserk right on cue. They were on their feet, stamping and yelling and waving their banners. Cynthia felt a perverse sense of elation. Even though they were manipulated bigots and probably crazy evil, she could not lose the feeling that they were cheering for her. Despite all her instincts, it was a feeling that she liked. She was enjoying the applause.

Speedboat

Johnny Cash was singing "Ring of Fire." The Grass Roots Tavern on St. Marks Place had one of the last real coin-operated jukeboxes in the city. Most of them had been destroyed through that terrible weekend two years earlier when the deacons purged the video games and pinball machines. Some fool in Washington had taken it into his head that video games were the instruments of Satan, and all across the country the dekes had gone to work with a vengeance. The dekes loved anything that involved conspicuous violence and destruction. Unfortunately they had acted with a fairly wide interpretation of their orders, and the jukeboxes had been smashed right along with the other machines. Only an administrative oversight had saved the pool tables.

The Grass Roots Tavern was something of a surviving relic itself. As far as he knew, the low-ceilinged semibasement had been there since the 1950s if not longer. It had always been the hangout for East Side bohemians. In its time, it had seen beatniks and hippies, punks, skinheads, and zippos all pass through its doors. Even though it had been plastered with all the anti-alcohol propaganda that covered the walls of every bar, and the bohemians of the Faithful era had been reduced to petty criminal lowlife, it still managed to retain a few shreds of its traditional atmosphere. The jukebox was one of those shreds.

Speedboat ordered himself a shot of bourbon and chased it with a draft beer. Normally he did not drink hard liquor, but he was tired and tense. He had unloaded the rock records and the pornosoft without too much sweat, and Jook Aroun had come through with the spansules. Speedboat had already moved half of those, and if he kept on going at the same rate, the rest would be gone by later that night. He had over a thousand dollars stashed in one of the secret pockets of his parka, and escape to Canada was close to becoming a reality. He had even run into a piece of luck. A pillhead who had bought his spansules at one of the rat traps had a line on where to get a set of forged travel documents. There was a guy who worked on the lighting crew at the Garden who could give him all he needed to get across the border for twelve hundred. The pillhead had given Speedboat a number, and he had dialed it, though not without a good deal of trepidation. Pillheads were notoriously unreliable, and there was always the chance that the deal might be a setup. Over the phone he had been given a list of instructions that seemed, on the surface, to be the real thing. In five days' time there was going to be an Arlen Proverb spectacular at the Garden. Speedboat was to go there and meet his contact after the show. Normally Speedboat would not have gone within a mile of that kind of Christian freakout, but if that's what he had to do, he would be there. At least it was a public place, which lowered the odds on getting robbed.

A bunch of mouthbreeders were feeding coins into the jukebox, and the country music was quickly replaced by a dirgelike, modern, no-bop instrumental. It was some doombeam band, probably Flugzeug. Speedboat had nothing but contempt for the doombeams and the way they pretended they were so goddamn subversive. All they did was play around at being self-destructive; at no stretch of the imagination was that going to bring down Faithful and his gang. The bands were a perfect example. They slid by the literal minds of the music censors by playing all instrumental music. They put out a lot of attitude that somehow their hollow, minor chords were going to change the world. To Speedboat's ear, it was nothing more than grim, depressing, industrial noise.

Speedboat ordered another drink. He needed to relax. As Canada came closer to reality, the fear grew that something would go wrong. He would be ripped off on the final deal, or, worse than that, he was somehow being set up for the big fall. Earl the bartender put his shot and beer in front of him.

"What's the matter with you? You look like there's a hell-hound on your trail."

Speedboat shook his head. "It ain't nothing. I just got a lot on my mind."

"You got to watch out for that thinking. It can make you crazy."

Speedboat forced a half smile. "Sure."

Earl shrugged. "Barkeep wisdom."

He moved off to serve another customer. An individual who went by the name of Rancid had come out of the toilet and was talking to the mouthbreeders by the jukebox. Speedboat had not spotted him before. The word on the street was that Rancid was a deke snitch, and the smart money said that sooner or later he would wind up dead in a dumpster. Speedboat watched him out of the corner of his eye. Rancid moved from the mouthbreeders to a pair of doomy blondes who worked a sheep and shepherd game up on Union Square. The blondes did not seem to be particularly pleased to see him, but he persevered. He seemed to be trying to sell them something. As he talked, he glanced in Speedboat's direction a couple of times. Speedboat inwardly twitched. Were they talking about him, or was Rancid watching him? Suddenly he wanted to get out of the bar. He downed the shot in one gulp and took a quick swallow of beer. He left a two-dollar tip and stood up.

Earl nodded. "Leaving so soon?"

"I got to see a guy."

"So take care out there."

As Speedboat reached the door, someone else was coming through—a tall man in a raincoat and an old-fashioned fedora. Speedboat stepped quickly back. The guy had to be a cop. Nobody else would have the gall to dress like that. To his great relief, the man paid him no attention at all and walked on into the bar. Speedboat scuttled off into the night.

He hurried down St. Marks. The whole street was covered in posters for the Arlen Proverb revival at the Garden. They were big 3D duraprints of Proverb against a dark, storm-cloud sky. The angry eyes that glared out of the poster seemed to follow Speedboat down the street. At the corner of Second Avenue, he ducked into Gem Spa for a pack of cigarettes and a candy bar.

Two meth maniacs, Jetson and Ratner, were hanging out inside. Ratner was nervously flipping through a copy of *Life*, hardly seeing the pages, and Jetson was staring with bug-eyed concentration at the TV behind the counter and chewing his lip. Speedboat could not imagine why someone like Jetson should be so engrossed in *Vern and Emily*. It was the kind of chance encounter that Speedboat would have liked to avoid. The pair had a reputation for being dangerous and usually armed. He hoped that he might slip away without them noticing him. As usual, his luck was lousy.

"Hey, Speedboat, we want to talk with you."

They followed him outside.

"We heard you got a bunch of spansules off Aroun."

"We sure could use a few of those."

Speedboat didn't doubt that. They both looked in bad shape. Their eyes seemed about to spin, and their hands were trembling. He began to back away. "You heard wrong. I don't have a thing."

"Maybe you sold 'em all and you got the money on you?"

Speedboat felt sick. "I'm telling you, you heard wrong. I'm tapped out."

"Maybe we should look through that funky coat of yours."

At that moment a police gunship clattered overhead, randomly probing the neighborhood with twin searchlights. Speedboat saw his chance and went for it. While Jetson and Ratner were looking up at the chopper, he took off at a dead run, his legs pounding for dear life.

Carlisle

The Grass Roots Tavern was not the kind of place that Harry Carlisle normally frequented, but it was close to the Astor Place complex, and he had a bad need to drink and think. The Grass Roots Tavern also was not the kind of place that cops were supposed to frequent. It was the hangout of all kinds of East Side scum. Its clients ran pills and pornography and low-rent prostitution. Cops who hung around in scum joints were generally frowned upon. The only reason for a detective to go in there was to anchor a snitch or bust a drug dealer on his home turf. If one wanted to get drunk, he was supposed to go to one of the cop bars up on Fourteenth Street. Anything else was suspect, and if he was seen going into the Grass Roots, it would doubtless go on his political file. Carlisle did not give a damn. He was so far in after the day's fun and games that there was virtually nothing they could do to him anymore. Besides, Harry Carlisle had had enough of cops for one day.

The clientele of the Grass Roots did not exactly make him welcome. A suedehead in a ragged parka, who was coming out as he was going in, turned white at the sight of him. The kid probably had a pocketful of Haitian speed, but Harry didn't give a damn. He had more on his mind than a cheap, off-duty bust. The bartender gave him a hard look as he poured his scotch, and a number of customers seemed to be thinking about leaving. Harry mitigated the effect that he was having by taking his drink to an empty table as far from the jukebox as he could get.

He was still disturbed by the conversation with Dreisler. The man was like no other deacon that Harry had ever encountered. There were plenty of swine among their ranks, but Dreisler transcended the usual choice of fanatic sadism or brute nastiness. He seemed to be totally without belief or principle. He was also quite without the bulldozing hypocrisy that was the usual deacon method of rationalizing their excesses. He looked at it all as one great game, and he played it with a chilling relish. He was either so compartmentalized that he had no real feelings, or he was a brilliant case of arrested development, a vicious child pulling the wings off flies, who had been layered with a cold, steely self-control and an urbane, scalpel-sharp wit. He was certainly a master of the oblique. In fact, now that it was all over, Carlisle realized that he had no real idea of what they had been talking about. Ostensibly Dreisler had been pumping him for his thoughts and suppositions regarding the Lefthand Path. Underneath it all, though, something else had been going on. Dreisler was so Machiavellian that he would certainly have covered all of Carlisle's theories and probably many more besides. It was as if Dreisler had been sounding him out about something deeper but was not revealing what.

There were times when the man's cynicism glided close to actual heresy. Perhaps, as chief headhunter of the city's deacons, he felt that the normal constraints did not apply to him. Even his manner amounted to an affront to the deacon orthodoxy. With his silk scarves, leather coat, immaculate black lounge suit, and languid attitude, he was nothing less than a sinister fop. At the same time, though, the dark dandyism was the velvet glove that covered the remorseless iron hand. If Faithful ever came up with a final solution, it would be Dreisler who would implement it.

Harry recalled how strange the conversation had become toward the end. Dreisler had given him an odd sideways look.

"When you think about it, the Lefthand Path was inevitable."

Carlisle had not rushed to reply. "What was inevitable?"

"The whole thing. It's almost Darwinian."

"It is?"

"Oh, yes. Any truly repressive regime is going eventually to produce a highly efficient clandestine opposition. I think we have ours."

Dreisler had looked quite pleased by the idea. Carlisle knew he had to call him on his choice of words.

"Are you saying that we're repressive?"

Dreisler had smiled, taken off his Raybans, and dangled them by one earpiece. "Not you, dear boy. You're much too busy being an honest cop."

Carlisle got up and went to the bar for another drink. His action caused only a slight ripple among some new arrivals who had failed to notice him sitting quietly in the corner away from the jukebox. The Grass Roots was getting used to him. He returned to his seat. There were levels of speculation about Dreisler that, for his own peace of mind, he did not particularly want to explore. The worst was that Dreisler had almost seemed proud of the Lefthand Path. Sure, he was pleased that the LP existed because it fitted in with his theory of cyclical cause and effect, but Carlisle was sure there was more to it than that. Dreisler had really seemed delighted that there was a terrorist operation running rings around the police and the deacons. A man like Dreisler scarcely seemed capable of being that delighted with something that was not his own creation. That was the thought that Harry did not want to think. If Dreisler was somehow involved with the LP, it opened a universe of wheels within wheels, and each wheel had cogs sharp enough to tear him apart. What really worried Harry was that he was becoming more and more certain that Dreisler had decided that he might be of some use to him. Harry Carlisle did not want to be of use to Deacon Matthew Dreisler, if for no other reason than the fact that he did not want to discover what might happen to him when he stopped being of use. Dreisler's parting remark had been the final enigma.

"Remember, Lieutenant, it is a natural process. Every so often there has to be a cleansing of the temple." He had given Carlisle a knowing smile. "I'll be in touch."

With that, he had summoned his aides and swept out.

Harry sat in the bar shaking his head. "I don't like this. I don't like this at all."

He realized that he was talking to his scotch on the rocks. He was spending too much time on his own. He rubbed his chin. Maybe he should flash his badge, take a complimentary bottle off the bartender, and head on home. With all the stuff that was running through his mind, he would have a hard time sleeping without a good deal of whiskey inside him.

He was just reaching for his hat when two men came in. They were local street punks, but bigger and badder than the usual. They were dressed in old, full-length military raincoats and heavy engineer boots. Their eyes, their expressions, and the way they moved combined to scream silently that they were in the advanced state of strung out where it hurt to be alive. Harry half recognized one of them, a guy with a record of low-class armed violence. What was his name? He used a street name, the title of some old TV show. Jetson. That was it.

They were too strung out to be drinking. Harry was reminded that he was still carrying the Magnum under his left arm. Jetson was walking toward the bartender while his partner just stood his ground, halfway down the long narrow barroom. Heads were starting to turn. Harry was not the only one who could sense the tension. Jetson opened his coat and laid a caseless, stripped-down autoload on the bar with the muzzle pointing at Earl. Harry sighed. It was going down.

Jetson sounded as if he had been gargling razor blades. "We needs a loan, Earl. All you got in the till."

The partner also opened his coat. He had an Israeli needler, the kind that fired bursts of metal slivers from its triangular barrel. "Don't nobody get excited. There's a transaction going on here that ain't no concern of any of you."

How the hell had that punk gotten his hands on a needler? A single burst could decimate the room, and turn the Grass Roots into a bloody slaughterhouse.

When Earl finally found his voice, he sounded as bad as Jetson. "You're crazy. You can't get away with this. Everyone knows you."

It was a fact that probably did not need pointing out.

"The money, Earl, get the money. When we out of here, we gone."

Were they crazy enough to waste everyone in the place? It had happened before in narcotics-related holdups. Carlisle had his hand on the Magnum. He was easing back his chair. Earl was emptying the till. The two punks were watching the bartender intently. Carlisle was on his feet in combat stance, the Magnum pushed out at arm's length. His voice was soft but absolutely audible.

"Police officer. This is your only warning."

The punks were half turned away from him, but they started to bring their guns around. Carlisle fired twice. The recoil of the old gun felt reassuring. Jetson went down, shot through the head. Blood and brains were spattered all over the mirror and bottles in back of the bar. The second shot was a little low on the partner—he took it in the chest and spun around. The needler went off. Carlisle ducked, but the blast tore harmlessly into the ceiling. Dirt, paint, and plaster cascaded down. A section of the decaying tin ceiling fell out. Harry walked slowly forward, the smoking Magnum held loosely at his side. Jetson was sprawled across the bar, flat on his back and stone dead. His partner was in a fetal position on the floor with his chest making sucking sounds.

Harry looked at Earl. "I don't expect tearful gratitude, but first you could pour me a drink. After that you could call some uniforms and get this mess out of here."

Earl poured Harry a very large straight scotch. He peered over the bar. "Should I call the paramedics for him?"

"That's up to you."

Carlisle removed himself from the place as soon as the uniforms had taken control. When the sergeant in charge had asked him if he wanted to tape a statement, he had wearily shaken his head.

"I'll do it tomorrow. I'm beat."

There was always a degree of shock after a shooting, a blank numbness, as if a bit of him had been left with the dead. He did not relish killing, the way some in the department did, but this time he felt a certain sense of release. There had been something real about pulling the trigger, a reality that was the perfect antidote to the shadow play of conspiracy in which he had been spending too much of his time. Harry Carlisle knew what he was going to do. He flagged down a cab and took it to Eighty-sixth and Broadway, one of those blocks where the police turned a blind eye. As he got out of the cab, he took off his hat and draped his raincoat over his arm—he did not want to look like a cop. He was approached by a dark-skinned girl with long legs and straight black hair. She was wearing an old fur coat, which she opened to allow him a flash of naked flesh.

"You want to go out?"

Carlisle's smile was crooked. "Sure, I want to go all the way out."

Winters

At three o'clock in the morning Winters was still at his desk. His eyelids felt gritty, and the hard neon light was boring into the back of his head. There was the metallic taste of machine coffee in his mouth. And nothing he was doing seemed to have any useful purpose. He and the other junior deacons, on duty for more than sixteen hours, had been given what amounted to little more than makework. He had interviewed four of the women from the house on Fifteenth Street, seen that they were locked down in the holding cells, and then completed four totally inconclusive reports. He had fed the reports into the database along with the transcripts of the interviews. His next task had been to run everything through an inconsistency filter and cross-match his results with those of the interviews that had been conducted by the other officers. The whole process had taken the best part of the day and had yielded nothing. The discrepancies in the prostitutes' statements were well within the parameters of standard eyewitness variations. If any of the whores knew anything about the triple assassination they were hiding it extremely well. In fact, they were hiding it like a professional. Oddly, the higher-ups still had not authorized a depth interrogation of any of them.

It was probable, of course, that the higher-ups had more pressing matters on their minds. Dreisler's headhunters were still all over the place. At regular intervals, one after another of the senior officers were taken out for questioning. Some returned to their duties quite quickly, while others did not come back at all. It was starting to look as if Dreisler and his Internal Affairs goons were using the murders of Bickerton, Baum, and Kinney to conduct a full-scale shakedown of the upper levels of the antiterrorism section. The junior deacons were more than a little resentful, in part because they felt their turf was being violated, but also because of a very definite fear that after IA had finished with the senior officers, the juniors' turns would come.

Around seven, the junior deacons who had been on continuous duty since eight that morning had expected to be ordered to stand down. No such order was given. The red condition that had been imposed after the news of the killings continued, and they were put on monitor status, watching the incoming crime reports, the stepped-up sweep of telecommunication patterns, and the random spy eyes in the major newspapers and TV stations. Again it was makework. They were overseeing complex computer programs that were quite capable of looking after themselves. It started to seem that they were simply being bottled up in the CCC complex and kept occupied. The suspicion was that the killings and the PD raid on Fifteenth Street had blown the lid off some kind of major scandal that they were not being told about.

The worst of it was that even in the skittish atmosphere of building tension and resentment, none of the junior deacons felt they could talk about it. Certain that their every word and deed was being observed and recorded, they either folded in on themselves in tight-lipped silence, or, if they talked at all, they reduced conversation to its blandest fundamentals. A few of the more competitive tried to trap their rivals into an unguarded moment of complaint. Rogers had taken a couple of shots at Winters. The last time had been as he had walked past Winters' desk carrying a pile of videotapes of the crime scene that had finally been confiscated from the Channel 15 news department. He had shot Winters a rueful glance.

"So when do you think we'll get out of here?"

Winters, who was staring uncomprehendingly at a graphic representation of pay-phone usage in lower Manhattan at the time of the killing and wishing that he were stretched out on the couch in his apartment watching Pretaped Football, was almost jolted into some grunted condemnation of the hierarchs. He caught himself in the nick of time. "I guess Satan doesn't work to our convenience."

Rogers treated him to a sour look and went on to the viewing room.

Around eleven-thirty, insult was suddenly added to injury. On the police blotter, which was running on his secondary screen, an item came up: Carlisle, off duty, had shot two armed holdup men in a bar on St. Marks. The bastard who had caused all the trouble that very morning was making himself a hero. He would probably be on TV. Grim junior deacons exchanged glances. Aside from the LPs themselves, Lt. Harry Carlisle was the one they would most have liked to see take a fall. Winters was instantly suspicious. The story had to be some phony PD media setup. Carlisle must have thought that a bit of publicity would keep him out of reach of the deacons. Screw you, Carlisle, Winters thought. We'll get you in the end.

The night dragged on, and the red condition dragged right on with it. It was starting to look as if he were never to go home. The stuff on the monitors had ceased to make any sense at all. His eyes were just starting to droop when, with no warning, both his screens blacked out. He was reaching for the helpkey when a single sentence glowed green, right across the middle of his primary screen.

THERE WILL BE A CLEANSING OF THE TEMPLE.

His jaw dropped. He blinked stupidly. What? The message lasted for five seconds, pulsing slowly, then it faded to black. Abruptly everything returned to normal. Winters looked around, trying to act as casual as possible. The others were all going about their business just as they had been doing all night. Was he the only one who had seen it? Should he report it? His paranoid conditioning warned that it could be a loyalty test. How he reacted to it could have a serious effect on his already precarious E&D scores. There was something else though. Something deep inside made the confident suggestion that God was talking to him. But that was ridiculous. God did not talk to junior deacons. Not through a computer terminal. Winters found that he was sweating.

Kline

By the time they arrived at the third party, Cynthia Kline had lost all sense of time. Immediately after the taping of the *Vern and Emily* show she had been picked up by Deacon Longstreet in a large black Lincoln Continental. The first party had been a fairly sedate affair at a reception suite on the fifty-sixth floor of the Trump Grand Tower. The situation had been explained to her as they had ridden up in the crystal elevator, through the melodramatic sweeps of the tower's neo-Egyptian architecture.

"It's very simple, Cynthia. We're here to show you off to the print media and the TV stations that have not, as yet, committed to going with you and your story. You don't have to say anything. Just smile nicely and let us do the talking."

There were maybe a hundred journalists in the suite. It was a brave magazine or TV talk show that turned down a party invitation from the deacon PR department. The decor was white and gold with a palm-tree motif. It looked like the set for a very crass production of *Antony and Cleopatra*. Once inside, Longstreet and his team of seven surrounded her like a beaming phalanx. They smiled and bantered, handed out press kits and ten-by-eight color glossies, and put amiable but quite determined pressure on those who remained unsold. Longstreet repeated the same pitch over and over again.

"What you have to understand is that this isn't simply about Cynthia and her act of courage. It isn't even a matter of making the Corps of Deacons look good. It goes much deeper than that. It you think about it, you'll realize that Cynthia is a symbol for everyone who has ever wished that he or she could strike back against the daily terror that plagues our city. Cynthia may be attached to the deacons as a clerical auxiliary, but when she drove off those Godless thugs, she wasn't doing it as a part of her duty. We don't put women in the danger zone. She was a woman on her own, fighting back. She'd seen the men with her shot down and she was determined to save her own life. I think everyone can relate to that."

A battery of TV sets against one wall was running a tape of Cynthia on *Vern and Emily*. Waitresses circulated with trays of champagne and plates of small sandwiches. When Cynthia began to reach for a glass, Longstreet quickly shook his head. She was starting to realize what being a media symbol really meant. It meant that PR men like Longstreet took over one's life.

The press party ended with a photo opportunity. Still cameramen and video crews closed in on Cynthia.

"Look this way, honey. Over here!"

"Come on, babe, push it out a bit."

"Yo, hike your skirt up just a tad."

"Let's see a little more leg!"

Cynthia did not know whether to bolt or to slug one of them.

They obviously had temporarily forgotten what she was supposed to be famous for.

Longstreet was beside her, whispering reassuringly. "Don't let them get to you. Just smile and take it. It'll soon be over."

The photographers were relentless.

"Hey, baby, how about a shot with the gun?"

"Yeah. What about the gun?"

Cynthia had expected Longstreet to rescue her when the demands for the gun started. To her amazement and considerable distaste, one of his assistants produced a standard-issue Remington Controller, just like the one that she had used on the two cops. She took it gingerly, took a deep breath, and brandished it. After a few moments, she looked from Longstreet to the photographers and back again.

"Is this thing loaded?"

Longstreet put on a show of cracking up for the audience, although something in his eyes warned her that he was the one who did the jokes.

Finally it was over. The press was leaving and busboys were clearing away the debris. Cynthia flopped into a chair, relieved that the show was over for the day. But Longstreet seemed to have other ideas.

"So, are you ready to have some fun?"

Cynthia had taken off one of her high heels and was massaging her right foot. She looked up in surprise. "Fun?"

"All work and no play. We have a couple of parties to go to."

"I thought that this was the party."

"This was business. The rest of the night is pleasure."

Cynthia frowned. "I don't know. I feel kind of beat."

"There are a lot of people waiting to meet you. You're the woman of the moment, after all."

Cynthia sighed. "So I'm still on duty?"

Longstreet lit a cigarette and handed her a glass of slightly flat champagne. "Not turning into a bolshevik prima donna already, are we?"

Cynthia looked down at her uniform. It had been instant-tailored for her. Figure hugging and made of Italian silk, it had nothing in common with her regular drab outfit except the insignia. At first, she had been amused by the idea of playing the wide-eyed innocent from inside this deacon killer-vamp creation. The costume had certainly helped her stand up to Emily, and when the taping was finished, Vern had become exceedingly friendly. After the TV show and the press bash, however, the outfit was beginning to wilt, and she was even starting to fear for its computer-stitched instant seams.

"Couldn't I go home and take a shower and change or something?"

Longstreet smiled. "It's all been taken care of."

"It has?"

Longstreet pointed. "You see that thing that over there looks like a mirror but is, in fact, a door?"

"Yes."

"So if you go through it, you'll find that you have a private bath and dressing room. A hot bath is waiting, and your clothes have been laid out."

Cynthia had known that the officers of the PR section were different from the rest of the deacons, but she was only starting to discover just how different. Longstreet himself summed it up completely and set the pattern for his handpicked underlings. With his patent-leather hair, effeminate gestures, and voice like a castrato W.C. Fields, he would have been called gay back in the old days, but no one was gay anymore—he was simply creative. His mannerisms became more extravagant now that they were alone and the show was over, but Cynthia did not let that fool her. She was also starting to realize that he was a master of his craft. His life probably depended on that.

Another uniform was laid out for her in the bathroom. Where the last one had been form fitting, the new one was a second skin of black satin. The perfunctory tunic was so low cut that it revealed more cleavage than she had shown since she had been a teenage bounce dancer in the summer of '96.

"I'm not sure about this outfit."

"Selling the deacons with sex bothers you?"

"Getting arrested bothers me."

"You can't be arrested. You're with deacons."

"But this? I look like a hooker."

"Give me a break, Cynthia dear. I know the corn-fed, prude act is a crock."

"What do you mean?"

"I've been watching you. You're taking to an audience like a glutton to punishment. There's always an audience for sex. Think about it. Everyone is fascinated by sex. They're even more fascinated now that they don't do it anymore. Besides, you won't exactly be playing to the great, dull, proletariat of Jesus this time. No Vern and Emily where we're going, stalwart in the service of the Lord as they may be. I said that we were going to have fun.''

Fun according to Longstreet turned out to be a frenetic, roller-coaster tour of the thin ice; high society that existed many floors above the yahoos howling for God, the spiritual cripples staring into the lights of their Jesus Waves, and the dark, miserable, strife-torn streets. Ground-level reality never penetrated their steel and crystal towers. It never got past the private security forces with their Uzis and electric clubs. Cynthia entered a Manhattan that was the last remnant of old-fashioned American hedonism. She was suddenly surrounded by people who still played and glittered against the shimmering skyline as if Cole Porter, Andy Warhol, and Sable Lydon had never been gone.

"Of course, there aren't as many of them as there were in the old days," Longstreet told her. "Most of them relocated to Rome or Brazilia when we took over. These are the rump of the rich. The real diehards, so to speak. You might even call them an endangered species.''

The night started at Der Blaue Engel, a private nightclub off Central Park West that, behind a blank basement façade, was a loving re-creation of a cabaret in Nazi Berlin. The singer dredged up Marlene Dietrich, the strippers were elaborately bizarre, and even the waiters and waitresses were like something out of *Salon Kitty*. The emcee was an elderly exquisite in a velvet tuxedo who loosed a stream of consciousness that was pure venom, sedition, and heresy.

". . . so Larry Faithful dies and goes to heaven.''

There was a ripple of applause. The exquisite looked at the audience curiously.

"And what are you people so pleased about? That he made it to heaven, or merely that he died?''

The drummer hit a rimshot. The crowd guffawed, and the exquisite started again.

"So anyway, Larry Faithful dies and goes to heaven and St. Peter comes out and he's wearing high heels and a dress . . .''

Longstreet leaned close to Cynthia. "The moment he stops being adorable, he'll be in Joshua.''

Cynthia had felt profoundly uncomfortable in the first place. There was the stupid outfit that exposed her as if she were some 1950s movie starlet out on display. There was also the desperate blatantness. If Longstreet was correct in his advanced cynicism, this endangered species thrilled to the danger. Why else had these last lonely jetsetters not taken the final jet out? There was a sprinkling of deacon dress gray among the suits and evening dresses. Despite Longstreet's apparent lack of concern, the place made her extremely nervous. There had to be a limit somewhere around the point that cynicism blurred into recklessness.

"Are those real deacons or just people masquerading as deacons?"

"Probably both. Does it really matter when you come down to it?"

Cynthia had shaken her head and ordered two martinis in quick succession. The alcohol had not made the place seem any less insane, but it had afforded her a certain level of detachment. The question of why anyone would want to fool around with Nazi-era decadence when there was a real live concentration camp just across the river in New Jersey became a little more academic.

"How do they get away with this stuff?"

"Probably because they think they don't care."

"Yes, but why do they have to play at I Am a Camera?"

Longstreet glanced at her with a raised eyebrow. "I Am a Camera? Your milk-and-cookies exterior really is a crock, isn't it?"

Cynthia realized that she had screwed up. The booze had made her careless. Longstreet read her expression and laughed.

"Don't look so upset, my dear. You're among friends. We all have pasts, you know. Only the very rich and the very stupid don't have to wear bland masks, but if you're going to swill martinis by the bucket, I suggest we order some food."

As Cynthia was finishing the best steak she had tasted since she left Canada, a man and two women joined them. The man was a short, Napoleonic Chilean called Raoul. Longstreet told her later that Raoul owned one of the biggest hack houses engaged in running the Japanese embargo. The deacons were never going to touch him, and he expected the pick of everything. Since he brought in 40 percent of the advanced software that reached the Eastern Seaboard, he normally got what he wanted. One of the women played small parts in the soaps. Her name was Donna, her hair was black, and she was voluptuous and wore a leather dress that suggested that pain might be amusing. She hardly said a word and rarely even smiled. The other was a willowy and anemic blonde with the unlikely name of Webster.

Her white jersey dress was quite as tight and revealing as Cynthia's satin uniform but, in addition, she had a Blackglama mink hanging over her shoulders. She was also stumbling drunk. At regular intervals, she would do a mood switch, stop giggling, petulantly announce that she was bored, and demand to be taken to Hell.

Hell turned out to be a clandestine nightspot among the ruins of Tenth Avenue. It was the renovated and heavily disguised basement of one of the blackened buildings beside the burned-out Javits Center. The five of them rode down there in Raoul's rented limousine. When they got out of the car, they had to pick their way along a narrow path between piles of rubble. Cynthia, who had drunk most of a bottle of Mouton Rothschild with her steak, as well as a couple more martinis, did not like this at all. Aside from the simple physical problems of negotiating the uneven surface in four-inch heels, an impossible skirt, and with her sense of balance more than a little impaired, it also reminded her too much of the dark vacant lot where she had shot the two cops.

There must have been some kind of heat sensor concealed in the rubble. Without any warning an automatic trap slowly lifted. Red light spilled out from below.

"Damn, it really is the entrance to hell."

A flight of steps led down to something out of the pre-AIDS '80s. Lasers flashed and holograms whirled in a huge, industrial-tech cavern. Porno loops were playing on a giant back-projection screen, and the music was oldies and outlawed. The live DJ, a tall black woman in spandex, seemed determined to run through the entire catalog of proscribed rock and roll. The dance floor was crowded with gyrating people, some of whom were practically naked.

Cynthia looked at Longstreet in amazement. "I didn't know anything like this existed."

"Everything exists. There have to be a few fleshpots, if only for foreign visitors. We're not Syria, you know. Most things can be accommodated if they're discreet and don't frighten the proles."

"This isn't discreet."

"That's why it has only three more weeks to go."

"You sound like you know that for a fact."

Longstreet laughed. "I'm already composing the media campaign that will accompany the bust."

"And what about all these people?"

"I'm afraid a lot of them will end up in the camps. Illicit thrills wouldn't be thrills if there wasn't a penalty attached to them. Besides, anyone who's important to me will be warned to stay away."

Cynthia blinked and shaded her eyes with her hand as a focused light effect hit her full in the face. "Don't have the fun if you can't do the time? Is that what you're saying?"

Longstreet nodded. "Exactly."

"There's something fucked up about all this."

"Of course there is. It's all a part of modern America."

They left after what purported to be a heavy metal band took the stage. Four young men in shag wigs and bondage costumes hammered loud raucous guitars and howled about Satan.

For the next party, they went uptown and across the park to Fifth Avenue. The Gotti Building was an art deco spire that had been financed by some very dubious millions during the mini-boom of the mid-'90s. Up in the penthouse, the music was smuggled hits from England and Australia, and the style was a brittle sparkle. The women were in designer originals and wore their own diamonds, and the men were in tuxedos. No doubt the tuxedos had been immaculate at the start of the evening, but by the time Longstreet's party arrived, jackets were unbuttoned and bowties undone, voices were loud, and the odd breast threatened to spill out of a low-cut Giva or Manetti. Cynthia felt more than ever like a freak on display, but she had passed the point of caring. Longstreet was treated like a major celebrity, and once it had been explained who Cynthia was, she found herself surrounded by her own circle of admirers. A breathless woman with cropped red hair and orange lipgloss wanted to know how it felt to kill someone.

Cynthia winked. "You just curl your finger around the trigger and pull, honey. You know how to pull, don't you?"

Later she heard the woman describing her to a group of friends as a psychopath. By that point, Cynthia was seriously drunk. Even coming up in the elevator, she had sagged against Longstreet.

"How do you keep this up night after night?" she had asked them.

"You probably haven't noticed, but I don't drink that much."

Cynthia lost all sense of time. The penthouse was starting to spin. Running on automatic, she headed for the bathroom, which turned out to be bigger than her apartment and decorated in black glass. Two women were leaning against one of the walls, caressing each other. One of them was Webster. She was half out of her clothes. She turned and looked blearily at Cynthia. "Your Longstreet's protégée, aren't you? What was your name again?"

"Cynthia."

"Hi, Cynthia."

Webster's companion also peered at her. Her bared breasts looked as if they had had the benefit of surgical implants.

"Hi, Cynthia."

Cynthia swayed and raised an ineffectual arm in greeting. "Hi."

Webster held out a small fold of blue paper and a rolled hundred-dollar bill. "You ever do cocaine, Cynthia?"

Cynthia's eyes widened. She had not seen cocaine since the '90s.

"Don't look so shocked. Although it is terribly illegal."

Webster's friend giggled. "They'll come and take us all away one of these days." She waved a fluttering butterfly hand. "All away."

Webster disengaged from her friend and moved unsteadily toward Cynthia. "You want some?"

It seemed to be a drunken dare. Or maybe it was a trap. Paranoia floated up through the haze.

"I don't know."

"Come on. You only live once."

"We're all witches and we're all going to burn. Might as well burn for something good."

Cynthia took the packet. Drunken bravado had swamped fear. She opened it and what she saw stopped her dead. Sure there was a small amount of white powder in the blue paper, but that wasn't it. There was a single symbol drawn on the inside of the pack. A simple right angle like an inverted L. It was the symbol of the Lefthand Path.

1346408 Stone

The hiss and staccato crack of the whip were immediately followed by the scream of the inmate. The sequence of sounds echoed around the concrete walls of the blockhouses that surrounded the main yard. There was nothing else. The whole camp, assembled there in the yard, seemed to have stopped breathing.

"Twenty!"

Voorhiss, the huge guard who acted as camp executioner, was bringing back his arm once again. He stretched to his full six five, leaning back slightly. The inmate was making soft whimpering noises. The scaffold on which the punishment was taking place had been fully miked. Every audio detail was being relayed over the PA. Voorhiss struck again. Again there was the hiss, the crack, and the scream. The inmate struggled and twisted against the heavy plastic restraints that secured her to the tall wooden triangle.

"Twenty-one!"

Armed bosses walked slowly up and down the overhead catwalks, ready to open fire at the first sign of any kind of protest. Punishments always raised the level of resentment among the inmates. Trusties paroled on ground levels, slapping their electric clubs into their gloved hands and scanning the eyes of the inmates. The prisoners had to watch every moment of the punishment. Closing one's eyes or looking away was an offense equal to three days in the bunker. The whip struck again. This time the scream strangled off into a series of racking sobs. The inmate's back was bleeding.

"Twenty-two!"

FOUR

Mansard

THE INTERIOR OF MADISON SQUARE GARDEN WAS AN EMPTY, echoing cavern that dwarfed the men working inside it. Their shouts, the hammering, the sharp bursts of noise from their belt radios, the hum of the cranes and servos, and the bump and scrape of heavy equipment being manhandled into position all reverberated around the girders of the roof and blended into a dull cacophony that signified a show was being set up. Mansard both loved and feared those sights and sounds, probably in much the same way that gladiators had loved and feared the smell of blood and sand, or that clowns loved and feared the sawdust and animal stench of the circus. The setup was the immediate prelude to Mansard's personal moment of truth. He could test and plan and check, but the time always came when there was nothing else to do except throw the switches and hope for the best. The start of the setup was the point where the tension began to build to its final peak.

He watched a rigger ride a lighting truss with professional nonchalance as it was hoisted up into the roof. The four massive scaffolds that, with their interlocking gantries, would carry the lights, the optic screens, and the image projectors were rapidly taking shape. Outside on the roof, a second crew was installing the equipment that would create the grand finale, the big Sony DL-70s, fresh off a chartered cargo plane from Chile, that would bring the Four Horsemen to life. The show was going to cost Arlen Proverb a fortune.

Mansard would soon have to go out onto the roof and check on how things were coming. The DL-70s were straight out of their packing grease and completely untested. If one of them had been damaged in transit, he would be totally screwed. Jimmy Gadd was working feverishly to get them ready for a trial run. Mansard was putting off going up there, however. It was not just that he did not want to hear the bad news, if any. Charlie Mansard, even though his life was dedicated to producing huge images in vast areas of empty space, had no particular love of heights. He could no more ride a lighting truss with the riggers' total lack of concern than he could fly in the air. He would ride the truss if he had to, but he would always be nervously looking down.

Rita was hurrying across the floor of the Garden, heading in his direction. She looked unusually agitated. "We just got a call. Proverb's on his way over."

"Damn. What the hell does he want to do that for? There's nothing for him to see yet. They should have told him that."

"Maybe he gets nervous, just like you."

"Why should he? He's got God on his side. All I've got is Jimmy."

"Which would you rather have?"

Mansard grinned despite himself. "You've got a point there."

Mansard's first impulse was to rush around and yell at people, to try to get something ready for the client. He knew that was ridiculous. Proverb was a professional: he knew that there were still two days to go and there was no way that Mansard would be ready to stage an effects run-through for at least eighteen hours. If he wanted to walk around and nod and watch the men putting up the scaffolds, that was up to him. It was nothing more than a waste of time.

"What the hell does he want to come bothering me for? Can't he stand in front of a mirror and rehearse his lines? I've got quite enough to do without conducting guided tours."

Rita shrugged. "You know what clients are like. They want to feel they're on top of things."

Arlen Proverb arrived with a small army at his back and the air of an occupying general. For someone who was so famous for his stage presence, he was of surprisingly small stature. He compensated for his lack of height by extreme flamboyance of dress. He was wearing a double-breasted white suit and a purple silk shirt; a black fur coat was thrown over his shoulders. The gold crucifix that bounced against his chest must have weighed close to a pound. The stitching on his white, high-heeled cowboy boots was also gold. As with so many of those who capitalized on their charisma, the first clue to Arlen Proverb's power was in his eyes. At rest, they were heavy-lidded and languid, almost lazy, but when he focused on something they came alive, knowing and penetrating, going right to the soul. He was flanked by his two huge bodyguards. According to the media, they went everywhere with him and even slept in the room next to his. On his right was Rashid Murjeen. The huge black man, who had been a heavyweight contender back in the old days, was quite probably the only Muslim in the employ of an American evangelist. Proverb had come in for a good deal of criticism on account of Rashid, but he had consistently ignored it. On his left was Joe Don Cutler, who had played for the '96 Steelers. He was the all-around cowboy. His black country singer's suit was decorated with white beadwork, and his Stetson had the feathers of an entire parakeet mounted on its front. It was very clear from the way the two of them carried themselves that anyone who interfered with Proverb could expect to be torn limb from limb. In addition to the two bodyguards, there was a six-man squad of private security guards in brown quasipolice uniforms, three aides in business suits, and a young, very well-developed blonde who was wearing a coat that matched Proverb's.

Proverb walked straight up to Mansard with his hand extended. He grasped Charlie's and shook it warmly. His energetic bonhomie came directly from his car salesman roots.

"Charlie, it's good to see you. How are you? How are things going?"

Mansard arranged his face into his best meeting-the-client smile. "I'm very well, Reverend Proverb, and everything seems to be coming together perfectly. So far, we're ahead of schedule."

"Arlen. How many times do I have to tell you, Charlie? It's Arlen. I can't be doing with my best men calling me Reverend Proverb. Makes me feel that I'm a hundred years old." He glanced at the two bodyguards. "Ain't that the truth, boys? No formalities around this family."

Rashid said nothing, but Joe Don grinned. "No standing on ceremony around us, boss."

The blonde giggled. Rashid gave her a hard look. Mansard

had had previous experience with Proverb's lack of formality. Everything stayed relentlessly downhome just as long as it was recognized that Arlen Proverb was the absolute dictator of the universe.

Proverb had changed quite a bit since Mansard had last seen him. Where his hair had previously been a nondescript brown, it was now dyed blue black, and the bow-wave pompadour was far more lavish than he remembered it. Proverb was also sporting thick triangular sideburns. The hair was one thing—the added length and the dye job could be attributed to a simple case of advanced show business. The sideburns were something else again. When one was as much in the spotlight as Proverb was, nothing could be dismissed as coincidental. The sideburns were too much of a symbol. They had to be perceived as an indication that Proverb really was moving closer to the Elvi—and if Arlen Proverb was moving closer to the Elvi, he was also further distancing himself from the Faithful establishment. Even though he claimed to be above it all, Mansard kept a fairly close watch on the political fluctuations of his clients.

Proverb was looking up at the giant scaffolds. "So, Charlie, where do we stand at the moment?"

"Well, Arlen, as you can see, most of the basic framework is in place. Pretty soon we'll start putting in the optical equipment. Once they're in place, we'll be ready for a visual run-through. If your sound men are ready in time, we could sync the audio."

Proverb nodded. "I'll goose them up some. Make sure they're ready when you are."

Mansard had to give Proverb credit for being well aware of the basics of the technology that went into his show. That was unusual among preachers. Most cultivated a smiling ignorance, as if pretending that they were living in some Old Testament world where special effects came straight from God.

"How are things going with the big final set piece?"

Mansard had expected that question. He maintained his air of calm confidence. "My best men are up on the roof rigging the gear, and the weather forecast looks good."

"You don't foresee any problems?"

Mansard shook his head. "Not at this point." He was not about to voice his fears about the DL-70s.

Proverb nodded again, then looked around as if he were hesitating to say something. "There is one thing I'd like to talk to you about."

He put an arm around Mansard's shoulders and led him out of earshot of the entourage.

"Now, I know, what with you being an artist and all, you ain't going to like what I want to ask, but I need a big favor."

Mansard had a suspicion of what was coming. "What do you want me to do?"

"I want you to juice the wave pushers."

"The script only called for undertow hypnotics."

"I've decided to go for broke."

Mansard sadly shook his head. "I really don't think you need to do that."

"I've got my reasons."

"Usually when a client wants me to juice the hypnotics, he's either got cold feet or he's no damn good, or both. I know that isn't the case with you. We've got an effects menu that'll knock their socks off. Most of them are spongy before they even come to the show from staring into a Jesus Wave all afternoon."

The hand on Mansard's shoulder tightened.

"You know me, Charlie. I trust your effects. Praise the Lord, Charlie, I'm counting on your effects. I have my own special reasons for wanting all the juice I can get. You'll have to trust me on that."

The eyes had come on, and Mansard knew that Proverb was determined to get what he wanted. What the hell was the man up to? He made a small gesture of capitulation. Proverb was God's own salesman.

"What levels do you want the pushers raised to?"

"Give me five with an override to eight."

Mansard let out a low whistle. "Are you sure about that?"

Proverb nodded. He looked almost grim. "I'm positive, and I want the override through to my sleeve control. I want to be able to zap the crowd if and when I need to."

The spangles on the sleeves of Proverb's costumes concealed a highly sophisticated electronic control system that he could play like a master. Mansard still was not happy.

"You want to go easy on the straight eight. You could start them flipping."

"If that's what it takes."

Mansard was surprised. He had never seen Proverb reveal that kind of ruthlessness. Clearly something was going down. Maybe he would rather not know about it.

He gave a small shrug. "It's your insurance coverage."

Proverb fixed him with the eyes again. "You're a good man, Charlie, but let me do the worrying."

There was more ritual handshaking and backslapping, and then Arlen Proverb swept out again. Charlie Mansard watched him go. This was shaping up to be no ordinary show.

Carlisle

"You really think he might be a target?" Carlisle asked.

"He's getting so much publicity that we have to seriously consider the possibility," Parnell replied.

"We don't have enough troubles?"

"Not as many as we'd have if a big-name preacher was shot dead live on stage at the Garden."

"Or blown up."

"Exactly."

"We could try to get him to cancel the show."

"Proverb's got too much swagger for that. He'd go on regardless. He'd probably go on even if the LPs issued a public warning."

Harry Carlisle had a leg cocked over the corner of Captain Parnell's desk. He was leaning forward peering at the large, hardcopy floorplan of Madison Square Garden. Both men had mugs of coffee in their hands. Parnell had his own coffee maker. It made real coffee that was infinitely superior to the bitter, darktan liquid that came out of the vending machines. Harry tapped the plan with his index finger.

"We can't give him absolute protection in a place this size."

"That's right."

"So what do we do?"

"All we can do is play the odds. Before the show, we do the place from top to bottom with sniffers. We beef up the weapons and explosives searches on the entrances. We run spotter scopes on the crowd and push the images through a hostile motion filter. We position snipers around the stage and have plainclothes squads in high saturation around the most likely vantage points from where a sniper might operate. After that we pray." He glanced up at Carlisle with a half smile. "Of course, you don't pray, do you?"

"Not if I can help it."

"You're going to wind up in a camp one of these days."

"Probably."

"You think you can stay out of trouble until after this Proverb spectacular is over?"

"I'll try. What do you want me to do?"

"I want you to take charge of the plainclothes squads on the floor."

"How many men do I get?"

"As many as I can spare. Hopefully something around a hundred."

"How much help can we count on from the deacons?"

Parnell shook his head. "I really don't know. They're acting ambivalent. There's a fairly powerful faction that'd be quite happy to see Proverb knocked off. They believe he's a dangerous maverick who borders on heresy."

"So even if they show up, we can't really trust them."

"That's how we have to approach the situation."

Carlisle scowled. "Just great. What about Proverb's own security people?"

"They can deal with the stage and backstage area. That's what they do best. Those two big bodyguards, the Muslim and the cowboy, they can have the honor of shielding their boss with their bodies if anyone opens fire. They can have that all to themselves."

"Can I pick my own men?"

"Sure, as long as you leave me all the sharpshooters."

Carlisle put down his coffee cup and pushed himself away from the desk. "I guess I'll go and get started."

"There'll be a detailed briefing after tomorrow's roll call. I suggest you go over to the Garden and familiarize yourself with the place. Proverb's people are already in there setting up."

"I've worked the Garden before. I know it pretty well."

Carlisle moved to the door. He hesitated before letting himself out. "Can I ask you som thing?"

"You usually do."

"How does the NYPD feel about Arlen Proverb?"

Parnell looked him straight in the eye. "Having a public figure killed in our jurisdiction can't do the department any good at all. Is that what you wanted to know?"

Carlisle nodded. Then he turned and left.

The theological advisory officer's steel-rimmed glasses were just sufficiently tinted to make it impossible to see his eyes. He could not have been past his early thirties, but his sandy blond hair was already thinning. The harsh white lights over the lecture room rostrum were reflected from his bald crown.

"Ostensibly we will be providing security backup to the NYPD, but in reality, we have a much more important mission at the Arlen Proverb service at Madison Square Garden."

The TAO carefully placed the flat palm of his hand on the lectern in front of him. It was the ultimately controlled version of slamming down his fist.

"Heresy, gentlemen. We will be there to detect heresy."

He paused for a moment to let his words sink in.

"Shall we think about heresy, gentlemen? Heresy is the worst of crimes, worse even than rape, murder, or terrorism. These others, although they are in themselves sufficiently heinous to warrant the putting to death of the perpetrator, are crimes against person and property and as such are the legitimate province of the secular police. Heresy, on the other hand, is a crime against the Lord our God, and without the Lord, our civilization would fail, and we would be back in the Satanic darkness that we only so recently struggled out of."

There was nodding among the keener of the junior deacons, led off by Rogers and a couple of others. Winters joined in just a little late. The TAO went on.

"We are the defenders of the faith, gentlemen, and the heretic is the greatest enemy of that faith. The heretic is a contagion that must be rooted out wherever it lurks. I repeat, wherever it lurks."

He put particular emphasis on the word "wherever."

"We will be at the Proverb service to observe. As of this moment, there is no investigation and no crime. No complaint has been laid, and there are no suspects, but as you all well know, the agents of Satan can reveal themselves anywhere and at any time. We must be constantly on our guard, watching for heretics both among the audience and on the stage."

Although it had not been stated, the message was clear: Proverb was under surveillance. There had been rumors about Arlen Proverb's lack of favor in Washington for some time. There had always been a gulf between him and the Faithful establishment, but recently it had grown visibly wider. It appeared that Proverb was doing everything to maximize the schism. He was appealing more and more to the wild and wooliest of nonconformists and even attracting out-and-out unbelievers. Proverb was still far too powerful to be directly accused, but the oblique instructions were clear. They were to start quietly collecting evidence. It was the first stage to laying a case.

Junior Deacon Milton raised his hand. "What if we detect overt heresy at the service? Do we attempt to make arrests?"

"You do nothing. No matter what the provocation."

The TAO half smiled. On the scarce occasions that he showed an emotion, his face became almost skull-like, with the tinted glasses providing the empty, shadow-filled sockets. It was as if his skin had been stretched too tight by the constant contempt in which he held an imperfect world.

"This is an occasion when the virtue of patience will have to be cultivated."

Winters raised his hand. "Intelligence reports indicate that a large number of the Presley people will be present at the service."

The TAO was no longer smiling. "I have seen the intelligence reports."

"Could this not have the potential of becoming a mass demonstration of heretical behavior?"

"You have touched on a less than well defined area, Junior Deacon . . . what was your name?"

"Winters, sir." Winters always dreaded what might happen when a superior asked him his name.

The TAO nodded. "Our first problem, Winters, is that there has never been a definite consensus regarding the exact nature of the Elvi. It has never been finally decided whether they are legally heretical or simply an extreme form of nonconformist sect akin to the snake handlers. The confusion is compounded by the fact that attitudes to this kind of extremism differ sharply from region to region. Here in the somewhat better educated North, we seek a certain orthodoxy and tend to be a little appalled by"—his face took on a brief expression of mild distaste—"the idea of worship via reptile. In the South and West, however, they have a much greater traditional tolerance of the bizarre. I have my own opinions about what should be done to the whole pack of them, but these are personal, and I would have no place expressing them here. Until we have specific instructions, we also do nothing about the Elvi.''

''Under no circumstances?''

''Under no circumstances whatsoever, Winters. I don't care if they are crawling on the floor and publicly fornicating. We do nothing except remind ourselves that our day will come and we will have everything.''

The skull-like half smile came again.

Kline

She drank coffee and tried to pull herself together. She felt awful. If this was what fame was, it might well kill her. She rummaged through her handbag, looking for the piece of paper from the night before, the blue paper that the cocaine had come in. From the moment that she had seen the Lefthand Path symbol on the inside of the packet, fear had tinged her drunken haze. Now it was morning, and all that remained was the hangover and the fear. The apartment looked even more cramped and dingy than it usually did, and the sunlight seemed to be struggling to cut through the smoggy air. Indeed, the whole of life seemed to be a depressing struggle. It was bad enough having a couple of drunken lesbian strangers offer her a drug that could get her five years, but to see the symbol of her secret and highly illegal organization on the inside of the packet had brought her close to hysteria. Fortunately Longstreet had simply assumed that she was drunk and incoherent. He had, in fact, seemed quite amused by her situation. In the cold gray of the morning, she wondered if he thought he was corrupting her.

She found the blue packet where she had hidden it in the lining of her bag. The woman Webster had not wanted the packet back. With a conspiratorial grin she and her companion had gone, leaving Cynthia swaying in the black-glass bathroom, looking blearily from the packet of coke to the infinite repetitions of her reflection in the multiple mirrors. With about the last shred of her presence of mind, she had sniffed up the remaining powder through the hundred-dollar bill and concealed the paper in the torn lining of her bag. The last thing she needed was to be caught with a quantity of coke.

She turned the paper over between her fingers. It seemed impossible that it could contain any kind of real message, considering the context in which it had been given to her, but she had to check. Standing up caused the pain in her head to increase sharply, and she had to stand still for a few seconds before going to the dressing table and searching through her jewelry box for the large antique dress ring with the huge fake ruby. With a practiced half twist she removed the stone. When she had been issued the thing back at the training camp there had been a lot of jokes about her secret decoder ring—but that was exactly what it was. She moved the microcode scanner across the surface of the paper. The first side was as blank as she had expected, but to her surprise, the second gave a positive reading.

"Damn."

She had truly hoped that this would not happen. The fact that the piece of paper contained a dot-coded message created a whole fresh set of questions. The prime among them was why she should be getting messages in a penthouse bathroom from a drugged-out party girl who was falling out of her dress. A close second was just how much trust she could put in a message that was delivered that way. She knew without being told that the organization had people in some very strange positions, but surely there had to be limits.

She loaded the dot data into her small laptop deck and ran a complex access code. The cipher program was hidden beneath a perfectly innocent-looking data management plan. The message that appeared on the screen was simple and to the point.

IT IS LIKELY THAT YOU WILL BE ASKED BY LONGSTREET TO GO TO THE ARLEN PROVERB SPECTACULAR AT MADISON SQUARE GARDEN. YOU WILL GO. IF HE DOESN'T SUGGEST IT, YOU WILL MAKE THE SUGGESTION TO HIM. WHATEVER HAPPENS, YOU WILL GO TO THE SHOW. YOU WILL BE CONTACTED THERE AND ISSUED WITH FURTHER INSTRUCTIONS.

Anslinger

Maude Anslinger could not afford to go to the Arlen Proverb rally. The money simply would not stretch that far. The monthly payments from George's life plan bought so little after all the years of inflation. Why did George have to be taken so early? Why, of all people, did he have to go with lung cancer? She knew that God had a plan for all things and that she should not question the ways of the Almighty, but it did seem a little unfair. Maybe she should be grateful that she still had the apartment. That was what President Faithful always said: Be grateful for your blessings and pray hopefully for the future. The trouble was that it proved to be so difficult merely feeding herself and Theodore that she felt her faith was being constantly tested.

At that moment, Theodore was curled contentedly in her lap. It had been a lucky week for the cat. Some strange fish stuff had appeared in the freezer cabinets at the market. Colored a peculiar pinkish white, it had come without either a label or a date stamp. She had bought it with a good deal of reluctance, but Theodore had fallen on it as if it were a rare delicacy. Afterward, he had shown no ill effects, so she had gone on feeding it to him and even considered eating it herself.

On TV, there was another commercial for the Arlen Proverb rally. She wished that she had the forty bucks to spare for a ticket. There was no way that she could come up with forty that week, or any other week, for that matter. That was something else that did not seem fair. The really poor got to go. An allocation of free passes was set aside for the unemployed, but she did not qualify. The fact that she owned her home and received an insurance pension, no matter how inadequate, disqualified her. The commercial caused a dull ache in her heart, as did the 3D posters that were plastered all over the neighborhood. It was as if Proverb's eyes, which at the moment were staring out of the screen, could see right through her. She had always liked Arlen Proverb. When George had been alive, they had gone to a number of Proverb's meetings. Of course, back then, they had been much smaller affairs than this huge spectacular at Madison Square Garden, but there had always been something warm about Arlen Proverb. Where President Faithful seemed so neat and controlled and maybe a little prim, even during his Sunday night fireside chats, there was a boyish energy about Arlen Proverb, a certain exhilarating wildness. He could create the image of a Jesus who laughed and danced and who could smile at the frailties of his people. It was a much more comfortable Jesus than the one that President Faithful brought to life. His was a motionless Jesus who only sadly judged.

She was dimly aware that the Arlen Proverb commercial, an extended, three-minute Jonah, was one that she had not seen before. At first she was uncertain. She had really been doing the Jesus Wave a little too much. Then the screen started flashing.

INSTACONTEST!
INSTACONTEST!
WIN!
WIN!

The flashing words and urgent beeping were replaced by a young, smiling blond woman who explained the deal.

"Yes, friends—you, too, can see Arlen Proverb, Sunday night at Madison Square Garden, absolutely free!"

That caught Maude Anslinger's attention.

"Now I don't in any way want any of you to be thinking that the Reverend Proverb condones gambling one little, teeny bit," the young woman continued. "The only reason that Arlen Proverb has authorized this Instacontest is, well—" The blonde smiled coyly. "—it's like Arlen always says . . ."

The camera cut to a laughing closeup of Arlen Proverb, with sweat pouring down his face, filmed at one of his live shows.

". . . figure the Lord has enough on his mind that he ain't going to be adverse to a little help now and again."

The image was replaced by a studio shot of Arlen Proverb.

"There may be some of you out there that aren't able to afford no tickets to my show and maybe others who aren't sure if they want to go or not. Either way, if the Lord really wants you to see this show, you're going to see it, because he's going to see that you win this special Instacontest. Of course, if you don't win, don't take it badly. The Good Lord has all kinds of plans for all of us."

A fast, scratchily distorted voice cut in. "Entry in this Instacontest requires a five-dollar service fee."

Maude knew that the contest was meant for her. She did not mind about the five dollars. After all, she so rarely responded to anything on TV. She was all but reduced to a watcher. Her credit on the shopping clubs and devotion houses had been canceled soon after George's paycheck had stopped coming in.

The smiling blond girl was back on the screen.

"Now, if any of you have forgotten the response codes on your particular set, we will get it to run a refresher for you."

Maude clapped off the refresher. She still knew how to make a response on her hook into the old Qube II.

The words were flashing again.

PLEASE RESPOND NOW!
PLEASE RESPOND NOW!

Maude moved slowly toward the big old forty-eight-inch monitor that George had bought after their wedding. She placed her hand flat on the touchfeel screen.

YOUR RESPONSE HAS BEEN RECEIVED.
YOUR RESPONSE HAS BEEN RECEIVED.

God was at least aware that she had tried. She waited, scarcely daring to hope. Then the screen greened out, and the monitor scrolled a personal message.

CONGRATULATIONS, MAUDE ANSLINGER! YOU HAVE WON A TICKET TO THE ARLEN PROVERB SPECTACULAR. TO HAVE A HARDCOPY PASS TRANSMITTED TO YOU, DIAL 9–800–7–900–555–111118.

Carlisle

The crowds outside the Garden started gathering a little before noon. The force of uniforms that waited for them was enormous, but the early arrivals were largely friendly. There was a certain nervousness among the squads of NYPD on the streets. Every cop who ringed the Garden, patrolled the back streets, or waited in reserve in the parked buses knew that the Garden was uncomfortably close to the scene of the recent supermarket riot on Eighth Avenue. It could be that there would be some who would use the event as the excuse for a rematch.

As the afternoon wore on, it started to look as if those fears were groundless. Despite high humidity, a gray, overcast sky, and the hammering of the constantly circling gunships, there was something close to a carnival atmosphere. The crowds bought hotdogs and sodas, radfex balloons, cotton candy, miniature Bibles, and mylar prints of Jesus. They streamed in and out of the big Roy Rogers on Seventh Avenue. Many just waited in long orderly lines. As Carlisle had expected, a lot of them were killing the time until the doors opened by staring into handheld Jesus Waves. He noticed that there was a good smattering of country people in worn blue jeans and threadbare dresses who appeared impoverished even by New York standards. Whole families, who looked as if they had been driving for days, made frugal picnics on the tailgates of their dusty, elderly cars.

Carlisle, Reeves, and Donahue made a slow circuit of the Garden in an unmarked car. They, too, were basically killing time until the crowds were let into the building. If anything went down on the outside, it was not their problem—they were concerned with an organized threat on the inside.

Reeves, who was driving, glanced back at Carlisle. "You want to go around again?"

Carlisle shook his head. "No. I don't even know what I'm looking for. All I've seen is a couple of gangs of kids who could be purse snatchers. Let's dump the car and go on inside with the others."

They pulled over to the curb. A burly, uniformed tac squad sergeant in full armor started to tell them that they could not stop there until they flashed their badges. Carlisle and Donahue left Reeves to park the car and walked toward the nearest entrance. They had to show their badges twice more, first to get through the final line of uniforms and then to pass the Garden's own rentacops. Once they were through the rentacops, Carlisle looked questioningly at Donahue.

"Have those guys been checked out? It'd be an ideal way to infiltrate a shooter. Hell, half of them are armed already."

"The uniforms ran their IDs and gun permits before they were allowed in to work."

Carlisle scowled. "And that was it? Anyone with half a brain could fake out a check like that."

Donahue shrugged. "It was out of our hands. Deacons were supposed to run background on everyone employed here. It all went to Virginia Beach. That's where the lists came from."

"Goddamn it."

"What's the problem?"

"The problem is, where this thing's concerned, we can't trust the deacons farther than we can shit."

With a puzzled look, Donahue ran a hand through his thatch of prematurely white hair. "Are you seriously telling me that the deacons might have a crack at Proverb themselves?"

Carlisle shook his head. "I doubt they'll go that far, but there's a feeling that they might well step aside if any third-party operator tried for the prize."

Donahue's expression hardened. "There's a feeling?"

"That's what I said."

"So where does that leave us?"

"It leaves us where we've always been. If Proverb gets it, it's our ass, and nobody's making our job any easier."

They had moved on to the main arena. Tech crews swarmed over the stage and towers, making last-minute adjustments.

"Did the deacons check Proverb's people, as well?" Carlisle asked.

"Proverb put a block on that. His own security is supposed to be one hundred percent watertight."

"Let's hope it is. In the meantime, make sure that our boys are fully aware that they can't look to anyone for support except their own team. You got that?"

"I got it, Lieutenant."

Carlisle had divided his force of a hundred plainclothes officers into four twenty-five-man teams. Two would operate on the main floor, while the others would spread out over the upper tiers. Before he sent them to their final positions, Carlisle moved around giving last-minute instructions and encouragement. All the time, he kept wishing that someone would encourage him. As he looked down from one of the top tiers, he realized that they didn't have a rat's-ass chance if someone was serious about getting Proverb.

The PA was counting down to the opening. "Doors will open in a half hour."

Someone picked that moment to bring down the house lights. Red swirling lasers blossomed from the overhead catwalks. In the darkness, Carlisle knew there was no point in pretending. Arlen Proverb would be an open target once the show got going.

Speedboat

The large number of cops outside the Garden made him nervous. Speedboat had arrived about twenty minutes before the doors were due to open. He had come early because he wanted to take a look at the layout before the lights went down and the show started. He had been given a ticket and a backstage pass, but he had been told not to use the pass until after the show. His contact for the travel papers had sounded as jumpy as he was.

The crowd waiting to get into the Garden should have been Speedboat's natural cover. He had expected Proverb's followers to be geeky, but he so seldom came out of the eastside ghetto that he tended to forget just how geeky geeky could be. Half of them were brain-canceled by those damned A-wave generators that they liked to stare into. It seemed as if half the world was in a zombie trance. The crowd did not make for very good cover. Speedboat stood out like a sore thumb with his parka and suede-head haircut. He did not belong out there, in what passed as the real world. He was sure that the cops had to be looking at him. The twelve hundred in cash in his secret pocket was quite enough to get him taken down to Astor Place if a couple of eager ass-holes decided to shake him down. They probably would not hold him, but the money would certainly vanish, and his efforts to get out to Canada would be back at square one.

He really had no option but to get in line and try to look as holy and inconspicuous as possible. He tucked himself in be-tween a sad-looking country family and an excited bunch of Elvi. The country family looked bad: a defeated husband, a washed-out wife, and three hopeless dispirited children in patched and handed-down work clothes. They looked as if they had been living on the edge for years. He could not understand why they stayed in the boonies. There was nothing out there but hunger and desperation since the big food conglomerates had finished running the small family farmers off the land. Maybe they were just too plain terrified of what might happen to them in the cities. What baffled Speedboat most of all was why, after those people had been handed every shitty deal imaginable, they still maintained their ridiculous faith. They might be living on turnips and hot water, but they still thought that Jesus was look-ing out for them and everything would be all right in the end. It could only be the passivity of the terminally stupid, and Speed-boat had no patience with it or sympathy for it. Those dummies could not even pull it together to vent their anger on the corpo-rations like Agricon and U.S. Grain that had made them the way they were. They did not burn barns or trash harvesters—they just sat around on their sorry butts and bought the official line that the Jews had done it to them.

The Elvi were a total contrast. The bunch that were standing behind him sounded as if they came from Jersey; they probably worked in the electronics or chemical plants out around Eliza-beth. The Elvi looked out for their own, and it was rare to see one of them that did not have a job. This bunch were definitely on a day out and determined to enjoy themselves. Speedboat had no time for their loony tune beliefs, but at least they seemed to have some spirit in them and to be somewhat in control of their own lives. The men wore the traditional pompadours, triangular sideburns, and mirrored aviator sunglasses, while the women were done up as if they were on their way to a high-school prom in the mid-1950s. The Elvi were as much locked into their particular timeframe as the Amish were in theirs.

Their beliefs were even more impenetrable to the average outsider. Everyone knew that the whole thing was a confused mishmash of UFO lore, Elvis Presley, and the Book of Revelations, but from that point on, the labyrinth of testament, epistle, and commandment became so complicated that only the faithful could even partially grasp what it was really about. Although technically it could be said that the Elvi had been born the night that Elvis Presley finally keeled over in his toilet at Graceland, the full-blown cult had not really taken hold until the mid-'90s. For a number of years, the media had gradually elevated obsessive fan behavior to a quasi-religion, but it was the publication of Dean Anthony's *Book of the King* that really twanged the string of fervent irrationality that appeared to run through all of the hard-core Presley fans. Dean Anthony was actually a drunken ex-rock writer who pulled together the mythology in the hope of making as much money as L. Ron Hubbard. The fat, twelve-hundred-page tome contained everything from the power of positive thinking to the second coming of the King and the rise of Atlantis. It was shameless in its plundering of virtually the entire catalog of twentieth-century weirdness, but the Elvi swallowed it whole and began to reshape their lives according to its convoluted tenets. The doctrine had been truly nailed down when Anthony had been shot dead in a fight in an East Memphis barroom. His plan had been to build a giant pyramid on a landfill just outside the city. He had been locked in a protracted legal battle with both Elvis Presley Industries and environmental groups that feared that the weight of the structure would force even more toxins into the Mississippi River. Although the police report said that he had been involved in an alcoholically escalating argument with a neighborhood pimp, the true believers smelled conspiracy. That was understandable. The *Book of the King* was chock-full of interlocking conspiracy theories. Anthony was canonized as the first martyred prophet of the Elvi, and Elvis Presley Industries, as the prime target of Elvi paranoia, lost all control of the Elvis iconography and subsequently went bankrupt.

With the coming of the Faithful administration, the Elvi had been forced to weather a series of storms. There had been more than one attempt to have them labeled as heretics, and Vanson Crowell, a syndicated faith healer out of Bloomington, Indiana, had even gone as far as to organize burnings of the *Book of the King*. Crowell had been the first to learn the lesson that one did not screw around with the Elvi. The moment he started his campaign, his grass-roots following vanished like the morning mist, and his cash contributions dropped away to nothing. The intense competition in the God business did the rest. Vanson Crowell vanished from sight and the airwaves. The truth was that Middle America rather liked the Elvi. They were different, maybe crazy, but they seemed harmless and good-natured. They were also rooted in a phenomenon that, for over half a century, had been very dear to the heart of blue-collar America. They worked alongside everyone else on the factory floor. They bitched about the pay cuts and the rising prices. After work, they went to the bar. They were permitted to get drunk, arm wrestle, and hold their own in a fight. Anthony, renowned for his bleary, saloon macho, had allowed himself plenty of slack when drawing up the Elvi moral code. The Elvi religion, above everything else, demanded that its members be good ol' boys and gals.

A ripple ran down the line. One of the Elvi grinned amiably at Speedboat. "Figure we should be getting inside pretty soon."

Speedboat nodded. It did not cost anything to be civil to the natural cover. He held up his computicket. "Says the doors open at five."

The Elvi consulted a huge, antique Rolex that was strapped to his left wrist. "Five on the nail."

As they filed forward, the Elvi kept up a stream of small talk. One thing that Speedboat thoroughly detested was nonconversations with total strangers. It was made worse by the fact that the line moved excruciatingly slowly. This Elvi might have been good-natured, but he was also extremely boring. It was the fate of many with fixed beliefs. Speedboat felt that it was best to humor the man, but even his minimal grunted replies came to an abrupt stop when he was confronted by the battery of security equipment that was deployed around the entrance.

"Holy shit."

The Elvi smiled indulgently as if to signify that he had heard a few cuss words in his time. "They do seem to be taking real good care of someone. I guess there's all kinds of nuts about. They say that Elvis himself was kind of leery about the possibility of a sniper trying for him from the audience."

Speedboat was about ready to bolt. The only thing that stopped him was that by the time that he actually saw the battery of security checks, it was already too late. There was no way that he could turn back without attracting attention. He was carried into the process by the momentum of the crowd. He dropped his ticket into the hopper and had its genuineness confirmed. Next he passed between a double line of armed and armored riot cops who stared impassively from behind dark visors. Speedboat could feel himself starting to sweat. The sensor banks were mounted in a cylindrical aluminum and plastic frame that formed a tunnel through which everyone in the line had to pass. Speedboat recognized some of the equipment. The mass detectors that ferreted out concealed weapons were larger versions of the portable frisk units that the deacons used. There were these dull black ceramic tubes that he could only assume sniffed for explosives. There was other stuff he had never encountered before—multiple lenses like the eyes of insects, tremor scoops, and curved ceramic panels. He could not start to guess at their function, but he did not like the look of them at all. Finally he was through the tunnel. The last obstacle was a huddle of Garden rentacops who amounted to very little after what had gone before. And then Speedboat was on his way down the tunnel that led into the main arena. If everything went according to plan, he had passed the first short stretch of a road that would lead all the way to Canada.

Mansard

The crowd was coming in like a flowing disorganized mass, spoiling and humanizing the symmetry of the ranked tiers of empty seats.

Charlie Mansard sighed. "I guess it's time for the preflight."

Jimmy Gadd placed his arm on the back of the coordinator's console chair and leaned forward so only Mansard could hear him. "You're certain you want to run the program yourself?"

Mansard scowled and nodded. "I want to run the program myself."

"You're sure?"

"I'm sure."

"You've been bitching all afternoon about how you can't do it because you're not up to it and you don't feel well."

"It's my way of psyching myself up for the show. Some people pace, others meditate. I whine and complain."

"You've got a couple of drinks in you."

"Did you ever know me to do a show without a couple of drinks in me?"

Jimmy Gadd shrugged. "Just checking."

"Stop treating me like you're my nanny."

"Did you hear anything more from the cops?"

Mansard slowly pulled off the two strips of fake plastic skin that hid the DNI input receptors behind each ear. "I didn't hear anything new. It's pretty clear they feel that Proverb is some major assassination target."

"How do you feel about that?"

"The money's in escrow. We're covered."

"But if it happens, it's liable to happen during the show while you're jacked into the board."

"So with my luck, I'll be in the middle of a straight D-interface. I'll overload, produce clear white light, and fuse both halves of my brain."

"And you're not worried?"

"It'd be a merciful release."

Jimmy Gadd shrugged. There was no talking to Mansard immediately before a show. "Have it your way."

"I intend to. Go and tend your business. Make sure those horsemen come up on cue."

Gadd gestured to the others at the effects control board. "Okay, folks, let's all get to our places. It's time to go to it."

Mansard held up the leads that were destined to fit into the plugs in his neck. He stared at the gold connectors and spoke to nobody in particular. "It's amazing, isn't it? The Russians are colonizing Mars. The Japanese have DNI, and the Home of the Brave has Jesus, nuclear power stations, and fake miracles." He eased the two plugs into his neck receptors. "Let's commit ourselves a felony."

Direct neutral interface—DNI—was a federal crime in the United States. The sin of cybercation could cost the perpetrator five to ten in a camp. Congress with a machine had been deemed to be an abomination in the eyes of God and legislated against accordingly. The fact that with the coming of artificial intelligence many machines were potentially smarter than Larry Faithful and the majority of his cabinet did not count for anything. In the new America prejudice prevailed. God-fearing folks did not run wires into their heads and turn themselves into some kind of Frankenstein monsters. The net result was that the country was becoming increasingly backward, a victim of its own ideological struggle with the Japanese.

Of course Mansard and the others in his crew who wore plugs were in no danger of arrest—not until the day came when they were really of no more use to the hierarchy. If or when that happened, it would not really matter. In that unpleasant eventuality, cybercation and neuromancy would be just two more charges way down on a long list of crimes that would be heralded by first-degree heresy. Even the Faithful administration was aware that software-based systems were pissing in the dark without DNI. The military had DNI, as did the major corporations, the remaining airlines, and even the deacons themselves. The real purpose of DNI prohibition was to stop potential kid cowboy hackers from interfacing their way beyond the reach of the thought control of Jesus.

Mansard experienced the unpleasant lurch of reality as he melded with the control software. It was a little too much like baring his innermost being to be strictly comfortable—it was a yielding to something bigger that himself. Each time he melded, he felt the loss of his strict singular identity. The physical leads that ran to the console and the mental channels that were opened to the whole of the complex system made him a component in an open-ended matrix that was part cybernetic and part human. That loss of self was, on its own, akin to a religious experience. Maybe that was why the hierarchy appeared so threatened by DNI. They probably saw it as competition.

What Mansard thought of as his second eyes came on and, with them, the exhilaration that followed the fear. The sheer depth of shared perception was what made jacking in such a source of pure excitement. He had been blind but now could see. The religious parallels always came thick and fast when anyone tried to describe the full depths of the DNI experience. Mansard was very much aware of the fact that, as the director of the whole operation, he occupied a unique position. They were his fantasies that were being projected as an illusion of light and form, and it was his will that directed the coordinated effort. He was the pivotal point around which everything else revolved. *I am the cyberking; I can do anything.* When anyone asked him how it felt to have that almost otherwordly power at his disposal, he had a stock reply. "From the top, you can see for fucking miles."

In a way, it was the absolute unvarnished truth. That was what the second eyes were really all about. Subjectively to the left and right of his physical vision, they provided an electronic overview of the entire control. "What can I tell you? I'm a visual artist, not a poet. It's like full-color radar—that's the only way that I can describe it." In that, he somewhat underplayed the truth. It might look like color radar, but it felt like playing God. His kingdom, the matrix, was laid out in front of him, a vast glowing landscape tailored to his hands and mind. If he thought it, it was done. The sense of omnipotence was all-consuming. About the only thing that rivaled it was the sense of the infinite. Although the second eyes did not show him anything but the single special-effects matrix, there was a awareness that, beyond the limits of his own universe, others existed. They were out there, glowing, distant things like island nebulae, linked by fiber optics or microwaves as surely as the stars are linked by mass energy and time. It was at that point that he envied the Japanese hardcore DNI ronin who had moved out in that space and freely roamed between the matrices. "One day," he told himself. "One day." In the meantime, even as limited as his circumstances were, he had enough consolations.

"Power!" Mansard broke the quiet in the control booth with a maniacal, mad-scientist laugh. "Let's bring up the power."

There were a number of smiles around the booth. The crew were all regulars and well aware of Mansard's flights of ego. Mansard moved back into the physical world and acknowledged the response with a nod. Then he was back to business.

"Bring the power up slow and be careful of surge. It's my brain in here."

He waited quietly while the crew built power and ran through the preflight. When his eyes had first come on, the image of the matrix had been a pale, ethereal thing, like a city in the dark, seen from a high and distant aircraft. Once power was fed into it, it came to shimmering life. As the dawnglow of first powerup surrounded Charlie Mansard, he realized just how big this job was. He had never handled anything this huge. It had looked manageable on paper and even in the miniaturizations, but now that he was confronted by the full-scale reality, he was not so sure.

"I'm going to need a drink after this sucker."

Jimmy Gadd was inside his head. "You always need a drink."

"Get out of my head, Gadd."

"Just reminding you that you aren't the only one who's jacked in."

Mansard sighed. In some respects he *was* the only one who was actually jacked in. He was the one in control. Most of the others on the crew who were on DNI would go through the show in a blissful half trance as they ran their functions. As more and more power was fed in, he started to move toward the center of the matrix. The control functions came to him as he moved forward. This was the subjective perception of entering the full interface.

"Damn, this really is big."

He was not even trying to run the Four Horsemen set piece himself. That would be controlled by its own program. Maybe he should have split the unit and used two controllers. He was almost at the center position. It was far too late for second thoughts, and what the hell, anyway. If he could not hack his own show he deserved to die trying.

There was a babble of audio at the periphery of his perception. Proverb's sound crew was syncing in. An alarm tone sounded, and the matrix flashed. That was immediately followed by an override voice.

"Showtime in ten minutes."

FIVE

Carlisle

"**R**ELEVATIONS NINE!"

The lights on the stage had dimmed to a velvet black. Arlen Proverb stood under a single pin spot that beamed straight down. The impression created was that of his being touched by the finger of God.

"Yes, my friends. Revelations nine."

As Proverb's voice resonated through the auditorium, a murmur ran through the crowd. Revelations nine was a Proverb showstopper. For him to use it so early in the show would seem to indicate that he was planning to go for broke. The crowd was excited at the promise of fireworks. Someone in the seats behind Harry Carlisle let out a whoop.

"Good rockin' tonight."

Some of the crowd laughed. Harry Carlisle shook his head in the darkness. It had to be an Elvi.

There was a high sustained note, somewhere between a trumpet and a violin. It seemed to hang in the roof darkness of the Garden. Tiny pinpoints of light danced high in the air.

"And the fifth angel sounded . . ."

Proverb's voice was as much a force as any other factor in the spectacle. The naturally powerful baritone had been amplified and deepened; it had been enhanced and juiced in every conceivable way until it sounded as if some holy orchestra were buried in the words. When he fell into the rolling rhythm of his Bible reading, during which he tacked a punching *aah* sound to

110

the ends of many of his words, the effect was even more pronounced. It became a voice ready to part the waters—Moses with the gift of advanced electronics.

". . . and I saw a star fall from heaven unto the earth: . . ."

The lights vanished, and the note faded. A deep subbass rumble seemed to be vibrating the foundations of the building. A deep glow, the color of blood, was crawling across the stage like something alive.

". . . and to him was given the key of the bottomless pit."

The voices became the roar of a hurricane.

"And he opened the bottomless pit!"

It was an illusion, but for an instant, it seemed as if the floor of the Garden had opened up. For a fraction of a second, the crowd felt as if they were falling. There were screams. Carlisle looked around. The show had only just started, and the Garden was already in total chaos. The cops who were supposed to be protecting Proverb were quite helpless. In the darkness, and with all the movement in the crowd, there was no way that they would be able to spot a sniper.

"And there arose a smoke out of the pit, as the smoke of a great furnace; and the sun and the air were darkened by reason of the smoke of the pit."

All hell was majestically breaking loose. Green and purple evil was crawling down the walls while magenta doom rose to meet it. The bloody glowing mist was flowing off the stage and down into the crowd. Things seemed to be moving in the middle of it. People were pushing back, recoiling from its advance. Carlisle's ears were assaulted by a cacophony of shouts and screams and the terrible flapping of leathery wings. All around him, people were clutching their ears: some were down on their knees, eyes closed, sobbing. Carlisle knew that Proverb was a wildman, but if the preacher kept the intensity up at this level through a full three-hour show, he would have half his flock clean out of their minds at the end—if they had not killed each other in some mass psych-out.

An atonal chorus cut through the desperate noise and hung in the air above the heads of the milling crowd like a blanket of doom.

"Come not, Lucifer."

"Come not, Lucifer."

"Come not, Lucifer."

Proverb himself was rising above the red glow on a small,

elevating platform. Hands seemed to be reaching out of the stuff to drag him back down.

"And there came out of the smoke locusts upon the earth: and unto them was given power."

"Power."

"Power."

"Power."

"And the shapes of the locusts were like unto horses prepared unto battle."

Proverb was down on one knee. The heavy Bible was brandished on high. Even forced to his knees, Arlen Proverb kept on fighting. He was high above the stage, surrounded by a golden aura. His voice had dropped to a terrifying whisper.

"And on their heads were as it were crowns like gold . . . And they had breastplates, as it were breastplates of iron; and the sound of their wings was as the sound of chariots of many horses running to battle."

The bloody glow was fading, but it was being replaced by lurking, hovering blackness that hinted of men on horses and threatening spears. Harsh metallic noise seemed to be coming from a long way off.

"And the four angels were loosed . . . for to slay the third part of men. And the number of the army of the horsemen were two hundred thousand thousand; and I heard the number of them."

"Kill meeeee!"

"Kill meeeee!"

The metallic noise was coming closer. The dark shapes loomed over the audience.

"And thus I saw the horses in the vision, and them that sat on them, having breastplates of fire, and of jacinth, and brimstone: and the heads of the horses were as of the heads of lions; and out of their mouths issued fire and smoke and brimstone."

Carlisle did not have a clue how the effects were achieved, but as the metallic noise grew louder and louder, the black shapes were in among the audience. White, skeletal forms appeared in the middle of them, indistinct but brandishing weapons, topped by the faces of screaming skulls. The crowd was reacting again. Carlisle started to realize that what Arlen Proverb was really providing was just a grand version of old-fashioned horror-movie grab and scream. It was a rollercoaster ride of fright-night biblical effects, and the crowd was more than happy to throw itself into it with a vengeance. It was all part of the show and probably provided those poor dumb bastards with more genuine thrills and spills than they had experienced all year. Carlisle's real worry was that since this was not merely an old-time horror show but something that touched psyches heavily dosed with years of religious mania, the spills might spill over into a full-blown bout of mass psychosis. He did not want to be officiating at a riot.

The metal noise had reached pain threshold. It was as if a dozen old-fashioned railroad trains were screaming through the place with their throttles wide open, while on board a barbarian horde was howling in unison and beating on steel shields. The vague skeletal shapes were much more clearly defined, demon holograms stalking the aisles and putting the very real fear of eternal damnation into the hearts of the crowd. Above it all, Proverb, protected by his aura, continued to rant.

"By these three was the third part of men killed, by the fire, and by the smoke, and by the brimstone, which issued out of their mouths . . . And the rest of the men which were not killed by these plagues yet repented not of the works of their hands, that they should not worship devils, and idols of gold, and silver, and brass, and stone, and of wood: which neither can see, nor hear, nor walk."

An indistinct, shifting demon face was projected onto the backdrop behind Proverb. It bore a definite resemblance to Larry Faithful.

"Neither repented they of their murders, nor of their sorceries, not of their fornication, nor of their thefts."

At the last ringing word, everything stopped with breathtaking suddenness. The interior of the Garden was full of ringing silence and pitch oppressive black.

After three seconds, there was a blinding white flash, and Proverb's voice rang out like a roll of thunder.

"I bring you tidings of great joy that shall be to all people."

The auditorium was filled with a golden light. Proverb was back down on the stage, no longer raised up on the elevated platform. Carlisle felt unnaturally good. He was at peace. He slowly looked around. Everyone in the place was beaming with brotherly love.

Carlisle quickly let out his breath. "Goddamn it to hell."

A couple of nearby people looked at him in amazement. He glared back at them, and they looked away. The good feeling had abruptly fallen off. Proverb was using some sort of high-speed visual hypnotic, an industrial version of the Jesus Wave. With this crowd, it was like shooting fish in a barrel. Over half of them were jelloed on the pocket-size A-wave already. Carlisle resented the indiscriminate use of mass mood movers. People were crazy enough as it was. For his own part, he objected to the intrusion on his privacy. He did not like anyone modifying his mind without his express permission. Ironically, the hypnotic was probably now heightening his irritation. Once one had fought the initial euphoria, the tendency was to plummet to the basement of ill temper.

A telescopic catwalk was extending down the central aisle, and Proverb was moving onto it. He was actually going out into the crowd. If a hitter was waiting there, Proverb's move was an open invitation. Every couple of paces he would pause and acknowledge some individual or group in the audience. He began handing out silk scarves. He seemed to be pulling scarves out of the high collar of his spangled costume as if it were a magic act. It was practically an Elvi ceremony. Between scarves, he would reach out and grasp the hands that were stretched up to him. He dropped to one knee and prayed to selected knots of people.

When he came to the end of the catwalk, he surveyed the crowd and slowly raised his hands. "Oh, my friends, I do bring you tidings of great joy and they shall be to all people. Very, very great joy."

Kline

Deacon Booth gripped a large glass of cognac and regarded the small, spotlit figure of Arlen Proverb with a bleak expression. "I think tonight he may finally go too far."

Longstreet, who was standing next to him, raised a questioning eyebrow. "It depends what you mean by too far."

"Far enough so we can finally wrap him with a full-scale, watertight heresy indictment."

"Is there such a thing as a watertight heresy indictment? Isn't it all a matter of theological interpretation?"

"There's a line beyond which interpretation no longer applies. That's why we've given this one so much rope."

Booth gave Longstreet a look that seemed to indicate he was another one who had had more than enough rope.

The smart cynical elite in the VIP lounge watched the performance with as much rapt attention as any of the common believers on the floor of the Garden, but their motivations were very different. The celebrities, the tycoons, and the city officials, who were staring through the panoramatic glass that looked out over the whole arena or else watching the banks of monitors that were mounted at strategic points all around the room, had come to see what amounted to an advanced freakshow. They accepted champagne from the circulating waiters and laughed at the excesses of both performer and audience.

"He is good. He really does have them in the palm of his hand."

"It's not hard to have morons in the palm of his hand. I mean, just look at them. They'd believe anything."

"He's also spending a fortune on special effects."

"He is good, though. He must be good to do what he does and have stayed out of a camp for this long."

"I don't think Proverb has anything to worry about. Faithful's afraid of him and his following."

"For God's sake, keep your voice down."

The last speaker, a well-fed, agribusiness executive in a quilted burgundy tuxedo, looked around nervously. There were also a great many senior deacons in the VIP lounge. They were not there to see a freakshow—they were looking for an excuse. They made absolutely no secret that they were there to see Proverb publicly nail his own coffin. The way things stood in the aftermath of the mess on Fifteenth Street and the continuing embarrassment of the Lefthand Path running loose, the deacons obviously needed the kind of spectacular arrest and show trial that the taking down of Proverb would provide. It went deeper than that, however. The agribusiness executive's companion was right. Faithful was afraid of Arlen Proverb, as were all of the hierarchy. He was an unpredictable maverick, and there was no place for mavericks in their brave new world. That, on the other hand, did not stop them looking around at the other guests as if speculating what their long-term fate might be. It was an old deacon trick, but that did not stop it from striking cold fear into anyone who faced one of those cold stares.

Cynthia Kline herself was close to cold fear. She had arrived, once again, as Longstreet's protégée and had been very much treated as such—she had been largely ignored. He had introduced her to a couple of people, but they had been singularly uninterested in her claim to fame. There was no way that she could compete with what was going on on the stage. If she had had less brain and more ego, she might have put it down to the much more conservative uniform that Longstreet had chosen for the night's outing. Cynthia, though, was smart enough to realize that she was already becoming yesterday's news, and that her moment of phony glory was into its final flare. The realization produced mixed feelings. There was a certain relief that she would soon be allowed to sink back into her previous covert anonymity, but it was tempered by a regret that she would no longer be in the public eye. There had been a certain exhilaration to being the center of attention.

In the VIP lounge at Madison Square Garden, Cynthia rapidly became aware that not to be the center of attention might actually constitute a blessing. The mild pique that came from hardly being noticed quickly subsided as she saw the nature of the crowd. The deacons, all high-ranking officers, some of whom she had seen around the corridors or in the elevators at the Astor Place complex, made up at least a third of those present. They looked like a pack of vultures waiting for a kill. The other two-thirds were the kind of successful self-satisfied sleaze who circled any concentration of power—not the leftover jetsetters of the previous night, but the predators, parasites, and scavengers who had actually prospered under the Faithful regime. The only one of them she recognized was Raoul, the Chilean software runner. She had felt a moment of panic when she had thought that Webster was with him and might accidentally let drop some incriminating remark. To her relief, she saw that his companion was some other willowy and anemic blonde.

The way in which she had been summoned to the event had made mingling with that kind of crowd even more difficult. A high level of paranoia had been established from the start. Longstreet had called only a matter of minutes after she had garbaged the mysterious instructions that had told her to go to the Proverb show.

"I think you should come with me to the Arlen Proverb extravaganza at the Garden. I've got passes for the VIP lounge."

As if she was not spooked already, that was more than enough to make her sit quickly down on the bed. The incidence of coincidence was well into the red. For a couple of seconds, she was unable to speak.

At the other end of the phone, Longstreet had sounded irritable. "You're that hung over?"

Finally she had found her voice. "I guess so. It was a long night."

"So drink some coffee and pull yourself together. I want you in my office here at five, and we'll go on from there."

"How should I dress?"

"That'll all be taken care of."

She sat on the bed for some minutes wondering if she should just cut and run. She had been told to go to the Garden and wait to be contacted. Was she going to be contacted in the VIP lounge? If that was the case, did it mean that Longstreet was somehow linked to the organization? Or did it mean that the whole thing was a setup? That was the very basic and absolute root of her fear. It was bad enough to feel that she was little more than a puppet with faceless people pulling invisible strings. The idea that these strings could be walking her to her death made her feel sick.

In the end, she decided reluctantly to go. It was not that she had all that courage; it was more because she could not think of a sound alternative. She only had the identity of Cynthia Kline, clerical auxiliary, and no travel papers would allow her to get back into Canada or away to Europe. Her only alternatives were either to become a nameless fugitive without money or support, or to continue to go with this increasingly dubious program. In the end she took a deep breath and started undressing to take a shower. It felt like walking naked straight into the lion's mouth.

Arrival at the Garden did not do anything to allay the gnawing fears. The streams of people that were still milling outside looked crazy, and the VIP lounge resembled nothing more than an anteroom to hell. Even Longstreet was fazed by the concentration of top deacons. As they walked past security on the door and were checked off on the guest list, he muttered under his breath. "My God, the brass is out in force and looking for blood."

Cynthia silently prayed that the blood would not be hers.

Longstreet quickly recovered. "Let's smile nicely and slide into the fray."

Fortunately, the fray proved to be less intense than she had expected. After the initial round of circulation, she was able to take a glass of champagne from a waiter and find a vantage point from where she could watch the show and hardly be noticed.

118

Longstreet hissed at her. "Try not to get drunk two days in a row."

"I'll watch it."

She sipped her drink and concentrated on what was happening on the stage. All her life she had done her best to avoid TV preachers. Even back in the old days, they had filled her with a restful unease. It was not just the creepy smiles, the overblown histrionics, and the constant demands for money—the thing that angered her the most was their absolute certainty about everything. How did anyone have the gall to presume to be so right? She had to admit, however, that this guy Proverb had a lot more going for him. He was a throwback to the scenery-chewing Elmer Gantrys of the mid-twentieth century, and the special effects were like something out of an old-time rock-and-roll spectacular. Despite herself, she found that she was soon halfway caught up in his act.

After an orgy of multimedia hellfire, he was pouring liquid honey over the masses. Bliss blue poured onto the stage, and an invisible choir of country-and-western angels harmonized in wrap sound.

"The word is joy, my friends. The word is rapture. Do you all know the meaning of the word 'rapture'? Do you know the meaning of the word 'joy'? Joy, my friends, my brothers and my sisters, that's the feeling when you feel so good that you want to jump up and yell out loud, when you want to throw your arms up in the air and just haul off and holler out: *Praise the Lord, I feel so good!*"

The sound was juiced on the final shout so that it came out as if Proverb were hollering from the mountaintop. Cynthia had to admit that the presentation was slick. All over the floor of the auditorium, the more exuberant sections were leaping in the air and yelling the line right back to the spangled figure on the stage.

"Praise the Lord!"

"Praise the Lord, I feel so good!"

"Praise the Lord!"

The deacons in the VIP lounge were watching in stony silence. There was no conversation above the music and the crowd noise that was being relayed through the monitor speakers. The choir was getting louder. Proverb raised a hand, and the faithful fell silent.

"I'll say it again." His delivery became stylized and rhythmic. "Joy-a is when you feel-a so good-a that you want to jump in the a-ir and holler out-a: *Praise the Lord, I feel so good-a!*"

That time the punchline had been shouted from an even higher mountain. The crowd repeated the jumping and shouting. The choir had grown to a couple of thousand strong and was smoothly sliding into a do-wop back beat.

"Doop-doop-doop-doop-doop-doop-doop-doop."

"Joyyyyyyyyyyyyyyy."

"Joyyyyyyyyyyyyyyy."

"The message of Jesus is joy-a to the world-a."

The audience roared their agreement, but even as they were roaring, the rollercoaster ride started to climb again. The choir was fading. The blue light was closing on Proverb. Again the crowd fell silent. Cynthia wondered how it must feel to have such power and control; what it felt like to have command of all those special effects. It was a miracle that Proverb was able to stay sane, if indeed he did. It was also quite clear why the deacons loathed him. He was now talking one on one, down home to the crowd.

"Now, I guess it's no secret that when I was a young boy, I was kinda wild. And I gotta tell you, way back then, one of the things that put me off coming to know Jesus sooner than I did was that I had this crazy idea that Christian folks didn't have no fun. I thought that being one with the Lord was a matter of giving up this and forgoing that and walking around with a long face and a sorrowful disposition. We know better than that now— *don't we?*"

The crowd howled, and Proverb beamed. A huge image of his face had come up on the back projection screen.

"We know that Jesus came to Earth to bring us joy. We know that Jesus came to Earth to make us know a true happiness. When I began to walk with Jesus, the first thing that I learned was that Jesus wants us all to have a good time."

Proverb paused to let that sink in. The eyes of the huge image seemed to be glowing slightly. For half a second Cynthia felt that they were looking deep inside her. She shook her head with a quick jerky motion. It was far too easy to be sucked in by this stuff.

"Now you may be saying, 'Hey, I may feel good right now, but there are times when I get downright miserable.' You may be saying, 'Hey, times are hard, Reverend Proverb. There are days when I ain't sure that I'm going to make it.' "

120

The stage began to darken. Gray storm clouds were driven across the screen behind the huge image of Proverb.

"Hard times, my friends. Hard times, friends and neighbors. Make no mistake about that. The whole of this country is being sorely tried and tested. The one thing you shouldn't believe, though, is that these hard times come from Jesus. It's the good times that come from Jesus. The hard times come from one place and one place only. They come straight from Hell. That's right! Straight from Hell! These hard times are the works of Satan—*and don't let anyone tell you different!*"

Proverb was in full cry.

"We all know them. We all know so-called good Christians who go around preaching doom and gloom, telling you that hard times are sent by Jesus because you've been weak, or because you've been bad. Well, my friends, I've got something right here and now to tell those so-called Christians. If they're not damned liars then they've been very badly informed."

There was the loudest roar yet from the crowd. They seemed to know who the damned liars were. Cynthia sneaked a covert glance at the deacons. They were in a tight knot around Senior Deacon Booth over on one side of the panoramatic window. They were watching Proverb like a flock of hawks. Booth was already red in the face and huffing and puffing. He barked at an aide.

"I want comprehensive tapes of this seditious nonsense on my desk first thing in the morning. You hear me?"

The aide nodded vigorously. Cynthia scowled. That had to be one bitch of a job, nursemaiding a piece of slime like Booth.

When he had sufficiently terrorized the aide, Booth turned to the other senior officers with a look of grim triumph. "I think, gentlemen, there's one thing of which we can be certain. After this display—" He nodded contemptuously in the direction of the stage. "—we have ample, legitimate grounds to require the Reverend Proverb to provide answers to the Fifteen Questions."

Cynthia raised an eyebrow. The Fifteen Questions, as laid out in the Second Amendment to the Mandatory Articles of Faith, were invariably the prelude to an indictment for capital heresy. She looked down at the roaring crowd and wondered: Did Booth and the others really think they could do that to Proverb without his millions of followers going violently bananas?

She saw that Longstreet was coming toward her. He had a wry look on his face.

He moved close to her and whispered. "I fear that my superiors are planning to make even bigger fools of themselves than they already are. They seriously believe that they can arrest Proverb, and his followers will just roll over. Do you want some more champagne? You seem to have been a good girl so far."

He signaled to a waiter. Longstreet apparently had not been a good boy. His breath smelled of brandy, and his eyes were unnaturally bright.

Cynthia accepted the glass. "You seem to have broken your drinking rule."

"Who wouldn't, at an affair like this? I feel the cold wind from the camps when I'm in the same room as Booth."

Cynthia quickly swallowed her champagne. If Longstreet was afraid, what hope did she have?

"What do you think would happen if they did try Proverb for heresy?" she asked.

"Civil war, if this crowd's anything to go by."

"Oh, come on."

"First-degree ghetto burning, at a very minimum."

"You shouldn't joke about all this. Not in public."

"I don't really—" He was suddenly staring across the room at a group of late arrivals. "What the hell is this? The Night of the Long Knives?"

Matthew Dreisler was in the center of the group.

"Dreisler the headhunter."

"The head of the DIA?"

"The very same, and he never socializes unless there's a purpose to it. He's no butterfly."

Cynthia could feel the ripple of fear go through the room.

Longstreet seemed transfixed. "God, he's always immaculate."

A black leather coat was thrown casually over the perfect shoulders of Dreisler's silk, double-breasted evening jacket. A black velour trilby was tilted over one eye, and, of course, there were the inevitable old-fashioned sunglasses. He was flanked by two large men who were clearly his bodyguards, and slightly behind him were two less strapping young men who had to be aides or assistants. The party was completed by a tall spindly figure wrapped in an all-enveloping cowled overcoat. It was hard to guess exactly what his function was, but he had the look of a personal spiritual advisor—and a strange one at that.

Advancing through the VIP lounge, they seemed to be very

much aware of the effect they were having on the rest of the guests. They did not swagger like stormtroopers—Dreisler was too sophisticated for that. The air of menace—and the relish that he clearly took in that menace—was subtle, almost understated. It was also quite unmistakable. It became plain that they were going for Booth.

Longstreet propelled Cynthia forward. "Let's move a little nearer. I don't want to miss any of this."

Cynthia resisted. "I don't want to be anywhere near those people. I'm not drunk, and they scare me to death."

The pressure on her arm was insistent. "We don't have anything to worry about. Dreisler fries bigger fish than us."

Cynthia let herself be pushed toward the other end of the room, hoping that Longstreet had not found his deathwish. To her relief, he stopped at what would be a safe distance from the confrontation between Dreisler and Booth.

Dreisler was affable and smiling, although his eyes were still hidden behind the black glasses. "How are you, Deacon Booth?"

Even Booth's florid cheeks seemed to have paled a little. "I'm well, thank you, Deacon Dreisler."

"I didn't know you were a follower of the Reverend Proverb."

It looked as if only an accustomed fear was keeping Booth from exploding. "Indeed I am not."

Dreisler was still smiling pleasantly. "Indeed?"

"I came here to see for myself how far the man would go."

"And how far has he gone so far?"

"Sadly, I have to tell you that serious questions are being raised regarding the loyalty of the Reverend Proverb."

Dreisler regarded Booth from over the top of his glasses. "But you haven't told me how far he's gone. Isn't that what you came here for?"

The pallor had gone from Booth's face. He was turning purple. "For a start, he's as good as—"

Dreisler waved a autocratic hand, summarily cutting Booth off. "I'll see for myself."

He stepped up to the window and looked down at the stage. He could not have picked a better time. Proverb was on a full tilt roll. The fire of damnation was all around him.

"Prophets of doom in the pulpit, and the money changers grow fat on the humble offerings of the poor. The chatter of commerce and the clash of the register drown the Word. The Light grows dim in the midnight of deception.''

Dreisler looked back at nobody in particular. "He really is a little radical.''

"John, chapter two, verse thirteen." Proverb gave the quote as if it was the ultimate authority. For many there, it was.

"And Jesus went up to Jerusalem, and found in the temple those who sold oxen and sheep and doves, and the changers of money sitting: and when he had made a scourge out of small cords, he drove them all out of the temple, and the sheep, and the oxen; and poured out the changers' money, and overthrew the tables; and said unto them that sold doves, take these things hence; make not my Father's house a house of merchandise.''

Dreisler glanced back at Booth. "He seems to be quoting holy scripture.''

"The Devil can quote scripture.''

Dreisler turned back to the window. "Of course.''

Proverb had put down his Bible.

"Now I don't think there are too many sheep and oxen around the temples of our land today—'' Proverb suddenly grinned. "—although there are times when I ain't so sure.'' He paused for the explosion of laughter and then became serious. "One thing I do know for sure is that there are plenty of money changers and the like hanging around, getting fat while the rest of us get poorer.''

There were some militant shouts. Everybody seemed to have overlooked the fact that the very last thing that Arlen Proverb ever got was poorer.

"Fat cats in Washington and fat cats in Los Angeles talking the name of Jesus but walking this country, this land of the free, into harder times than we've ever seen.''

Booth flashed Dreisler a look of triumph. "He's directly refering to the administration and the hierarchy.''

Proverb had his arms outstretched. "But let me promise you one thing, friends and neighbors. The fat cats' days are numbered.''

There was a blaze of light in the auditorium.

"There will be a cleansing of the temple. Believe me, friends and neighbors . . .'' Again the voice came from the mountain-top. *"There will be a cleansing of the temple!''*

Dreisler turned away from the window. Cynthia was looking directly at him. For a fleeting instant, she saw a smile of intense and pure delight, that of a small boy who was seeing an elaborate practical joke coming together. Then it was gone. In shock she glanced at Longstreet, but he appeared not to have noticed anything.

Winters

All around him, people were shouting and cheering. It was like a battle cry.

"There will be a cleansing of the temple!"

Winters was lost. He did not know what to think. There was open sedition and heresy right there in Madison Square Garden and then, at the height of Proverb's headlong flight into blasphemy, out came that phrase, trumpeted in that terrible amplified voice. It was that same phrase that had so mysteriously appeared on his primary computer screen a few days earlier and, from that moment on, had caused him so much soul-nagging unease. He looked about for another of the deacons from his team. No one was in sight. All around him was a chaos of jumping, waving people, bumping and jostling him as they allowed themselves to become obscenely carried away by Proverb's cheap tricks. They were out of their seats and out of control, surging toward the stage like mindless lemmings. The security did nothing to stop them. It was a pagan hysteria that verged on violence. All order and control was deliberately being broken down, and if that was not criminal, Winters did not know what was. He was being carried forward by the bovine stampede. He pushed back, hunching his shoulders and letting them flow around him. They had to be insane, the staring eyes, the outstretched hands. Wordless noise came from the gaping mouths. There was something terribly perverted in the way that Proverb was able to take hold of those people's minds. He had to be more than just a cynical hustler. Was he a real agent of the Antichrist?

The crowd had closed in around him, and he was being carried forward again. In that instant, he hated those people. He hated them with a cold, unforgiving venom. They were ugly, stupid, and dangerous, and there was no place for them in the world that they were trying to create. Why did they not just move the army in and clean out the whole bunch of them? It would have to come one day. He was repulsed by the physical intensity of the whole thing. It was the complete and extreme opposite of the clean, cold godliness that was the core of his beliefs. A big burly man with triangular sideburns and greasy hair, and smelling of beer and cheap aftershave was thumping him on the back and yelling into his face. The man had to be an Elvi. There was sweat running down his cheeks and flecks of spittle on his chin.

"Praise the Lord, brother. The day is coming. There will be a cleansing of the temple."

Winters was eaten up with a blind fury. He loathed being touched by strangers. He wanted to strike out at the man, but the offender was already gone.

"You stupid hillbilly bastard!"

He wanted to go on screaming at the crowd that they were sick, that they were abandoning themselves to an unnatural evil. His hatred and outrage were, however, tempered by a deep-seated fear. Those very same words had appeared on his primary screen, and he did not know what they meant. Could he somehow be a part of all this?

He spotted Rogers through the mass of people. Rogers, too, was pushing his way backward, struggling against the tide. Winters cupped his hands around his mouth and yelled. "Hey, Rogers! Over here!"

Rogers did not respond.

Winters yelled again. "Rogers! Over here!"

Rogers was looking around. He spotted Winters and began moving toward him. "This is getting to be a mess."

"He ought to be arrested right now."

"There'd be a riot."

They kept moving back. Now that there were two of them, it was a great deal easier. The identical dark suits immediately labeled them as deacons, and people stepped out of their way. Finally they were behind the main milling body of the audience. They stopped for breath.

Winters, feeling dizzy from the A-waves, shook his head. "This should never have been permitted."

Rogers nodded. He looked around the floor of the Garden with bleak, narrowed eyes. "This is going to be the last one. He's gone too far this time. If this cleansing the temple stuff isn't stamped on hard, we're going to see it scrawled on every wall in the city. It'll be a rallying cry for every hell-spawned subversive."

Winters experienced a sudden flash of guilt. He was on the

verge of telling Rogers about the way that the slogan had appeared on his terminal, but at the last minute he stopped himself. An instinct told him that it was something he had to hide, but in that instant of holding back, he also felt that he had become a part of whatever it meant. The words had appeared on his terminal and, as far as he knew, no one else's. It was as if the Antichrist already had a hold on him.

Speedboat

The woman was down on her knees, speaking in tongues; her eyes rolled, and her body jerked and spasmed. Speedboat watched in horrified fascination. All round her, male Elvi swayed in unison through their knee-snapping, hip-swaying, ritual dance. A second woman, young and quite pretty by the archaic standards of the Elvi, dropped into a glazed, unsteady duck-walk, arms thrashing and face contorting from vacant bliss to teeth-clenching paroxysm. She teetered precariously on tiptoe and toppled over on to her side. Her legs started kicking. Some of the male Elvi whooped and hollered as her skirt flew up to reveal pink stockings and garters, white thighs, and black lace panties. Speedboat wondered what really happened to them when they had those fits. What went on in their minds? Did they simply blank out, or did they really go to some other place. The wordless raving of both women was lost in the general din, but that did not seem to bother any of those, Elvi and non-Elvi alike, who had gathered around. As far as they were concerned, the Lord was manifesting himself right there on the floor of Madison Square Garden, and that was what they had paid their money to see. It was the direct intervention of God, and maybe a look at a girl's underwear into the bargain.

"Praise the Lord!"

"Amen!"

All over the auditorium, similar groups had gathered around other individuals who had dropped into their own random mystic states. Up on the stage, Proverb was milking it to the maximum.

"Total communion, brothers and sisters! Let's take it to total communion! Jesus is among us! *He has arrived!*"

The bursts of A-waves were coming like hammer blows, and the lights were strobing close to the epileptic frequencies. The music was deafening. Speedboat had never realized that the

Christians allowed themselves to become so radically crazed. If the doombeams had known about this, they would have joined in droves: It was not too different from dropping doomers. Either way, the person fell over.

Speedboat had had the foresight to swallow a couple of ten-milligram icebergs as the show started; otherwise some of the excesses of Proverb's special effects, coupled with the antics of the crowd, might have panicked him out of the place. They also helped prevent him being bent out of alignment by the subliminal hypnotics. The damn place was awash with audiovisual moodifiers, and he preferred to maintain a certain chemical distance from so much religion. After all, he could not afford to lose sight of the reason he was there.

Through with the total communion bit, Proverb had backed off again, and soaring electronics were playing "Love Me Tender." It was the Elvi's moment. They were moving up to the front of the stage. The lights were going down, and a velvet darkness was settling over the arena. Tiny blue stars floated high in the roof, orbiting each other with slow dignity as the music soared. The crowd fell silent. It was the hush of expectancy. Suddenly there were more blue lights in among the audience. At first Speedboat thought that it was another special effect, but then he saw that it was the Elvi themselves. Men and women alike were taking out small spheres, each about the size of a softball, which they appeared to warm in their hands. The spheres started to glow, the same soft blue as the stars above. When an Elvi right next to him took out a sphere and activated it, Speedboat had a chance to look at one close up. The glow was not the simple diffused light of a regular bulb. It was as if there was a tiny pinpoint of intensely bright light at the center of a solid globe of blue glass. Speedboat could not figure out exactly how it worked. It was probably nothing more than some new knicknack from one of the home shopping outfits, but a thousand or more of them, all softly shining in the darkness, had an eerie beauty. Those who did not have the spheres began striking matches, or flipping lighters and holding them up. The music fell away. Proverb's voice came over the top of it.

"Love me tender, love me true. All my dreams fulfill."

Speedboat knew that it was nothing but crafty manipulation, but despite himself, he found that a lump was forming in his throat. Half-ashamed that such a tear-jerk setup could even start to get to him, he focused hard on his own business at hand. The only dream he wanted fulfilled was to be out of this insane country.

1346408 Stone

The screen had abruptly blanked out, as if someone had jerked the plug on the program feed. The prisoners in D block glanced at each other. Nobody wanted to be the first to venture an explanation as to why the Arlen Proverb show had so abruptly gone off the air—they never knew when their conversations were being monitored.

It was Sunday night and the end of a bad week. There were few good weeks in the Joshua Redemption Center, but this one had been particularly awful. Early in the week, a gray, polluted overcast had descended on the camp and the swampland that surrounded it, accentuating the everpresent atmosphere of depression and hopelessness. Midweek, there had been the punishment. The grapevine said that the two women prisoners were already dead when they had been brought to the infirmary. They had died while still secured to the whipping post, maybe even before the flogging had run its course. A full-blown, ceremonial punishment, whether a flogging or a hanging, always left a lasting impression not unlike a grim emotional hangover on both inmates and guards. The prisoners adopted a hunched, glassy-eyed shuffle as if weighted down by a heightened awareness of their own fragile mortality. The hope that they might one day leave Joshua, other than in a blue plastic bodybag, diminished until it was all but invisible. The guards went to the opposite extreme, becoming viciously buoyant. Trivial infractions of the rules that they normally blind-eyed were penalized with considerable relish. The bosses seemed dedicated to making the prisoners' lives even more miserable than they already were. Kicks and blows were freely given, and the abuse was nonstop during the waking hours and salted with constant references to the two women who had been publically beaten to death.

Sunday had arrived with a certain measure of relief. The inmates had been marched to the compulsory three hours of remedial prayer and Bible study. Once that was over they were, by camp tradition, returned to their cell blocks and their own devices. Even heretics were permitted a God-given day of rest. But this Sunday, in keeping with the rest of the week, proved to be the exception to the general rule. A tour party of Young Crusaders and their parents had come through to look at sinners and observe their fate. It seemed a thoroughly sick way to spend the weekend, but the prisoners had no say over who came to inspect them. "In this hell, Dante comes in a tour bus with his whole damned family," 1346597 Ravel had muttered to Stone as they had been paraded for an extra two hours of special religious services staged for the visitors.

"Except this is no divine comedy."

"That's a fact. What do you think these kids did to qualify for such a treat?"

"Who the hell knows? Probably turned in their teacher to the deacons."

A boss was looking in their direction, and they quickly shut up. Ravel was a convicted porno dealer and comparatively new to Joshua. He was still a little too fond of taking chances for his own good. Sooner or later, they would break him in the bunker.

Even when the Young Crusaders had gone and the inmates were finally returned to their blocks, they still were not left alone. The TV monitor was blaring, relaying the Arlen Proverb rally from Madison Square Garden. There was no way either to shut it off or even to turn down the volume. At first, the prisoners in D block sat sullenly on their bunks staring at the raucous TV, taking minimal consolation in the fact that they were sitting down and not being marched anywhere or harangued by the guards. After a while, though, they started to sit up and take notice. Something weird was happening on the screen. Proverb was completely deviating from the normal routine of the TV preacher. He actually seemed to be issuing a direct challenge to the Faithful establishment, as good as calling the president and his people crooks and charlatans and promising a cleansing of the temple. And then the screen went blank. Someone had decided that Proverb needed to be censored. The only question was whether that censorship was confined to the camp, or if the plugs had been pulled on him all across the country.

After five minutes of silence and a blank screen, the TV flickered and a Danny & Crank cartoon appeared. Under the cover of the noisy audio, Ravel ventured the first comment.

"Looks to me like the Reverend Proverb might be joining us all in the quite near future."

Carlisle

Harry Carlisle positioned himself near one of the exits. If anyone had been intending to kill Proverb, he would have done it by now. The show was winding toward its grand finale. All he wanted to do was to get out of this madhouse as soon as possible. Proverb was going for broke, and Carlisle did not want to be around when things started getting broken. His cop's instinct told him that something bad was going to happen. Bad invariably put the PD right in the line of fire. He had no clear idea of how it was going to go down, but however and whenever, he intended to stay out from under. He had been detailed to stop an assassin. The assassin had failed to show, and when Proverb's act was through, Carlisle would be signing off. He wanted no part of what might come later. He would not put it past the deacons to be stupid enough to try to bust Proverb on the spot. He had heard that most of the deke brass were up in the VIP lounge. On a much more mundane level, he would also prefer to be long gone when the true believers came streaming out and hit the streets around the Garden, loaded to the gills on A-wave and audivid.

He had plenty to think about. When that phrase had come up, it had completely thrown him. "There will be a cleansing of the temple." First Dreisler, and then Arlen Proverb. His cop's instinct would not swallow coincidence. It was a sign, a signal, a code. It was a secret, maybe even a conspiracy. It went even deeper. He was certain that, whatever it was, Dreisler was trying to pull him into it. That on its own scared the hell out of him.

Mansard

They were coming up to the reprise of Revelations 9 and the final set piece. It was getting to be hard going. Despite the double glazing in the control booth, he could feel that the juiced waves from the stage were getting to him. He was having trouble maintaining control of the second eyes. The bright electronic landscape wavered and slid. At the periphery, it was breaking down into hilly undulations. He was becoming very much aware of the close promixity of the big audio net. He was even having trouble focusing his physical eyes. It was like being drunk but with none of the relaxation. He was well aware that he had, at a number of points in the show, pushed the effects much closer to the limits than he had intended. As far as he was concerned, Proverb had gone recklessly hog wild in his use of the hypnotics. Mansard, protected by two layers of armored glass, was being seriously hindered by them. Out in the auditorium, the crowd had to be plain crazy.

"Precue Rev nine reprise."

Mansard pulled what remained of his senses together. It was the final haul.

"On precue. Fading to black."

He pulled the hellfire to his fingertips. The monster shapes were parked in the middistance of the second eyes' landscape. He was ready. And as soon as this was over, he could throw on the Horsemen program and let it rip.

"Last set is down. Cue on my mark."

Mansard tensed.

"Three . . . two . . . one . . . mark!"

Speedboat

The bloodred fire was creeping down the wall. Purple flames leapt up behind the dark figure of Proverb. They were back in a rerun of the opening horror show. The ghosts were starting to crowd the aisles, and the hologram monsters stalked the artificial gloom. The wraparound electronic choir filled the air with its voices.

"Come not Lucifer!"

"Come not Lucifer!"

"Come not Lucifer!"

The crowd was beyond nuts. Some danced, loose-limbed, heads lolling, eyes unfocused, apparently unaware of the light and sound effects that swirled around them. Others sagged back in their seats, staring openmouthed, awed into limp submission. Still more went to the opposite extreme and lost themselves in deep-seated hellfear. They moaned and screamed. They wrung their hands and clutched for religious charms and tokens. For them, the special effects had become horribly real. A knot of Elvi held up their blue globes as if they believed that some inner magic would keep the devil at bay.

"Come not Lucifer!"

"Come not Lucifer!"

"Come not Lucifer!"

Speedboat glanced down at a woman next to him. She had sunk to her knees, sobbing and covering her face. Her body was racked with spasms, and she pleaded with the demons that she so obviously believed had come to get her.

"No, please, not me. I've lived a good life. Don't take me. Please don't take me!"

Speedboat held out a hand. "It's okay lady. Nothing's going to get you. It's only a show."

Speedboat could not have received a more hostile reception if he had exposed himself. She recoiled from his hand as if it were a striking snake and started to back away from him, scrabbling sideways on all fours with a contorted, crablike motion and making terrified mewing sounds. Her pantihose were ripped, her makeup was streaked and smeared, and her beehive hairdo had fallen into straggling disrepair.

Speedboat held up his hands. "Okay, okay. I was only trying to help."

He had seen enough freakouts in his time, but this had to beat all. The crowd itself had started to resemble extras in a scene from the Inferno. A gaping death's head hologram passed right through him, and he felt a shuddering chill. The icebergs had to be wearing off.

"Come not Lucifer!"
"Come not Lucifer!"
"Come not Lucifer!"

He started easing back through the disorganized throng. He wanted to get as far as he could from the stage and its A-wave pushers. He also started looking around, trying to figure out the easiest way to reach the backstage area after all the craziness was over. He had retreated about half way up the main floor when everything abruptly changed. A high, melodic tone, like a sudden breath of ice-cold air, cut through the "Come not Lucifer" chorus. The flames and demons faded into the darkness, and a single, intense white light grew on the stage. It was as if Proverb himself had become white hot. The light expanded into a single, blinding horizontal band. Proverb's voice rolled through the Garden as if carving the words on stone.

"Lucifer shall not come. He has no dominion over the children of the living God!"

It was like the sun coming up. Even Speedboat had to stand and stare. The choir's harmonics went straight up to heaven.

Golden light streamed from Proverb, its warmth melting away the audience's previous hysteria. The music was climbing to a final crescendo.

"Go forth and rejoice. The day is at hand. Go forth and rejoice. There will be a cleansing of the temple."

The lights on the stage slowly went down. The show was over. The house lights had not yet come up, but a lot of the crowd were starting to gather themselves together to face the real world. Then a strange rhythm started. At first it was just a feeling, low and indistinct, but it quickly gathered momentum. It was the hubbub of thousands of whispering voices.

"Go outside, look to the skies."

"Go outside, look to the skies."

The audience was picking up the cadence.

"Go outside, look to the skies."

"Go outside, look to the skies."

They were marching to the exits with a dogged, shell-shocked determination. They really believed that their day was at hand.

Mansard

He let out a long, heartfelt sigh, pulled off his headset, and slumped back into the chair. He felt like a pilot who had just flown around the world single-handed. He lay for almost a minute with his eyes closed, then reached up and gingerly eased the plugs from the DNI receptors in his neck. The physical world took back his senses. Sweat was running down his face, and his shirt was soaked. The light seemed unnaturally bright, and the roar of voices around him seemed deafening. People were slapping him on the back and applauding. He smiled automatically.

"I think we hit them where they live."

There was a red light flashing on the board in front of him. He picked up the headset again and put it to his ear. The voice of Jimmy Gadd came through loud and clear.

"Ready to go with the Horsemen when you are."

"Everything checks out?"

"Perfect."

"You're sure?"

"Sure, I'm sure. It's perfect."

"How's the weather?"

"Perfect."

"Is the crowd out on the street yet?"

"The first ones are coming out now."

"What's the status on the streetlights?"

"The Con Ed guy got the envelope, and there ain't one alight for three blocks in any direction."

"Traffic?"

"Eighth Avenue diverted from Twenty-third up to Thirty-eighth. Seventh Avenue is normal. We're going to have to live with that. It doesn't really matter though. Most of the light from the traffic is blocked by the Penn Plaza Tower."

"So we got about as much as we could have hoped for?"

"We did pretty damn good."

"Okay, so give it a fifteen count and let the Horsemen ride. If they don't push things over the edge, nothing will."

Someone had put a drink in front of him.

SIX

Carlisle

He ran the tracy on his wrist through a quick function check. The screen was still distorting, but the communicator was working again. Outside the auditorium, in one of the tunnels that led to the street, there was enough protection from the storm of leakage that was coming from the stage to allow the audio to function. He touched the send stem.

"Carlisle here. Control, do you copy?"

"Opcon here. We copy you, Lieutenant, but no visual."

"I know that. It's the best I can do."

"Audio loud and clear."

"So listen, the Arlen Proverb show is over. There have been no incidents. I am signing out and returning to Astor Place."

"We've logged that. What about the rest of the team?"

"They're off the air until they move away from Proverb's special effects. You'll just have to pick them up individually as they come out. Tell them to regroup downtown. I've had enough of this bullshit. The damned A-waves have given me a headache."

"Ten four, Lieutenant."

"Yeah."

He closed the channel. Harry Carlisle was in a foul temper. What had all the paranoia been about? Was it celebrity chic to imagine death threats? He felt that he and his men had yet again been used, and he fully intended to stop at a bar before he returned to Astor Place.

The street door led out onto Eighth Avenue. Carlisle's temper

135

was not improved by his discovery that the street lamps were out. It was a hell of a time for a power failure. Or was it a power failure? It was certainly limited. From the corner of Thirty-third Street, he could see the Empire State Building, shining in its halo of cloud, just blocks away. He could also see that the traffic was not running. People were strolling along the empty expanse of the avenue. What the hell was going on? He looked around. There were plenty of cops about, but they seemed to be standing in tight watchful groups, certainly not deployed to handle the crowd that would be coming out of the Garden at any minute. They had the look of men who were waiting for an order. He walked over to the nearest group and flashed his badge.

"What happened to the lights?" he asked.

"It's all part of the show."

"What show?"

The patrolman was inscrutable behind his armored visor. His name tag read "Rennweiler." He imperceptibly jerked his shoulders. "You better talk to the sergeant."

"At any minute, thousands of these fools will come streaming out of the Garden, twisted out of shape on A-waves, and find themselves in total darkness."

"Really, Lieutenant, you'd better talk to the sergeant."

"Where is he?"

"He's here someplace. I'm not sure exactly where. It's hard to keep track in the dark."

Carlisle knew that he was getting the uniformed runaround. He looked about for someone in authority but failed to see any stripes or gold braid. The first of the Proverb audience had begun to emerge from the exits. He shook his head, trying to clear it. Oh, Christ, they were chanting something. What was it they were saying? It sounded like "Go outside, look to the skies." They were crazier than he had thought.

They were spilling out of the exits in earnest. The chanting could be heard coming from those who were still inside, but once they reached the sidewalk, the cohesion faltered. They seemed to become confused. They walked aimlessly, turning and peering upward, spreading out over the closed-off width of Eighth Avenue. Only a handful seemed to be going for their cars or turning for the subway. By far the majority seemed to be holding on, waiting for something to happen. The squads of uniforms were not doing anything. It was insane. The way things were being handled went against all the most basic rules of crowd control. In a situation like this it was a matter of get 'em out and get 'em gone.

A crowd could never be allowed to linger after any event, and that went double when the event had been as emotionally charged as this one. He was starting to suspect that someone had failed to tell him something. What did that jiveass Rennweiler mean by "it's all part of the show"?

Then it started.

They simply glimmered into silent life, like apparitions from another dimension. There was a concerted gasp from the crowd on the street. The things were huge. At first, Carlisle was too close to the building to be able to see them. With a host of other people, he hurried across the sidewalk and out onto the avenue. When he turned and looked, he was instantly rooted to the spot.

"God almighty!"

The Four Horsemen of the Apocalypse, maybe a hundred feet high, were charging across the city. War, Famine, Pestilence, and Death, armor gleaming, spear raised, scythe swinging. They seemed to be galloping full tilt for the Hudson, New Jersey, and the rest of America. Fire burned from the horses' nostrils, and sparks flew from the giant hooves. The Horsemen's eyes were hidden beneath cowl, behind visor, or in the dark hollows of black skull sockets. Their spectral images were reflected over and over in the curtain glass of the neighboring towers. Even though Harry knew it was all an electronic illusion, the first sight took his breath away. It was magnificent.

It was also an explosive situation. All around him, those who were not simply standing and staring as he was were dropping to their knees in prayer. Many were walking backward, gazing up, transfixed. Someone had started shouting.

"The day has come!"

Others took up the cry.

"The day has come!"

"The day has come!"

Carlisle was very much aware that word would soon be spreading across the city about the vision above the Garden as people saw it from their windows and started to call friends. It was possible that literally millions of people would soon be converging on the area. Just a few blocks downtown, the burned and blackened buildings that had been torched in the recent bread riot stood as testimony to a crowd's madness. He opened a channel on the tracy.

"This is Carlisle. I'm on Eighth Avenue, outside the building. Do you know what's going on out here?"

"This is opcon. What is going on out there, Lieutenant?"

"There's a hundred-foot-high hologram on the top of the building."

"The Four Horsemen, right?"

"That's right. The goddamn Horsemen. Why wasn't I told about any of this?"

The tracy was now working perfectly. The opcon operator on the small screen shrugged.

"Don't ask me, Lieutenant. I just work here. Maybe someone didn't think it was your territory."

"But who sanctioned this damned thing? It could start a riot."

"I don't know, Lieutenant. I heard the deacons approved it."

"Can you patch me through to Captain Parnell?"

The operator shook his head. "I can't, Lieutenant. He went into the auditorium just before the end of the show. He's still off the air."

"Goddamn it."

"I'm sorry, Lieutenant."

Carlisle knew that he was helpless. He spotted a sergeant with a squad of uniforms. The sergeant's name tag read "Muncie," and he looked as if a conversation with a lieutenant of detectives was the very last thing he wanted. Carlisle didn't give a damn. He had had enough of closed-minded departmentalization. He glanced pointedly at the huge hologram images. "This could easily come unhinged."

"Tell me about it, but we've got orders from the brass to let it happen."

"And you're just following orders?"

"You said it, Lieutenant, not me. Get me some new orders and I'll move them out of here and get the traffic running. Until then, I'm not offering up my ass for sacrifice."

Carlisle sighed. "I hear you."

In fact, the crowd, although growing increasingly dense, was surprisingly orderly. The chanting and screaming only came in brief bursts, and comparatively few were still on their knees. The majority simply stood, heads tilted back, gazing up at the giant Horsemen. The first ones out had moved up onto the block-long stone steps of the big post office building across the street and were using them as granite bleachers. He could see blue pinpoints of light from the Elvi's globes. War's mount reared, and its rider stabbed down at the mass of people with his spear. There was the murmur of thousands of voices. Carlisle spotted a gang of street kids moving through the growing throng like sharks through a school of tuna. They were almost certainly making a preliminary pass before the first purse- or chain-snatching runs of fast larceny. The calm would not last long.

"But what the hell, it's not my problem."

Unfortunately, he couldn't quite believe himself. Sometime— it seemed like centuries ago—he had sworn an oath to protect the public. It had not said anything about all deals being off if the public put itself willfully at risk or his superiors acted like morons. He couldn't just walk away. He looked around for someone who might be a little more help than Sergeant Muncie. It was then that he spotted the deacons.

There were eight of them, coming out of the Garden at a fast walk. They all wore bulky, dark-blue, three-quarter-length rain-coats and porkpie hats. Carlisle knew those raincoats. Their cut sufficiently loose to hide automatic weapons and lightweight body armor. Something was absolutely wrong. They looked like a deacon hit team—and what in the name of merciful heaven was a hit team doing in this already lunatic situation?

They turned sharp right and followed the curve of the building around into Thirty-third Street. He decided to follow them. They seemed to be heading for the gates where cars and trucks had access to the inside of the Garden.

Speedboat

He knew that he had taken a wrong turn somewhere. He pushed through a set of double doors and found himself in an approach lane to an underground loading bay. There was a black and heavily armored stretch limousine parked under a light. It might have been a Mercedes when it started out, but the exten-sive customizing made identification difficult. There was a cow-catcher on the front, and the windshield and windows were just slits surrounded by steel plate. The ceramic eggbox panels cov-ering the sides and top could stop anything short of a rocket attack. Whoever owned the car took his or her personal safety very seriously.

It was not the car, however, that made him duck back into the doorway. It was the five armed men who stood around it. At first he thought that they were cops, but then he saw the pale-blue trim on their uniforms. They were Garden security. Speedboat did not know too much about private rentacops. He didn't have a great deal of contact with them down on the Lower East Side. In theory, he should have been able to stroll up to them with his backstage pass prominently displayed and ask directions. The pass was legit, and it had worked perfectly well on the guards who had let him through the security screens into the backstage area and who had explained how to find the guy he had to contact. Though the explanation had turned out to be garbled, it had been freely and civilly given.

Theory and practice were, unfortunately, two different things. Speedboat fished out the pass from one of his deep pockets and stuck it on the front of his parka, but he hesitated before walking out into plain sight. What kept him there in the doorway, peering furtively at the car and its escort, were the machine pistols that they held at high port. These guys were serious. In a culture where shooting first and asking questions afterward was far too common, an individual with a uniform and a machine pistol required a good deal of consideration and respect.

He had all but finished considering and was about to pull out his pass and walk boldly up to the armed security men when the five of them stiffened. He quickly changed his mind and stayed put. Something was about to happen. There were voices in the darkness beyond the pool of light around the car. Figures came into the light. There were four of them, backed up by even more armed Madison Square Garden security. On the outside, there was a mountain of a man dressed like a western gunfighter, complete with Stetson and fancy suit, and an almost-as-large black man in a scarlet sweatsuit. They flanked a flashy blonde with a gold leather evening coat tossed over her shoulders and a small man wearing a rhinestone suit, dark glasses, and a towel draped around his neck. Disconnected cables trailed from his pants leg. Speedboat froze. It was Arlen Proverb himself.

The cowboy opened the door of the limo, and first the blonde and then Proverb got into the back. The cowboy slammed the door. There was a brief conversation with security personnel, and then he and the black man climbed into the front. The long car was started, and it accelerated quickly up the tunnel. The Garden security and the unnoticed Speedboat watched it go. Speedboat was a little bemused; he rarely came close to celebs.

Once again he readied himself to seek directions from the

security men, but once again he shrank back into the shelter of the doorway. There was a commotion beyond the lights—shouts and running feet. Another group of men also brandishing guns ran into the space where the armored limo had just been. Speedboat's eyes widened. There was no mistaking the blue raincoats and dark suits. They were dekes. They yelled something indistinguishable at the security men and started up the tunnel at a run. Speedboat did not hesitate. He jerked back through the doors behind him and fled.

Carlisle

There was a sizable crowd around the gates. They were quiet, with no pleading, pushing, or hysteria, and the line of security directly in front of the vehicle entrance had no difficulty in holding them back. These were the hardcore, the fans rather than the faithful. Despite the Four Horsemen, they were waiting for Proverb to come driving out of the bowels of the building in his limousine. They just wanted to be close, maybe to see his face, and they stood quietly holding souvenirs or programs. Two had raised a banner that read "Next to Jesus, We Love You." There was a high proportion of Elvi among them, holding up those blue globes.

Carlisle was about eight yards behind the deacons, and he slowed a little as they came up to the knot of fans by the gates. Nothing had prepared him for the sudden and completely purposeless violence. They simply went through the crowd, barking and manhandling, counting on ingrained fear to make the people melt away in front of them. And their tactic might have worked if it had not been for one burly Elvi. His wife was not fast enough in getting out of the way. One of the deacons pushed her roughly. She stumbled on her Minnie Mouse shoes and fell with a shriek. Her previously quiet husband, who had been docilely holding a pair of polytone 3D pictures, one of Elvis Presley in his ceremonial costume and a slightly smaller one of Proverb in his, instantly turned into a mean and outraged good ol' boy. He grabbed the deacon by his lapels and threw him.

"I don't care who you are. Nobody pushes my wife to the ground."

He turned to help his wife to her feet but was immediately jumped by three deacons. Two others pulled guns from under their raincoats. At the very same moment, the gates started to slide open. A large and heavily armored black limo was coming through from inside. It was coming fast, and the Garden security started to move the crowd out of its path. They immediately ran up against the remaining deacons, who seemed to by trying to push through to the gate. There was total confusion. The deacons who were struggling with the furious Elvi tried to break away and go for the car. But the Elvi had not finished with them. He brought one down with a mighty, double-handed chop to the back of his neck. The fallout from that act cannoned into the security men and the now-panicking fans they were attempting to control, resulting in a tangle of struggling people right in front of the car. Whoever was driving the black limo slammed on the brakes, and it screeched to a shuddering halt. The deacons were straight on it, brandishing their weapons and grabbing for the car's door handles.

For Carlisle, everything fell into place. Maybe he was going to see an assassination after all. The idiots were going after Proverb, and they did not look particularly bothered as to whether they took him alive. That in itself was a measure of how far gone they were. The bastards thought that they could get away with anything.

The black limo was resisting all their efforts to open the door. The engine roared. The people in front of it, caught in the blazing headlights, scrambled to get out of the way. The car shot forward. Its lowered cowcatcher clipped one of the deacons and sent him sprawling on the hard road surface. It made a hard right and sped the wrong way down Thirty-third Street, scattering the stream of people who were coming in the opposite direction to see the Horsemen. A deacon loosed off with a burst from his machine pistol at the disappearing limousine. The bullets struck orange sparks off the sheet steel in the car's armor. The car did not stop, but gunfire started a mass panic on Thirty-third as screaming bystanders dived for cover anywhere they could find it. Carlisle clipped his badge to his lapel and reached for his own gun. The deacons all seemed to be equipped with the latest .10 Krupp HVs, which made his own automag seem puny.

The big Elvi did not seem at all deterred by the show of weapons. With three or four more at his back, he ran straight at the deacon who had fired and blindsided him. The deacon went flying. The way he hit the ground, rolled, and fired did credit to his training. The burst took the Elvi in the chest. He was lifted off the ground and thrown backward. His wife started screaming. The deacon lost his gun as the other Elvi ran over him, kicking and stomping with pointed Italian shoes.

The second burst of gunfire started the stampede. People were running in every direction. The echoes from the surrounding buildings made it impossible to tell where the firing was coming from unless one was very close to the incident. Somewhere a woman was screaming.

"They're killing us! The deacons are killing us!"

It was the kind of blind hysteria that could spread like wildfire through a crowd. Carlisle looked down at his tracy. His first instinct was to call in, but what was the point? He didn't need anyone confirming that there was nothing that could be done.

There was a lot of noise coming from Eighth Avenue. The panic must have reached the main body of the crowd. A second tight, angry group of deacons came running up the ramp from inside the Garden. As they came through the gate, Carlisle grabbed one of them by the arm. He spun the man quickly around and yelled in his face.

"Who's in charge of this nonsense?"

It was only after he had yelled that he recognized the deacon. It was that sanctimonious little jerk Winters. The recognition was simultaneous and mutual.

"Carlisle."

"I asked you a question, boy."

An unpleasant smile spread over Winters's scrubbed, unctuous face. He was out of breath and clearly running on adrenaline. "You don't talk to me like that, Carlisle. After the end of tonight, things are going to be very different."

They both ducked as a bottle smashed against the wall behind them. An angry mob had started to ring the gate, and the deacons were pulling back into a protective formation in the gateway. The crowd did not seem willing to force the confrontation yet. The firepower that the deacons had between them was more than enough to keep them sullenly at bay. They contented themselves with throwing things from the back rows and yelling abuse. Carlisle knew that it was a situation that would not continue indefinitely. It had to deteriorate. Either the mob would work itself up until it was irrational enough to charge the deacons, or else the deacons would lose control and start shooting. In either scenario, people would die. He knew that he really had to get himself out of there. He could not do anything, and he was damned if he would let himself be caught in the crossfire.

He was still holding on to Winters. They were in a kind of no man's land.

Winters glanced down at the ten caliber in his hand. "You realize that I could shoot you out of hand and nobody would do a thing."

Carlisle's own gun was in his free hand. The moment's angry impulse that had caused him to grab Winters was creating a ridiculous and dangerous standoff. It was time to take the initiative. He smiled back. "You could, at that."

Winters's eyes flickered. It was obviously not the response that he had expected.

Carlisle laughed. "For all your bullshit, you deacons really don't have it, do you?"

Without warning, he kicked Winters hard in the crotch and turned to run. Three steps, and he was in among the crowd. They parted to let him through.

Winters

His eyes were watering and he wanted to vomit. He lay on his side, doubled up, his body curled around the throbbing agony between his legs. Only rage stopped him from crying out. That bastard Carlisle. He would kill him. The next time he saw him, he would kill him. Through the pain and the violent fantasies of what he would do to Carlisle, he heard shouts in among the mob.

"Get his gun! Quick, get his gun!"

He realized in horror that when Carlisle had kicked him, he had dropped his weapon. He opened his eyes and saw the brand-new Krupp lying some six feet away on the sidewalk. He had only been issued it half an hour earlier. He tried to move, but the pain redoubled. There were footsteps coming toward him. He tried dragging himself. Hands reached for the gun. He stretched for it, too, but his arm was kicked aside. Then, right on top of him, there was a thunderous explosion of gunfire. Rogers was standing, straddling him, firing over the heads of the crowd. They were backing away, and some had turned tail and run. Rogers's first burst had been aimed at the scum who had been trying to get the HV. Four of them lay sprawled on the sidewalk. There was a lot of blood.

Rogers moved quickly forward, picked up the fallen gun, then stepped back to Winters. "Can you walk?"

"I don't know."

"You'd better."

Meredith, the team leader, was yelling to them. "Everyone move back inside the gates! Move back!"

Rogers slung Winters's machine pistol over his shoulder and put a hand under his armpit. "Come on, I'll help you."

Winters found that his legs were working again. With Rogers holding him up, he hobbled back to where the other deacons were slowly retreating to the vehicle entrance. That withdrawal made the crowd a good deal bolder. They were closing in again. Meredith had found himself a bullhorn somewhere. He faced the mob. He cut a heroic figure, the ramrod-straight embodiment of authority facing the milling forces of darkness and disorder.

"There will be no more warnings. If you don't disperse, I will order my men to open fire."

Winters dropped to one knee. He took his Krupp back from Rogers. The ring of angry faces stopped coming on, but the crowd showed no inclination to disperse.

Meredith looked grimly at the other deacons. "They've had their chance. Fire at will."

The muzzle flashes spat into the night. Winters' gun vibrated in his hand. The Krupp HVs made an angry, high-pitched sound. Winters was surprised at how easy it was. They went down like mown corn. Bodies kicked and contorted on the street and sidewalk. The ones who were not hit in the first withering fire took to their heels, scrambling for their lives. They immediately ran into the crowds behind them who were still pressing forward. All of Thirty-third Street was choked by terrified, struggling humanity. On the far sidewalk, the front window of Toots Shor's bar exploded.

"Hold your fire. Back through the gate, right now."

As he moved back with the others, Winters had almost forgotten about his pain. He felt breathless and light-headed. That'll show the bastards. That'll show them who gives the orders. That'll show those inferior scum what kind of God we worship.

There had been a chorus of protests when they had been told that they could not leave the VIP lounge. Everyone had something to do or someplace to be. They had parties and dinner dates to go to, or lovers waiting for them. The Yorkshire terrier that was clutched under the arm of the overweight wife of the president of Good Shepherd Inc. started yapping. Maybe it, too, had plans, Cynthia reflected wryly. Only the senior deacons had left, after making a curt announcement that, because of possible street disturbances, everyone should remain where they were. Only official vehicles would be going in and out of the Garden until it was considered safe. They had left Longstreet to take the flak, with a couple of junior aides to do spin control on the disgruntled guests. Longstreet immediately had the waiters push out the booze as if it were New Year's Eve, and then he got on the phone to his department at Astor Place.

"What the hell is going on?"

During the lengthy pause that followed, Longstreet's face had grown increasingly disbelieving.

"The Four Horsemen of the Apocalypse? Has the world gone completely insane?"

There was a shorter pause.

"Why, in God's name, weren't we told about it? Was it supposed to be a surprise?"

Pause.

"What do mean you just got it from NBC? Do you realize how that makes us look? Who authorized this?"

Pause.

"What is Dreisler's office doing authorizing sky spectacles? I'm getting a little tired of the assumption that he can do exactly as he pleases. In the meantime, I'm bottled up in here with a party of extremely miffed bigshots. If this Four Horsemen thing is happening, they might as well see the damn thing. I want you to get on to somebody at the Garden and have a video picture piped in here. In the meantime, I'll do my best to smooth the feathers."

He hung up and turned to the circle of impatiently waiting guests.

"Well, we may not be going anywhere for a while but at least we'll be able to see what's happening."

His words were not greeted with any degree of enthusiasm.

The detainees did not want to see what was happening—they wanted to get on with their planned evenings.

After about five minutes, the monitor screens came to life. Some, apparently being fed from a camera mounted on the roof of the big post office building on the other side of Eighth Avenue, showed an upward-angled shot of the Four Horsemen. A second view was provided by a camera crew in a helicopter hovering over the Hudson. A third set of images came from a mobile unit down in the crowd. The video hookup, far from calming the protesters in the VIP lounge, actually started a new round of complaints.

"How big are those things?"

"I heard that they were over a hundred feet high."

"Why can't we go out and see them?"

"You want to be down in among those people?"

"They don't look too bad."

Indeed, at that moment the crowd was orderly and quiet, simply staring up at the huge images.

"Crowds can change very quickly. A mob like that may look okay, but there's always a proportion of criminals and sickoes in among them."

"What about the roof? Why can't we go up to the roof and watch things from there?"

Longstreet was quick to squash that idea. "The images are being projected from the roof. There's too much equipment up there for it to be safe."

"The real question, Deacon Longstreet, is how long do you intend to keep us cooped up in here?"

The vocal leader of the complainers was the president of Good Shepherd Inc., whose fat wife was now feeding canapés to the Yorkshire terrier. Cynthia figured that he had probably been planning to dump the wife and dog and go to see his mistress. That was no doubt why he was so agitated. Longstreet's amiable concern was showing signs of strain. He started enunciating his words very carefully, as if he were explaining to a fractious child that he could not have his own way.

"All I know is that people much more important than me have decided that we'd be better off staying where we are. I think the best thing we could all do is to go along with them."

"You deacons have to remember that you don't run everything."

An irresistible nastiness was starting to twist Longstreet's bland, public smile. "Oh, we do, sir, we do. Except, in this instance, we're doing our best to protect your lives and health."

"But there's nothing going on out there."

"Actually, there is."

Everyone turned. The voice belonged to the rather strange figure in the voluminous cowled overcoat who had come in with Matthew Dreisler. When Dreisler had left, a few minutes after the rest of the deacon brass, he had taken his aide and bodyguards with him, but for some inexplicable reason he had left the tall, thin individual there. This was the first time that he had spoken. The other guests looked from him to the monitor screens.

"He's right."

People were running past the camera. It shook and went out of focus as the camera car was jostled. Then there was the sound of gunfire. The ground-level crew were down with their microcams and pushing toward the source of the disturbance. The screen was streaked with afterburn from the lights. Suddenly the cameras were jerked aside as a squad of police pushed through. The president of Good Shepherd Inc. was immediately demanding answers from Longstreet.

"What the hell is going on down there? Why doesn't somebody tell us? Why's there no voiceover?"

Longstreet was happier when he had something to explain. "What we're seeing here is the direct feed to the network. The voiceover isn't put on until the raw input is processed."

He did not add that this footage would be processed straight into the garbage. The censors would never let anything so inflammatory reach the domestic screens.

The guests fell silent as they watched the deteriorating situation on the monitor screens. Cynthia was near the back of the crowd, helping herself to more champagne than was strictly good for her. The man in the cowled coat came up beside her.

"Am I right in thinking that you're Cynthia Kline?"

Cynthia looked up in surprise and not a little alarm. "That's right. That's me."

For the first time she had the chance to get a good look at the face beneath the cowl. There was something almost biblical about the deep-set eyes and hollow cheeks. He had the look of a genuine ascetic, a rare animal in that day and age.

He smiled slightly. "I've been asked to give you something."

"You have?"

Cynthia felt extremely uncomfortable. The man in the cowled coat glanced pointedly at where Longstreet was once again on the phone, trying to get additional information about the disturbance that was boiling up on the streets outside. She could only assume that the strange man was making a deliberate show of checking that they were not being observed. When he seemed satisfied, he took a small plastic pouch from his sleeve. She assumed that it contained some kind of software diskette.

"Please take this quickly."

Cynthia looked at it as if it were a venomous insect, but took it anyway. Refusing to touch the thing would not save her from whatever was going to happen next.

The cowled coat made a slight bow. "You will treat this as wholly confidential."

He quickly moved away, mixing in with the knot of people gathered around Longstreet. His timing was impeccable. Longstreet was just hanging up the phone.

"They're going to send the STG in to clear the streets."

The president of Good Shepherd Inc. grunted. "It's the only way to deal with this rabble."

Carlisle

The woman's arms were windmilling, clawing at anything that came within reach as she stumbled along blindly. Tears were streaming down her face, and she was sobbing a revolving litany about how the Seventh Seal was broken and everyone was going to die. All around, there were hundreds like her taking simultaneous leave of their senses. The Four Horsemen towered above them all as if they really were presiding over the fall of civilization. Carlisle himself was not too far from believing that the end of the world had come. He tried to push backward, but the crush would not let him. The woman lurched straight into him and grabbed him round the neck. Her eyes did not even focus. Carlisle ducked out of her clutching embrace but, in so doing, momentarily lost his footing. He was starting to get frightened. He was in the middle of an escalating, milling panic, and if he was knocked to the ground, his badge or gun or all of his training would not do him the slightest bit of good. He could be trampled just like anyone else. He took advantage of a brief eddy in the crowd to get his breath and bearings. His tracy was flashing. He touched the RECEIVE button.

Parnell appeared on the tiny screen. "Where are you?"

"I'm on Eighth, in the middle of a hundred thousand maniacs."

"Get out of there. Right now. The deacons have ordered in the STG. Unrestricted pacification. They're going to clear the streets the hard way."

The Special Tactical Group was the last resort when it came to urban disorder. Based on the British and French models, it was an independent, paramilitary force under the direct control of the deacons. They used it like a blunt instrument. Once they were let loose in a situation, there was no stopping them. They went at their target with a singleminded, mad-dog brutality.

"The STG? Has everybody gone nuts?"

"Quite possibly."

"The deacons had a crack at Proverb, but they missed him."

"We know. They had a couple of tries, but he beat them. They picked up the car in the forties, but he'd already switched vehicles. But listen, Harry, you don't have time to talk. Get the hell away from there. The STG is coming. It's going to turn into a massacre and there isn't a damn thing we can do about it."

"Okay, I'm going. Which direction will they be coming from?"

"Straight down Eighth from the north. They're grouping at the U-Tran terminal. The Herods will come through first laying gas."

"They're using gunships? You were serious about a massacre."

"Just get out of there."

He signed off. Carlisle tried to push his way down the avenue, but right at that moment a surge of people decided to go in the opposite direction, and he was carried backward.

Mansard

Charlie Mansard was on the roof when the STG arrived. He was not aware of them at first. He was standing in the very center of the complex of laser projectors, staring up at the sky and admiring his creation. It was impossible to see the image from that angle, but he was quite content to just gaze up at the pillars of light seemingly going straight to infinity. It was like being inside some radiant cathedral, a cathedral that he had designed and created himself, the biggest skywalker ever staged. He laughed out loud in pure delight.

"It's alive!"

He felt like Victor Frankenstein as the lightning energized his monster. In his case, though, the lightning itself was his monster.

"God, it's beautiful!"

The first he knew about the trouble on the street below was when a Herod gunship cut clear through the image, disrupting the columns of mist with its rotors and producing a temporary hole though Famine and Pestilence. Mansard had heard some noise and shouting down on the street, but he had not paid any attention to it. Crowds were like that. The helicopter, on the other hand, was a direct affront.

He turned angrily in the direction of Jimmy Gadd. "What the hell was that?"

Gadd was over on the other side the roof, running the control board. "It's an STG chopper, chief. There's two more coming down Eighth Avenue. I think there's trouble in the crowd."

Mansard quickly picked his way through the snaking complex of cables to the parapet. Gadd was right. There were two more choppers coming slowly down the street. They were the urban combat model, the kind with the ultrashort rotors that could operate down between the buildings. Below them, on the ground, a dozen or more armored personnel carriers were rolling forward with blazing searchlights mounted on their front turrets. The choppers kept pace with the armor until they were opposite the old New Yorker Hotel, then suddenly accelerated and swung up and over the crowd outside the Garden. A second chopper cut through the image of the Horsemen, punching a hole through Death.

Mansard cursed after it. "What do you think you're doing?"

He got a firm grip on his fear of heights and peered down at the crowd. They were milling in chaotic confusion. What had spooked them? Surely not his Horsemen? The first line of armor had halted at Thirty-fourth Street and was disgorging dark, disciplined squads of men.

Gadd had come up beside him. "This looks like it's going to turn ugly."

"Is there anything we can do?"

Gadd sighed. "Not much. Not unless . . ."

Mansard looked at him suspiciously. "Unless what?"

"Unless we kill the image. It might minimize the confusion."

Mansard was outraged. "Take down my Four Horsemen?"

"We'd have to shut it down soon. It won't be long before the fog generators start overheating."

The STG troops were spreading out over the entire width of Eighth Avenue. Even from where Mansard sat it was possible to see the light reflecting off their Plexiglas riot shields. The Herods had turned around and were heading back up town in a wide loop that took them close to the Empire State Building. Their first pass had obviously been a dummy run. Presumably they were turning around to come back for the real thing.

"This is going to be very unpleasant."

The lead chopper was coming back down Eighth Avenue at high speed with its nose lights blazing. It could not have been more than twenty feet from the ground. It zipped over the lines of STG and barrelled toward the crowd. People started to run, but there was nowhere to run to. Trails of white vapor arrowed from beneath the gunship's stubby wings. It pulled quickly upward as the rocket cannisters hit and bounced end over end, spewing clouds of EZA riot gas. The second and third Herods followed suit. When they had made their runs, the whole area in front of the Garden was awash with the incapacitating gas.

While the helicopters hovered over the post office, the front ranks of the STG ground force started jogging on the spot. There was a sinister rhythmic drumming sound. They were beating on their shields with their electric clubs, working themselves up for the attack.

Mansard turned away. "What do they think they are? A goddamn Roman legion?"

Jimmy Gadd looked at him questioningly but did not say anything. The STG was moving forward, gas masks sealed, closing on the hysterical crowd.

Mansard shook his head. "Kill the image. We're not a part of this."

Anslinger

First it had been a dream and then it became a nightmare. There had been moments, back inside, during the service, when she had been frightened. She had been scared to death during the dark part when the demons had moved among them, but then the Reverend Proverb had made the golden light come and everything had been all right. They had gone out of Madison Square Garden chanting, all together.

"Go outside, look to the skies."

On the outside, Maude Anslinger had looked up and seen the terrible Horsemen towering over her. The first sight of the huge figures had turned her heart to ice. What was this? Had Judgment Day really come? Would the graves really give up their dead? Would George be coming back to her? She had a sudden vision, like one of those old movies: the living dead walking through the night, lost and confused. She was lost and confused herself. It was so hard to think. The Jesus Waves made her mind cloudy and hard to focus. Perhaps she should go to the cemetery in Queens were George was buried; perhaps she should go and find him. Thinking about George helped clear her head a little and calm her fear. There was no way that she could get to Queens. The important thing was that she was safe. No harm was going to come to her. The Horsemen were not coming for her. She believed in Jesus. She had signed the pledges; she had sent what little money she had. It was not much, but she did not have much. Jesus knew that. She would receive her golden crown and be reunited with George.

Some of the people in the crowd did not seem to share her calm faith. They screamed and shouted and dropped to their knees to pray. There was pushing and shoving. She was repeatedly jostled. She began to worry that she would be knocked down when the crowd made one of its wild surges. Over on the other side of the street, some people were climbing the big flight of stone steps in front of the post office, using them as a vantage point. She decided to follow suit. On the steps she would be out of the main body of the crowd and high enough up to see what was going on. She made her way toward them, avoiding the rowdier sections.

After determinedly easing her way through the crush, she eventually found herself on the third step from the top, looking out over the massed heads. Another woman, roughly her age, was standing next to her. The woman wore small, round, old-fashioned wire-rimmed glasses and seemed to be staring transfixed at the Four Horsemen. Maude Anslinger remembered her own initial fear and put a hand on the woman's shoulder.

"There's no need to be afraid. They won't hurt us. They're here for the sinners."

The woman shook her head. There was something a little strange about her eyes. "It's only an apparition. The Day hasn't come yet. It's just a vision to show the sinners what to expect."

The woman seemed a little crazy, but Maude smiled pleasantly anyway. "I sure hope you're right."

The woman nodded. "The voices told me. They tell me everything."

"I don't hear voices."

"You're lucky. There are times that I wish they'd go away." She put a hand quickly to her mouth. "I suppose I shouldn't say that."

There seemed to be a lot of noise coming from the direction of Thirty-third Street. A violent rush of running people caused a huge ripple in the crowd at the foot of the steps. There was a lot of shouting and screaming. Maude Anslinger frowned. The crowd was huge, and it did not seem to be calming down. If anything, it was getting more agitated. The people on the steps shuffled uncomfortably. It was as if everyone sensed that, somewhere on the other side of this sea of people, something was very wrong. When the shots came, the feeling was confirmed. Everyone was looking for a way out. Like all the others, Maude failed to see one. There were more shots and the flashing lights of emergency vehicles.

Maude Anslinger was seriously frightened. A surge of humanity broke over the bottom of the post office steps like a crashing wave. Dozens of people fell in an extended tangle of arms and legs. She knew that if she went down, she would never get up again. A new thought danced into her fear. If anything happened to her, who would take care of Theodore? The cat would starve.

The helicopters screamed past with their blazing lights. The noise was so loud that Maude clapped her hands to her ears. It was all going so fast that she could not really absorb it. People like her watched helicopters on TV. They did not stand in crowds of people who were going mad. There had to be some way out. She looked behind her. People were hugging the pillars that held up the post office's massive portico and pressing back into the dark spaces between them. There was no room for her up there. The helicopters screamed past once more. This time they dropped the gas. It came up the steps in a single rolling billow.

When it reached them, it burned. Maude was doubled over, racked by stomach cramps. Her eyes were streaming. It was the Day of Judgment, and they were all sinners. The terrible, face-less men that advanced through the swirling gas were like de-mons from the pit.

They were beating people as they came up and across the steps. Lashing out at them with bulky clubs that made blue electric sparks when they struck home. The violence was cold and impersonal. Anonymous in their dark-blue armor and iden-tical insect masks, they were quite literally a line of grim reap-ers. The crowd fled in front of them in blind choking panic. Men and women fell and were trampled. The woman of the voices went down, her old-fashioned glasses falling at Maude Anslinger's feet. In the next moment, a foot came down and crushed them. Maude hunched her shoulders and closed her eyes. She was jostled and pushed, but she did not fall. Miracu-lously, the crowd had gone around her. She opened her eyes and found herself face to face with the locust-headed demon from the pit. The club came down, and there was a single flash of pain and then nothing. Maude Anslinger did not know that her neck broke when she fell backward down the steps. She would not know that her cat would be rescued from starvation in just three days. Nobody would know or even care whether she spent the hereafter walking and talking with Jesus or in the atheist's oblivion. To the world, Maude Anslinger was just part of the death count.

Carlisle

"Get back inside the Garden, right now!" Carlisle yelled through the handkerchief he had pressed to his face. He held up his badge with his free hand. His exposed skin felt as if it were being peeled. "That's an order!"

He had seen the small knot of NYPD uniforms struggling against the tide, and he had fought his way through to them. The STG's plan was simple and obvious. They were going to drive the crowd south on Eighth. They would probably run the hardcore all the way down into the twenties, down as far as the devastation left by the recent bread riot. There they would finish them. The lucky ones would be arrested, and the rest would be left for dead.

The uniforms did not need a second urging. They were as glad as he was to get out of that deadly chaos. They formed a tight phalanx around him and started fighting their way to the nearest entrance. They were not particularly gentle about it. Once they had made it to the door, Carlisle was surprised to find that nobody responded when they beat on it. He looked around anxiously.

"Anybody got a track on this?"

He was delighted when one of the uniforms broke about fifteen regulations by blowing off the inspection plate and running an illegal-looking DU through the lock system like a hot knife. The door slid back, and they tumbled through.

SEVEN

Kline

CYNTHIA KLINE WOKE WITH A STRANGE MAN IN HER BED. It took her half a minute to remember his name. Harry. Harry Carlisle. She had brought a cop home. Not only a cop, but a lieutenant attached to the counterterrorist task force. Was she developing a deathwish? She had heard that could happen to some agents who stayed undercover for too long. The greatest irony was that she did not feel bad about it. It was hard to think of this Harry Carlisle as the enemy—he behaved too much like a human being. Of course, she had taken care of the basic practicalities. There was nothing in the apartment that would betray her. The diskette that the man in the cowled coat had given her was still in her bag. She was certain that Carlisle was not the kind who would get up from a woman's bed and go through her purse. And even if he ran the disk, it would no doubt appear quite innocuous on the surface.

Cynthia sat up in bed and lit a cigarette. There was no way she could pretend that she had brought him back there with some ulterior motive. She was not seducing for the cause. After the violence and insanity of the previous night, she simply had not wanted to sleep alone. She had picked up Harry Carlisle because he was there and he seemed normal, at least in comparison to the psychotic bloody deacons and the rest of the smug, self-satisfied leeches with whom she had recently been spending the majority of her time. She dragged angrily on her cigarette. The enthusiastic applause in the VIP lounge as the monitors showed

157

the STG club and gas their way down Eighth Avenue was still too vivid.

She had spotted Harry Carlisle after they had come down from the VIP lounge and were waiting in the main entrance area to be allowed to leave. There had been quite an assortment of people marking time in the area. The tech crews from the show sat on flight cases and complained about how they should have been back at the hotel hours earlier. Groups of exhausted-looking NYPD drank coffee and also complained. Deacons tried to hold up their steel-eyed image while the STG stole their thunder.

Harry Carlisle had been sitting by himself on the bottom step of a stationary escalator. He had found a fifth of scotch somewhere and was drinking it from the bottle. Cynthia had been coping with three particularly obnoxious deacons who were trying to hit on her and she had used Carlisle as an excuse to get away from them. She had walked over to the escalator and sat down beside him on the step. Up close, it was clear that he had been battered by the riot. There was blood on his cheek, and his jacket was ripped at the shoulder. The scotch was probably emotional first aid.

She nodded at the bottle. "Could I get a taste of that?"

He looked quizzically at her clerical auxiliary's dress uniform. "Aren't you bothered that someone will see you?"

"Screw them. I've had enough of religion for one night."

He nodded wearily and passed over the bottle. "You can say that again."

She took a long pull on the scotch and then coughed. Harry Carlisle laughed.

"Never did see a deacon drink like that, particularly a lady one."

"Deacons are something else I've had it with."

As he took back the bottle, he looked at her closely. "Don't I know you?"

"I work at Astor Place. I've seen you around the corridors. My name's Cynthia Kline."

"Hello, Cynthia."

"You're Lieutenant Carlisle, right?"

"Right. But you can call me Harry."

He took a long drink and looked reflectively at the bottle. "I kicked a deacon in the balls earlier. You probably know him, too. Goes by the name of Winters."

She giggled. "I know Winters."

It had been about that time that the first bunch of STG had come in, swaggering, fresh from the kill. Their insect gas masks were pulled aside to reveal the flushed faces of hard-eyed, brutalized farmboys. The center *T*s of the STG stenciled on their helmets were painted over so they became large white crosses. The very sight of them had started Carlisle on a slow burn that, fueled by whisky and the STGs' loud boasting, quickly escalated to a white-knuckled anger. It was only with the greatest difficulty that she had talked him out of going after a couple of them and probably getting himself killed in the process. It was around that point that she had decided to sleep with him. Transportation had started arriving and the conversation had reached a certain impasse. She knew that he was thinking about suggesting they go somewhere, but he seemed unwilling to come to the point. Finally she had taken the initiative.

"Why don't you come to my place for a nightcap? I don't live too far away."

He had nodded with an expression that suggested that one part of him had surrendered to another. "Thanks. I'd like that."

She mashed out the cigarette. Harry Carlisle was still asleep. His light-brown hair fell over his forehead. He looked so peaceful and vulnerable. Almost like a little boy. As she watched him, he stirred in his sleep but did not wake. When they had first started to make love, he had seemed almost reluctant. It was not as though he didn't find her attractive or he had any doubts about himself. He certainly was not one of those simultaneously horny and guilt-ridden individuals that she had started to think were the norm in these soul-sick times. It was more as if some serious pain in his immediate past had frozen his capacity to be freely and openly sensual. This Harry Carlisle was a complex one. It had taken him awhile to thaw, but once he had put his thoughts on hold and warmed to the purely physical thrill, Cynthia found that her patience had been amply rewarded. He had been very good. His frustrations channeled themselves into pure thrusting energy and, stage by stage, they had worked their way toward noisy, clawing, and more than merely satisfactory orgasm.

She put out a hand and stroked his hair. His eyes opened. He slowly raised his head. For a few seconds, he looked as if he did not know where he was. Then a kind of recognition dawned. His face broke into a lopsided smile.

"Hi."

"You know who I am?"

"Sure, Cynthia, I know who you are."

He was grinning. He stretched out a hand and stroked her breast. "Is there anywhere we have to be?"

She was grinning, too. "I don't think so."

His arms slid around her body and he pulled her to him. She did not resist.

Thirty-five minutes later, she wrapped a sheet around herself, kissed him on the cheek, and padded barefoot to the shower. He watched her go. Hot water actually came out of the shower head on the first try, and Cynthia suddenly felt so irrationally pleased with life that she sang to herself as she lathered. Maybe, despite the odds, it was going to be a good day. When she emerged from the tiny bathroom, he was sitting on the edge of the bed, smoking one of her cigarettes. His face was serious.

"It'd be a very bad idea if we fell in love with each other. We could wind up in a whole lot of trouble."

Her good mood diminished considerably. She sat down in front of the dressing-table mirror and started to brush out her hair. There was a controlled anger in the strokes.

"What makes you think we're going to fall in love with each other? Aren't you taking a hell of a lot for granted? I mean, you're cute and all and good in the sack but—"

"People often do when they feel comfortable around each other."

"And you're comfortable around me?"

"More comfortable than I've been in a long time."

"How come you don't have a girlfriend or something?"

"It's more like or something."

"What's that supposed to mean?"

"I had a girlfriend. She's in a camp out in the Midwest. I haven't heard from her in more than eight months."

Cynthia looked at the image of his back in the mirror. So that was what had caused his first reluctance. "I'm sorry."

"So am I."

The outside world, with its peeling paint, poverty, and paranoia, was starting to close in on them. Harry Carlisle must have sensed it, too. He covered the moment by searching on the floor for his shorts. Cynthia could see no way but to go along with it. The day had started.

"You want some coffee?"

"Sure."

The diskette was in her bag, and the games of deceit were waiting to be played. There was no more time to hide under the bedclothes and pretend. For the first time, she noticed that he had old white scar tissue over his left shoulder blade. She picked up the coffeepot and went to the sink. This time, the tap only coughed out a cupful of rust-colored liquid and then quit altogether. Suddenly angry, she slammed down the coffeepot.

"There's no goddamn water."

"It's probably a result of last night's unpleasantness."

"It's off half the time these days. The West Side's been falling apart ever since the Javits Center burned down. I've got some of that generic Coke that tastes funny, or there's half a bottle of vodka in the freezer."

"You're kind of a free spirit for a deacon."

"I'm not a deacon, goddamn it. I'm nothing more than a glorified secretary."

"You look better out of that uniform."

First the water and now this. Cynthia's face froze. "You take a job where you can get it."

"I'm not too proud of what I do, either."

She did not believe him. "Oh, yeah? I thought you cops regarded yourselves as the blue knights."

"That was when we used to chase the bad guys. Now all I do is kiss the asses of psychotic bigots. No disrespect intended."

"Aren't you worried that I might pass the word of this conversation along to my bosses?"

Harry laughed. "You're not wearing any clothes. How would you explain that?"

"Seriously. Don't you worry about what they could do to you for talking like that?"

"I think I'm actually past caring. There could be a warrant out for me now, after what went down last night. Aggravated assault on a holy officer should be worth dismissal from the force and three to five years."

"Winters?"

"The very same. He'd love to hand me my head. If not him, it'll be another one. They're going to get me sooner or later."

"Aren't you frightened?"

"Sure I'm frightened, but what the hell can I do about it? Fear eventually becomes something that you live with."

Cynthia was discovering that she had a lot of sympathy for Harry Carlisle and his attitudes. She could not tell him, however, without coming clear out of her character. She had let it slip quite far enough already.

"You could run. Go to Canada or Brazil. You've got to have the contacts."

Harry Carlisle was struggling into his T-shirt. "I don't know. I may be crazy but I still feel like sticking around. I have this feeling that something's going to go down very soon. I don't know what it is, but I can feel it. Something big's about to happen. That shit last night was only an opener."

Cynthia sat down. His instincts were almost certainly correct, but she did not want to think about the future right there and then.

"Could you do something for me, Harry Carlisle?"

"Sure, anything."

"Bring that bottle of vodka and come and fuck me some more. There's too many people walking on our graves."

Winters

Rogers pulled the car over to the curb in disgust. He slapped the wheel hard with the heels of his hands. "This can't be right."

Winters slowly twisted his Academy ring. He felt the shock just as strongly as his companion. Only moments earlier they had been informed that the warrants for Arlen Proverb had been revoked on the authority of no less than the president himself. To make matters worse, a number of the lesser warrants had also been canceled, including the one for Carlisle that he had sworn out himself.

"What are they trying to do to us, make us look like complete idiots?"

For the last three hours, they had been chasing their tails all over the city following fruitless leads on Proverb and his people. Neither man could ever remember when a day had gone so disastrously wrong. As Monday dawned, the deacons had been on top of the world. The first shift at Astor Place had strutted like roosters. The riot outside the Garden had been crushed and, although the civilian casualty figures were running just under two hundred, the general feeling was that those numbers were acceptable. There had also been two deacons, one STG, and three regular cops slain. It was the arithmetic of eyes and teeth. Proverb was still at large, but it was only a matter of time. A figure as public as he was could not hide for long. Even if he went to Canada, they would get him in the end. The opposition that he represented appeared to have been effectively crushed. It was starting to look as if they were on the threshold of a glorious new era. Proverb was down for the count. The PD would be quickly brought to heel. Soon they would have a free hand to deal with the Lefthand Path and all the other terrorist groups. The officers in the corridors of CCC had a light in their eye and a spring in their step.

By noon, the light had faded and the spring was a great deal more tentative. Things were starting to come apart like an old pair of overalls and nobody could quite understand why. Someone appeared to have caught the ear of the president, and whoever it was had been no friend of the New York deacons. At ten-thirty, a videoconference was netted between New York and Washington. Those wired in included the vice president, Attorney General Harrison, the mayor, the police commissioner, the local military commandant, and Senior Deacon Booth.

The deacons were effectively isolated by a threat from Washington to place the city under martial law. The other city agencies were quick to point the finger. Words like "excessive force" and "incompetence" were being bandied about. At twelve-thirty, Dreisler had been summoned and Booth had been placed under arrest. The senior deacon was to be the scapegoat of the moment. The shock spread through deacon posts all over the city. The final blow had come with this most recent bulletin. Proverb was going to get away with it, at least for the time being.

The city itself had a strange feel to it. The streets were unnaturally empty for a Monday afternoon. Large numbers had stayed home from work, and even the lines outside the supermarkets were noticeably shorter. The usual schizophrenia of the censored media had almost reached its breaking strain. Everyone in the city knew about the bloodshed of the night before, but the media in no way acknowledged that it had even happened. There were reports coming in via Virginia Beach of how rumors were spreading through other cities that a vision of the Four Horsemen had appeared right in the heart of Manhattan. It was being treated as a harbinger of The End.

Something else that was spreading was the slogan "There will be a cleansing of the temple." Some bunch of subversives had been busy in the night. The words were daubed on walls all over town. Winters felt very uneasy when he looked at them. He could not forget the moment when the same phrase had appeared on his computer terminal. He and Rogers were parked in front of a boarded-up storefront on Park Avenue South a little to the north of Union Square. It was covered with half-torn-down dur-aprint posters for the Proverb show. "There will be a cleansing of the temple" had been pressure-painted right across them all in foot-high, vibrating yellow letters.

"You want to go and rip that thing down?"

Rogers, who seemed to be taking the catastrophic course of events very personally, shook his head. "Why bother? There are hundreds of them."

"So what do we do? Head back to Astor Place?"

"I should imagine that CCC is the last place we want to be. There's probably feces hitting the fan all over the building."

Winters was thoughtful. The bruising around his groin was still painful. "You know what I'd like to do? I'd like to forget that we heard about the warrant on Carlisle being dropped and go and pick him up anyway. We know where he is. He went home with that whore Cynthia Kline."

Rogers shook his head. "They'd crucify you if you mess with Carlisle after what happened today. Besides, it's not only Carlisle, you'd also be messing with this month's party girl."

"This week's party girl, the way that she's going."

"You still don't want to put your neck on the rail."

Winters scowled. He didn't like Rogers and was not happy about being paired with him, but he had not imagined that the man would be so chickenshit.

"I'd like to do something about him. He isn't going to get away with what he did to me."

"There are more ways of skinning a cat."

Winters glanced sidelong at him. "What's that supposed to mean?"

"Think about it."

Rogers dropped the slightest hint of a wink. Winters looked at him long and hard. He had not suspected it of Rogers. He was seeing him in a new light. "You mean you're a—"

Rogers grinned. "Don't say it. There's no such thing."

The word that they were not using was "magician." The Magicians were a legend among the deacons, and in other quarters as well. They were a powerful and highly secret society of officers with a very radical attitude toward the enforcement of social order and the elimination of enemies. They were called the Magicians because they made people disappear. Membership of the Magicians was also supposed to be an inside track to promotion. They were the clandestine cream of the agency.

Rogers had taken out his wallet. He pulled out a small pink card. "You know that a replacement for Fifteenth Street has opened up?"

"I didn't. I . . ."

Rogers indicated that he should take the card. "Why don't you come along tonight?"

Winters quickly shook his head. The thought of dim lights and perfume started an uncomfortable constriction in his chest. "I don't think . . ."

Rogers did not let him finish. "You're not hearing me. I said why don't you come along tonight, relax, and have a little fun? You'll be contacted, and you'll meet with some people. It's possible that the case of Lieutenant Harry Carlisle will come under discussion."

Winters swallowed hard. The constriction had gone and there was an excitement building inside him. "I'll be there."

"Good."

Rogers put the car in gear and pulled away from the curb. He was grinning cheerfully, his mood totally changed. "I tell you what, let's roust some street punk and work off a few frustrations."

Mansard

Rita looked up from the intercom. "There's three deacons on their way up."

Fear clutched at Charlie Mansard's brain. He prayed that he had heard wrong. "Say that again."

"Three deacons, to see you."

Suddenly there was cold sweat under his armpits and beading his back. Even the normally unshakable Rita had turned the color of a corpse.

"Did they look serious?"

"Of course they looked serious. Deacons always look serious."

"Oh, Christ."

Here was the moment that he had been dreading all night. Indeed, here was the moment that he had been dreading ever since the Fundamentalists had first taken power. It was only the best part of a bottle of scotch inside him that stopped him from going headfirst out of the window. He had always joked about the day when the deacons came for him, but now that the day seemed to have really arrived, he was more terrified than he could ever remember. All the torture stories started to close in on him. He was not going to be tortured. At the very suggestion of physical pain, he would talk. He would cooperate fully. He would tell them anything.

Rita was looking at him uncertainly. "Do you want me to stay?"

Mansard quickly shook his head. "No, get the hell out of here. Tell all the others you see to make themselves scarce. The fewer of us involved in this the better."

Most of the crew were scattered around the building or in the bar down the street. By far the majority had come there straight from the Garden; the others had drifted in quite soon after. Nobody seemed to know where to go or what to do. They had put up the biggest projected image ever, and then two hundred people had died. Mansard's crew seemed to want to stay together as a group and share the confused depression.

Rita did not need any second urging. She gathered up her coat and bag and slipped out the side door. Mansard sat back in his chair and did his best to compose himself for the arrival of the deacons. Without thinking about it, he took a pencil out of the organizer on the desk and started tapping it on the Lucite top. With Proverb on the run, he did not have a friend in the world. He had called a few of the preachers for whom he worked regularly, but they had all been in meetings or at prayer. None of them could be disturbed.

The deacons knocked. Mansard raised his eyebrows. They were observing the niceties. Maybe he still had some value. He counted to five.

"Come in."

A junior officer came through the door first, holding it open for his boss. The top man of the trio sauntered in with studied deacon arrogance. His lip was slightly curled as if there were a bad smell under his nose. The heavy brought up the rear. He had a machine pistol slung under his right arm. The situation did not have the air of a social call. The three arranged themselves in front of his desk in positions of courteous menace. Charlie Mansard looked at each of them in turn. They were all variations on the same theme, cold-eyed and clean-shaven with those thin, smug, lipless mouths. The young one was a mere flunky, nodding and opening doors and absorbing the moves. The heavy was wider and flatter, flat mid-European cheekbones and a flat forehead. He had huge hands that looked built for crushing. Mansard did not even want to look at those hands. The top deacon did the talking. He was one of the ones with that constant aura of amused superiority. Soon they would be cloning the bastards.

"Charles Mansard?"

"Yes."

"Charles Everett Mansard?"

Mansard sighed. "Right. Charles Everett Mansard."

"Would you please come with us?"

The deacon's tone left no space for a refusal. Mansard felt sick, but he did not immediately move. He tried to maintain as much dignity as he could. He carefully replaced the pencil in the organizer.

"Am I being arrested?"

"Not at this moment, but we do want to ask you a number of questions."

"So please ask them."

"It'd be better if you came with us."

"I'm a very busy man. Couldn't you simply ask your questions here?"

The heavy started giving him a very hard stare. The top deacon leaned forward and placed a black-gloved hand on the top of Mansard's desk. "It would be better if the questioning was conducted down at the Astor Place complex."

Mansard was wondering if his legs would actually support him. He did not want to have to be carried from his own office. The top deacon straightened up. He glanced at the heavy, who managed to flex his muscles without actually moving. Mansard pushed himself up from the chair. His legs held.

"I'll get my coat."

The phone rang.

The top deacon put a hand on it but did not pick up the handset. Mansard looked at him questioningly. The top deacon shook his head.

"The phone will have to wait."

It continued to ring, nine times in all. When it stopped the deacon removed his hand.

"Shall we go?"

The door was pushed open, and Rita walked in just as if it were any other day. There was no sign of her coat or bag. "Charlie, you'd better take this call. It sounds important."

The booze was slowing him down. He did not have a clue as to what was happening.

The top deacon swung around. "There will be no phone calls."

Rita looked at the deacons as if she were seeing them for the first time and did not like what she saw. "I think you'll want him to take this one. It's from the White House."

The deacons froze. Junior and the heavy both looked at their boss for some sort of signal. He seemed at a loss as to which way to jump. Mansard took advantage of his indecision and slowly picked up the phone. He wished that he had not drunk so much. The top deacon reached for the handset.

Mansard leaned back out of reach. "I don't think you want to be asking the White House if it's really them."

The top deacon stopped in his tracks. If Mansard had not already been so shook up, he would have enjoyed the man's discomfort. He spoke into the phone. "Mansard here."

The voice on the other end was as smooth as silk and twice as professional. "Charles Mansard?"

"Speaking."

"This is Ron Cableman, Charles. I'm President Faithful's Director of Special Projects. I'll be in New York tomorrow, and I wonder if we might meet."

Mansard hated to be called Charles, particularly by people he had never met. "Could you give me some idea what we might be discussing, Ron?"

"Despite last night's very tragic incidents, the president was greatly impressed with your skywalker. I'd like to talk about the possibility of you doing the same kind of thing at a future presidential event."

Mansard laughed with relief. "I'd be delighted to meet you, Ron. There is, however, one small problem."

Ron Cableman's voice was suddenly very cautious. "A problem, Charles?"

"Right at the moment, I have an office full of deacons, and they seem to be trying to arrest me."

Ron Cableman sounded less than happy. "Why are they arresting you, Charles?"

"They seem to think I'm somehow responsible for last night's tragic incidents."

Ron sounded considerably relieved. "Perhaps I should speak to these deacons, Charles."

"I wish you would, Ron."

Ron Cableman spoke to the top deacon for just over a minute, during which time the deacon said almost nothing. By the end of it, he was all but standing to attention. Finally he handed the phone back to Mansard. When he spoke, his voice sounded as if it were choking him. He avoided Mansard's eyes.

"I think there's been some kind of misunderstanding. I'm sorry you've been troubled."

Mansard waved them away. They left quickly. Only the heavy looked back. His eyes indicated that, as far as he was concerned, it was only a reprieve, not a pardon. Mansard went back to Ron Cableman with a slight shudder. That had been much too close.

"Well, I guess I have to thank you for that, Ron. I never have been very good with policemen. About tomorrow, shall we say the Skylounge at one? You know it? I thought you would. Ciao to you, too."

He hung up and regarded Rita with some suspicion. "So who cooked up the phony call?"

"It wasn't a phony call."

"They'll be straight back and madder than hell. I don't think it's helped anything."

"It wasn't a phony call."

Mansard shook his head. His mind had to be caving in. "What?"

"The call was the real deal."

"Are you telling me that the president wants to hire us, after everything that's happened?"

Rita nodded. Mansard stood up. He moved like a man in shock.

"I'm going to the bar. I have to think about this."

Speedboat

The cab slowed to a stop in front of Terminal 4 at La Guardia. Speedboat slowly climbed out and handed the driver three twenties.

"Keep the change."

For a few seconds he just stood on the curb and looked around. He had seen too many old movies where people jumped on planes without a second thought, and airports were bright gleaming places with cocktail bars and newsstands packed with souvenirs, where sexy flight attendants made dates with handsome men in expensive suits. Speedboat pulled his parka around his shoulders. This place was like an armed camp. Ever since the cab had turned off the Brooklyn-Queens Expressway, they had been driving through various levels of antiterrorist defenses. Armored cars and light tanks were parked along the service roads and runways. The major intersections were controlled by quadguns in sandbagged emplacements. Even the most minimal security area was surrounded by rusting razor wire. The cab driver told him that there were even patrol boats out on the water under the flight paths.

He thought he had never been so pleased to see a cab for hire in his life. The scene outside the Garden, when he finally managed to get out of there with his forged travel passes in his pocket, had been like a scene from a World War II horror show. There were bodies strewn all across Eighth Avenue, and the road surface was slick and black with drying blood. The air was filled with sirens and the gut-wrenching stench of EZA. Emergency medical units came and went, but there were not enough of them to clear the hundreds of injured. Detainees in prison gray had been drafted up from the Tombs to help load the dead onto sanitation trucks. The helicopters that still clattered overhead were the sleek modern craft used by the STG, not the old and battered Cobras and Hueys that belonged to the police department. When people inside the Garden had talked about a massacre going on, he had thought they were exaggerating. The first step outside, however, proved them to have been perfectly accurate.

He had been extremely reluctant to leave the comparative safety of the Garden. The STG was everywhere. Their squad captains were having the greatest difficulty stopping their troops from randomly savaging people who had done nothing but have the bad fortune to be out on the street. Scarcely a minute passed without the crack of an electric club and the resulting screams. Proverb's biblical hell had been made flesh. At first, Speedboat found safety in numbers, sheltering behind a crowd of the tech crew who had all left together, but as they dispersed to go their separate ways, he struck out on his own. Most of the STG seemed to be straggling back up Eighth Avenue from the twenties, so he headed due east to get away from them in the fastest possible time. His objective was a derelict tenement on East Third where he had cached the remainder of his money. The streets were busy for the small hours of a Monday morning. Every block had its straggling gangs of the stumbling, the glazed-eyed, and the all-too-frequently bloody. Wary knots of uncomfortable nightstick-tapping cops were gathered under the few streetlamps that were still working. Many of the stragglers were drunk, having tried and failed to blot out the horror with alcohol. The bars had been shut down when the trouble started, but the downtown shebeens and speakeasies were doing a roaring, if grim, trade. It was like the end of some nightmarish blood-soaked New Year's Eve.

Once inside the building on Third, Speedboat had worked in complete darkness. He turned off his jury-rigged electronics and emptied the hidden homemade safe. Back on the street, he was even more nervous now that he was carrying his traveling money. To his amazement, he had walked only a block when the cab came into sight with its "For Hire" sign glowing like the morning sun. He had actually waved money to get it to stop.

The wind at La Guardia was chill. Speedboat realized that he had been standing on the curb for too long. Two of the airport's own paramilitary rentacops had started looking him over. If he did not move on into the system, they would begin to get interested. He walked toward the first-stage security check. It was the same basic system as the sensor tunnel that he had walked through to get into the Garden, but it was much older and therefore much less sophisticated. Nothing took an objection to him, and he found himself in the main body of the airport. It was a dirty, dilapidated place of cracked and smeared glass and degenerate plastic. The walls were plastered with cheap government posters, mainly red and black ones warning of the criminality of various kinds of behavior and the penalties that might be expected. There were quite a number that referred to forgery and undocumented travel. A distorting sound system played sacred feelgood music. One closed-off section of the arrival area was still scarred and blackened from last year's bomb attack.

At least half of those traveling were in some branch of the military. Again it was reminiscent of a World War II movie. Brown, tan, and olive-drab uniforms were stretched out on benches or sprawled in broken TV chairs. Some had even sacked out on the gum-crusted carpet with their heads on their kits. The traveling civilians were a sorry bunch who had the dull, hopeless look of people who were far from convinced that their plane would come at all. Of course, La Guardia was the poor folk's airport, from which the domestic cattle cars went to Chicago and Dallas–Fort Worth. Forty miles away at Koch International there were cocktail bars and restaurants and people who took the suborbitals to Manila and Rio de Janeiro.

Before a person could even purchase a ticket, there was a three-phase document check. The first level was comparatively benign, a counter where airport clerks checked out the documents before the bearer moved on to population control and finally the deacons.

Speedboat joined that line. It took him almost an hour to reach the counter, and by that point he was more bored than worried. But when he faced the unsmiling clerk with sandy hair, bad teeth, and a receding chin, all his fears came back.

The clerk looked over the two flimsy plastic strips that gave him the right to travel and then looked at him. "Mr. Evan?"

The documents identified Speedboat as Leroy Evan, a U.S. citizen with a Canadian grandmother in Toronto. She was dying, and he had compassionate permission to visit her.

"Yes?" he said politely.

"Mr. Leroy Evan?"

"That's right."

The clerk dropped the plastic into the scan slot in his computer terminal.

"I'm sorry to hear about your grandmother."

"You're very kind."

The clerk took a red folder from under the counter and put Speedboat's plastic slips in it. He handed the folder to Speedboat. "Please follow the red line to the bench, Mr. Evan, and wait there."

He indicated a bench against the wall. Two sorry-looking men were already sitting there, clutching red folders. Speedboat's heart sank. The papers were no good. He had been ripped off and now he was busted.

The unsmiling clerk processed two more people and then put up the "Use Next Position" sign. He walked over to where Speedboat was sitting.

"Please come with me, Mr. Evan."

There was a line of private interview cubicles behind the counter. As Speedboat followed the clerk toward them, he was certain that he was terminally screwed. That bastard at the Garden—if he ever got out of all this, he would kill the creep.

Inside the cubicle, there was a desk and a chair. The clerk sat in the chair. Speedboat had to stand. The clerk held up the flimsy plastic strips.

"You understand that one of these allows you to fly to Buffalo and the other to cross the border on the Trailways bus to Toronto?"

"Right."

The clerk shook his head. "Wrong."

"Wrong?"

"These are really terrible."

"What do you mean?"

"You actually paid for these?"

"I don't understand."

"These are very poor forgeries. You were robbed, my friend."

"I don't know what you're talking about."

"Sure you do." He held out the documents to Speedboat. "Look at the ink, look at the embossing. The data fix only just holds up."

Speedboat sagged. There was no point in going on pretending. "So what happens now?"

"The one for the flight to Buffalo isn't too bad. Nobody looks too closely at domestic flights, and you could get away with using it. The one for Toronto is a joke. It'll never stand up to the kind of scrutiny that you'll get at the border. I'd sell it if I was you."

"Say what?"

"Sell it to another sucker. Try to cut your losses."

Speedboat could not believe what he was hearing. "Are you serious?"

"Sure I'm serious. You look like you know your way around. In fact, I'll do you a favor. I'll give you a hundred for it right now."

Speedboat was at a loss. "Why should you do that?"

The clerk smiled for the first time. "Because I can get five hundred for it inside of an hour."

Speedboat knew that corruption was endemic, but this was

absurd. It was also reeked of a possible con job. "I don't know about this."

The clerk made a dismissive gesture. "I suppose I could do my job and turn you in."

"How do I know it's bad forgery? I've only got your word for that."

The clerk had pulled out a dirty hundred. "You want to take a chance on it?"

"What about the one for Buffalo? You want to buy that, too?"

The clerk shook his head. "If you've got some money, you might as well go on to Buffalo."

"What's the point of going to Buffalo, if I can't cross the border?"

The clerk was smiling again. "It's easy to find someone in Buffalo to take you across. It's a local industry in Buffalo."

"It is?"

"Sure."

The clerk had produced a pen. He wrote a phone number on the hundred. "Call this number when you get there. They'll take care of you."

Speedboat was certain that the goddamn clerk was running a con on him, but he was not so certain that he was going to bet his life on it. In this game, the loser went to a camp.

"I'll take the hundred."

Kline

Harry Carlisle had fallen asleep in front of the TV. He and Cynthia had spent the afternoon drinking and making love until a smug, bleary exhaustion had set in. Unfortunately Cynthia could not quite enjoy the sensation. The software in her bag had to be checked out. She could not completely bury it in the back of her mind. The uneasiness kept coming back. There could be urgent instructions or even some kind of warning. There could be real trouble bearing down on her while she was trying to lose herself drinking and fucking this quietly charming police lieutenant.

She looked closely at Carlisle. He was dead to the world. Even the noisy chatter of Channel 8's *Happy Talk News* did not show any sign of waking him. She climbed out of bed and slipped into the hapi coat she used as a robe. She removed the cover from the laptop. A second glance at Carlisle assured her that he was sound asleep. She turned on the power, took the software from her bag, and loaded it. She scrolled quickly through the cover program. It was a rather dull piece of cheap porn based on the romance stories of Lydia Lovelock. She fed in her recognition code, and the software downleveled to her hidden instructions. A message appeared on the screen.

IN THE NEXT WEEK YOU WILL CEASE TO WORK WITH LONG-STREET. YOU WILL BE TRANSFERRED TO C86 COMPUTER COM-PLEX. ONCE THAT HAS HAPPENED, YOU WILL ALWAYS CARRY THIS SOFTWARE WITH YOU DURING YOUR DUTY HOURS. THERE MUST BE NO MISTAKE ABOUT THIS. THE SOFTWARE MUST ALWAYS BE WITH YOU. AT SOME POINT IN THE NEXT MONTH, THE CODE PHRASE "LOOK TO THE SKIES" WILL APPEAR ON YOUR WORKSTATION MONITOR. THE MOMENT THE CODE HAS BEEN DISPLAYED, YOU WILL LOAD THE SOFT-WARE CONTAINED ON THIS DISK AND DIRECTFEED TO VIR-GINIA BEACH ON THE 771-36971-2458-666 I-LINE INTERFACE. WHEN THIS TASK HAS BEEN COMPLETED, YOU WILL RECEIVE FURTHER INSTRUCTIONS.

Harry Carlisle mumbled something in his sleep. Cynthia quickly closed the file and turned off the laptop. At least the instructions were not something that needed instant attention. She slid quietly back into bed. Harry mumbled again. He turned over and, without opening his eyes, reached out and placed a hand on her stomach. She wriggled close to him. There was security in the warmth of his body.

Winters

"You and I are going on a journey of discovery together to the dark of your soul. I will be both your mistress and your guide and I will expect your absolute obedience. I will take you to places that you have only imagined and didn't think could exist. I will take you even farther than that, beyond your petty fears and inhibitions, to a place where you will see visions of yourself that you will hardly recognize. Do you understand me?"

"I think so . . . mistress."

The tip of the leather crop moved slowly down the length of

176

his spine. "You don't think. You are my slave and you merely obey. Repeat that."

"I don't think. I am your slave and I merely obey, mistress."

The tip of the leather crop had reached the top of his buttocks. Although its touch was as light as a feather, the skin beneath it crawled. It had to be in anticipation of the cruelties that would undoubtedly come later. Anticipation was half the experience. He knew she was well aware of that. The whip tapped against his flesh, emphasizing the point.

"Obedience is everything. As we go along, you will discover that our relationship is controlled by rules, and the punishments that I shall inflict on you when you break them. My word is the law, and you mean nothing. I require just two things from you. You obey me absolutely, and you pay me for the privilege. I don't even have to like you. I merely tolerate. Now do you understand me?"

"I understand you, mistress."

Winters was naked and completely helpless. His arms were stretched above his head and secured at the wrists by thick leather straps with chrome buckles. There was a second, wider strap around his waist, cinching him tight to the polished mahogany post in the center of the room. It was the need to be helpless that had really brought him to this place and caused him to strip and abase himself in front of a strange young whore in an exotic costume. It was a release of tensions and frustration, but the pain and the ritual somehow made it something for which he was not responsible. He did not do anything—it was all done to him. It was as she said: he paid and obeyed. The pleasure and the punishment were one. The flesh lusted and was mortified. The sin was paid for even as it was committed. Jesus could surely go along with that. There were times in the night, however, when he was not sure that Jesus was quite so accommodating.

The walls of the room were mirrored. If he turned his head in either direction he could see multiple images of himself bound to the whipping post and the woman standing arrogantly behind him, flexing the leather crop as if she were undecided as to where on his body to lay the first stripe. She was a figure of costume fantasy. Her legs and arms were swathed in black, form-fitting patent leather; sleek thigh-length boots with high, spiked heels; and long evening gloves that reached to her upper arms. Her torso was laced into a corset of the same material in a cruel flame red. It was cut so that it exposed her pubic hair and allowed her ample breasts to swing free each time she moved. Her wig was a high-teased black bouf with flame tips, and her stark, dramatic makeup gave her the look of a depraved, contemptuous corpse.

"There will be times when you may feel that I'm too cruel to you. There will be times when you may wonder if my punishments are too harsh, too out of proportion to your wretched little transgressions. There will be times when you'll beg for mercy."

"I wouldn't do that, mistress."

"Did I ask you to speak?"

It was all part of the game.

"I'm sorry, I—"

"I'm tired of listening to your whining, I'm going to gag you."

He watched her in the mirrors as she went to the equipment rack on the far wall. When she came back with the rubber ball gag, he struggled a little as she forced the gag into his mouth.

"No . . . please . . ."

His protest earned him three quick cuts of the crop. All that was part of the game, too. He might struggle and protest, but they both knew that she was doing exactly what he wanted.

When she finally released him from his bonds, he sank to the floor at the bottom of the post. He was emotionally drained, so drained, in fact, that he did not move when the phone on the wall by the soundproof door gave a soft purring ring. The whore's high heels clapped across the hardwood floor. She picked up the phone and listened. Finally she nodded and hung up.

She looked down at Winters. "You better get your clothes on. They want you down in the basement right now."

Winters was confused. "The basement?"

"The private dining room, where they get down to the really weird shit."

She hung the whip on the equipment board and opened the door. "Behave yourself."

She was gone. A bemused Winters picked himself up off the floor. It had to be the Magicians. Rogers had as good as said so. Winters had no idea what to expect. He pictured some dark Masonic Temple with ceremonies and swords, but somehow that was not quite right. The Magicians were more than just playacting businessmen. They meted out life and death. They were faceless and all-powerful.

As he took his shirt from the hanger, he caught sight of his back in the mirror. It was a mass of crisscrossing red welts. The skin was broken in a number of places, and he could see streaks of fresh blood. He quickly dressed. Guilt had started to set in, and the usual questions were beginning to nag at him. Why did he come to places like this? Why did he always have to give in to his dark impulses? The routine was always the same, and he could usually count on the guilt lasting well into the next day. But this time, the pattern was broken. As he rode down in the elevator, guilt was quickly replaced by an excited anticipation and more than a little fear. If this was really the start of his induction into the Magicians, it could well be the making of his career. He felt as if he were on his way to an examination or an audition.

The elevator doors opened, and Winters had to restrain himself from taking a quick step back. A tall bulky figure in a dark suit was waiting for him; a blue metalflake helmet completely covered the man's head, and a black visor hid his face. "I am the Master-at-Arms," he announced ominously.

Winters force himself to step out of the elevator. "Where do we go?"

"We wait here until we are summoned."

There was an electronic distortion on the Master-at-Arms' voice, no doubt some kind of gizmo built into the helmet. The Magicians appeared to take pains to maintain their anonymity, Winters reflected. The two of them waited in front of the basement elevator for almost five minutes before a red light flashed and a tone sounded. The Master-at-Arms indicated that Winters should follow. They walked down a short corridor that led to a pair of solid double doors with Victorian brass fittings. The huge man opened them with a solemn flourish.

"Deacon Winters waits without, in answer to summons."

Another electronically distorted voice came from beyond the doors. "Let Deacon Winters enter and be recognized."

The Master-at-Arms beckoned. Winters took a deep breath and walked forward. The private dining room was large and gloomy. It was not exactly the Masonic Temple he had imagined, but it had many of the same elements. The walls were draped in purple velvet, giving the long, narrow room a kind of ecclesiastic hush. A long dining table was the centerpiece of the room, and a very lavish dinner had just been completed. Port and cognac had been circulating, and the smell of cigar smoke was in the air. The Magicians, if that was who they really were, appeared to look after themselves very well.

By far the most striking feature of the basement dining room was the men grouped around the table. There were thirteen of them, six on each side and one presiding at the head. Each wore a different color motorcycle-style helmet and a black, all-concealing visor just like the Master-at-Arms. The presiding officer's helmet was gold. The overall effect was not unlike a high-tech version of the Ku Klux Klan. Winters had to presume that the helmets had been put on for his benefit. He could not see how anyone could eat, drink, or smoke a cigar while wearing one of those things.

There was a vacant chair at the foot of the table. Winters suspected that it was for him. He was also pretty sure that the thirteen for dinner was a symbolic number and not the entire membership of the Magicians.

The presiding officer in the gold helmet raised a hand. "You are Winters?"

Winters wondered how many familiar faces were hidden behind the dark visors. Maybe Rogers was among them. "I am."

"Please remain standing and raise your right hand."

Winters did exactly as he was told. It seemed to be a night for unquestioning obedience.

"Please repeat after me. 'I swear by almighty God and on my oath as a deacon . . .' "

"I swear by almighty God and on my oath as a deacon . . ."

" '. . . that I will never reveal to any third party the nature of this meeting or anything that may pass between us at this or subsequent meetings.' "

". . . that I will never reveal to any third party the nature of this meeting or anything that may pass between us at this or subsequent meetings."

" 'On pain of death.' "

"On pain of death."

"Do you understand the oath that you have just sworn?"

"I do."

"You may be seated."

Winters sat down. The man to the right of him, wearing a green metalflake helmet, leaned forward.

"Would you care for a cognac, Winters?" His voice, too, was artificially distorted.

Winters hesitated. It could be a personality test. "I . . ."

The presiding officer laughed. The sound came out of the distortion gizmo as a harsh grate. "Have a drink, man. Here we judge a deacon by his spirit, not by his capacity for abstinence."

The others laughed. The helmets and the distorted voices put a decidedly bizarre edge on the whole proceedings. The officer in the gold helmet again raised his hand. It was the sign for what appeared to be a prepared speech.

"Deacon Winters, we are off duty, and we allow ourselves a degree of informality, but please don't be confused. The founding principles of this society—The Society That Does Not Speak Its Name—are deadly serious. We are all well aware that our nation and our faith are in a state of siege. All around us there are enemies, threatening our borders and even infiltrating the very fabric of our culture. The heretics, the communists, the Satan worshipers, and the atheists are ranged against us in a war to the death. The shuffling hordes of the genetically inferior are poised to overrun us. They would show us no mercy, and we, in turn, must show no mercy to them. It is unfortunate that what we think of the civilized niceties make it all too easy for the agents of chaos and Godlessness to move in among us, causing murder and destruction, and for their sympathizers and fellow travelers to spread their poisonous and pornographic sedition."

Gold Helmet paused to let his words sink in. Winters nodded to show that he was in complete agreement. There had been a moment when he had thought he recognized the voice, but then he was not sure. Gold Helmet continued.

"This society was formed by a small group of officers who decided that, although regrettable, it was time for them to sacrifice those niceties and to take the fight to the enemy with the single-minded determination and cold ruthlessness that makes our enemy so implacable. We work alone and in secret, but make no mistake about the reasons for this. We are in no way ashamed of what we do. There can be no shame in doing the Lord's work, no matter how distasteful it may be. In a conflict of this kind, secrecy is power, secrecy is freedom, secrecy enables us to operate as unhindered as our enemies. Do you understand me, Deacon Winters?"

Winters nodded vigorously. "Indeed I do. I understand fully."

"We do not suffer a Satanist to live, Deacon Winters."

"Those are my sentiments entirely."

Green Helmet refilled Winters's brandy snifter.

The officer on Gold Helmet's left took up the story. His helmet was silver.

"Before the enemy can be eradicated, he must first be identified. Although society has the considerable resources of the service at its disposal, it still depends on individual input to detect the degenerates who walk among us. Many of them are in protected positions and can only be reached by unorthodox means. I believe you have information regarding just such a subversive?"

This time Winters's nod was slow and deliberate. "Yes, I do."

"His name?"

"Lieutenant Harry Carlisle of the NYPD. Even in his public conversation, he constantly borders on open heresy. God knows what he—"

Silver Helmet cut him off. "We have already had a number of reports on Lieutenant Carlisle."

"You mean I'm not the only one?"

"Far from it."

Winters was puzzled. If other people had already fingered Carlisle to the Magicians, why had he been summoned? It hardly made any sense. Then Gold Helmet gave him the answer.

"Deacon Winters, would you be willing to assist in the execution of Lieutenant Harry Carlisle?"

It was better than he had hoped. They did not only want his information, they actually wanted him to take part in the hit. They had to be considering him for admission to the society. He thought of the pain that Carlisle's kick to his groin had caused, and he answered without hesitation.

"I'd be honored."

"Then you will be contacted."

EIGHT

Mansard

CHARLIE MANSARD LAY FLAT ON HIS BACK ON THE KING-size bed, staring at Lynette working out on the La Lanne unit. She was bent forward in what he thought of as the doggy position, and all she had on was a pair of net stockings. Her eyes were closed, and her body was covered in a fine sheen of sweat. He had called Lynette earlier in the hope that a little sexplay might help to slow down the army of ideas that insisted on marching about in his head. But after three bottles of champagne, a doomer apiece, and some rather inconclusive dalliance, he still felt strange, in what he could describe only as a state of counterexcitement. His imagination simply would not quit; it also would not focus. He could not lose himself in Lynette's accommodating body, and he could not get drunk. Even when he admitted that he was physically exhausted and settled for the role of the passive voyeur, he could not concentrate on her moving flesh for any protracted period. His mind refused to stop jumping, and his whirling thoughts carried him along from one random point to the next.

His single consolation was that Lynette probably did not mind. Apart from anything else, Lynette was paid very well not to mind. Right at that moment, he was using her as a piece of living pornography, and he was not even able to give her his full attention. Still, she did not complain. Over the years they had maintained their strange relationship, he had given Lynette a great deal of money to tolerate his foibles and mood shifts.

182

There were times when he felt almost paternal toward her. Back in the old days, before Faithful and his jackals had grabbed power, she probably would have been a lawyer, perhaps an actress, at least a corporate executive. Now all those options, with the exception of that of the actress, had gone. She had to settle for being the plaything of an alcoholic but highly paid sky designer. The worse condemnation of the times was that a woman in New York, alone and without money, could have done a great deal worse. He paid for her apartment, and he gave her ample pocket money. At the very least, she had time to read, to listen to music; she even had time to think, something that made him very envious now and then.

He had also given her one other thing that also explained why Lynette complained so little about what he did. He had had her fitted with illegal DNI plugs and set her up with a connection for bootlegged Japanese software. At that moment, as she pumped the La Lanne unit and sweated, she was jacked into one of the lastest erofeeds to be smuggled out of Tokyo. She was somewhere else, in some erotic wonderland of endorphins and microcurrents.

He had to admit that the sight of her bare buttocks, making frenzied coital movements as she half-consciously interacted with the machine, was close to arousing the beast in him. However, each time he was almost ready to get up and make a move, he became distracted. The last couple of days had produced more than enough to distract him.

Ron Cableman had turned out to be a smooth, third-generation Washington sharpie. He belonged in the Faithful White House. His daddy had survived the plot and counterplot of the last days of the Reagan administration, and his grandaddy had played poker with Richard Nixon. They had started drinking at the Skylounge, had a late lunch at 21, and from there they had gone downtown to Ruskin's. Cableman had matched Mansard drink for drink. As the happy hour had started to grow maudlin, Cableman had offered to call a couple of girls that he knew. Mansard had declined. He was fairly faithful to Lynette, although he did spend the rest of the evening wondering what if. Along the way, it had transpired that Larry Faithful was planning a major spectacular. Although it was not stated as such, the president and those around him thought that the country needed a major diversion. It had been decided that Larry Faithful would declare a special public holiday. In one month's time, there would be a Day of National Reconciliation. To mark the occasion, he would hold a special service at Liberty Island. The plan for the grand finale and crowning glory was to have four of Mansard's giant holograms moving up the Hudson. They wanted him to use the Four Horsemen again.

"Plus we want you to do the other figures from Revelations— the Beast, the Whore of Babylon, and Jesus himself, the Lamb of God. Storming up the river and terrifying the hell out of the sinners. It'll be on all the networks, plus it'll go out on satellite so it can be holostructured in all the major cities."

Mansard had put down his scotch and looked at Ron Cableman in blank amazement. "It's impossible. There's no way that my people could pull something like that together in the time."

Cableman had smiled blandly. "It'll be a rush job, but all of the country's resources will be at your disposal."

Mansard had firmly shaken his head. "That's the trouble, Ron. The country doesn't have the resources. The skywalker we put up last Sunday used state-of-the-art Japanese hardware that's subject to the full prohibitions of the embargo. The projectors themselves are close to impossible. I think we had all that there are on this side of the Pacific. And don't ask me how we got them. You wouldn't like the answer."

Cableman had laughed. "Listen, Charles, I'm pretty sure that the U.S. Government is quite capable of getting you a bunch of Sony DL-70s. I don't think we'd need to go through Chile, either."

Mansard had looked at him with considerably more respect. Ron Cableman had done his homework.

"Could you get me thirty of them?"

"I expect so."

"In two weeks?"

"If necessary."

"Then it might just be possible, if the money was right and everything else fell into place. I'm not saying I'll do it, but in theory . . ."

Cableman had raised an amused eyebrow. "This is the government, the price is always right."

"I'd also need a lot of trained, experienced riggers."

"We could get them from the military."

"I want good people."

"Believe it or not, there are people in the military who know what they're doing."

Mansard continued to put up objections, but he knew in his heart that he was going to try for the job. Cableman knew it, too. Another part of his homework had told him that Mansard had the kind of ego that would not be able to turn down a challenge of this size.

The program on the La Lanne unit had changed, and Lynette was doing a slow sinuous stretch. Mansard watched her for a while, then thoughtfully got up from the bed. He looked around the penthouse suite as if he had not seen it in days. The place was a mess. He had been working and sleeping there for weeks. A debris of beer cans, empty bottles, and Styrofoam food containers was beginning to bury the more permanent clutter of accumulated junk and toys with which he liked to surround himself. It was all mixed in with the professional litter of plans and drawings and scale models of work in progress. The six-foot thirteenth-century Buddha of which he was so proud seemed to be contemplating a slob's nirvana. The mess was his own fault. He was too paranoid to allow the cleaning people in to do their work. He had to get a grip on himself. The luxury squalor was verging on the disgusting and would probably soon be a health hazard. It was time to get it cleaned—or to move.

He stepped over a pile of foreign newspapers and magazines, mostly banned, which one day he would get around to reading, and gazed out the wraparound window that took up most of two walls. He flattened his hands on the curved expanse of glass and peered into the night. A steady rain was falling on the city. To the south and west, in the twenties and thirties, there were deep pools of darkness where power had yet to be restored. If this was the legacy of just one of his figures, what chaos would four of them create? There was little or no remorse riding his train of thought. Charlie Mansard had no illusions about himself. He would go on creating the biggest possible optical images for as long as they would let him and whatever the consequences.

In the distance he could see the river. He imagined the four giant figures moving majestically against the tide. Of course, it would be a nightmare to pull together, and despite Cableman's optimism, the odds were still against him. To sell it to his own people alone would be a major task. They would bitch like shit and demand triple overtime, but in the end, they would make it happen. If—when—those images went up, it would be a triumph. It might also convince half the crazies in the nation that the Day of Judgment had really come. If that happened, he wouldn't lose any sleep. In fact, he'd be secretly delighted. Scare the hell out of the sinners? Cableman and his bosses did not know the half of it. By the time he was through it would be the final fall of civilization. He had three weeks to create something that would have them begging for mercy.

He was starting to get excited. The huge project really wasn't going to be that hard. There was simply a great deal of work. No new systems had to be devised. The program they had developed to run the Horsemen was capable of adapting to the new designs. The designs themselves might take a little time, but that was Manny's department, and Mansard could bully Manny. If the army provided the barges on which to float the hardware and enough technicians to do the scut work, they could make it. His fingers were drumming on the glass. He had completely forgotten about Lynette.

A soft moaning reminded him. She had killed the La Lanne unit and rolled out of it onto the rug. She was still jacked in to the erofeed with leads trailing from the plugs in her neck. She was lying on her back, languidly caressing herself. When she spoke, her voice was slurred and husky.

"Charlie? What are you doing?"

He continued to stare out through the curved window. "Just designing the end of the world, honey."

"That's nice, Charlie. Real nice."

Carlisle

"Proverb's agreed to give himself up."

"Why should he give himself up? The warrants have been cancelled. He isn't a fugitive."

"He says, and I quote the statement, 'Although my own conscience is absolutely clear, I feel that unresolved questions remain that may prove an impediment to the normally cordial relations enjoyed between myself and the deacons of New York. Accordingly, I shall present myself at the main entrance of the CCC Astor Place complex at noon of Tuesday next, in the hope that any misunderstandings may be clarified.' "

"And he wants us to see that he gets in and out alive?"

"In a nutshell."

"He sounds like a very paranoid individual."

"He has every reason to be. The deacons want him dead."

Carlisle, Reeves, and Donahue were crowded in the captain's office: It was the latest in a series of grim meetings. Parnell was sitting behind his desk patiently fielding their questions. It was clear from the drift of the conversation that Carlisle and the others were less than happy about the situation.

"And we're expected to stand in the line of fire?"

"Where else should we be?"

Reeves grunted. "I don't recall signing on for some holy war."

Parnell was not amused. "Do you recall what you did sign on for?"

Reeves shrugged. "What I don't understand is why this has to be turned into a sideshow. Surely, whatever the problems are, they could all be settled in private? This high-noon grandstand seems like Proverb's just sticking it to the dekes one more time."

"It's not something that we were consulted about."

"Ours not to reason, right?"

The captain was starting to lose patience. "This is a delicate situation and there's pressure coming down on all sides. Washington feels that our deacons went too far with that mess at the Garden, and they want the appearance of reconciliation between them and Proverb. They've also put the block on their arresting any more Elvi, because that's making waves in the South. Proverb is obviously going to do his best to turn the whole thing into a media event, and that suits Washington because they need to do something to stop the rumors that are running loose in the rest of the country. When the real story of what happened at the Garden was censored out of existence, all kinds of weird tales started spreading. Half the country thinks that we're having nightly supernatural visitations."

"What about the deacons? Where do they stand in all this?"

Parnell half smiled. "They're madder than a bunch of wet cats."

"They're not crazy enough to try something against Proverb, are they?"

"Not officially, but we all know they've got their death squads."

"Yeah, but—"

"Yeah, but nothing. We can't afford to take any chances. There are deacons who might just be far enough over the edge to pull something. We also still have to take the Lefthand Path's death threat against Proverb seriously."

"So where do *we* figure in all this? Surely this is primarily a job for the uniforms."

"I want a large concentration of plainclothes officers in the crowd."

"Are we expecting a crowd?"

"There'll be TV cameras and the whole bit. I already told you that Proverb's going to make the biggest possible deal out of this. You can bet that he'll get his followers out on the street."

"So there's no way to screen everyone who's going to get close to him."

"None."

Carlisle shook his head. "I'm getting awfully tired of this nonsense."

Parnell had the look of a man who had heard it all too often. "We're all tired, Harry. It goes with the territory."

Parnell clearly wanted the meeting to move on and get down to details, but Carlisle was not ready to let it go.

"It does? It was only a couple of days ago that the deacons had a warrant out for me. Is that part of the territory? To get thrown in a camp for just doing your job?"

Parnell stared at him bleakly. "So what are you saying? You want to resign?"

Harry Carlisle sighed. "No, I don't want to resign."

Parnell nodded. He knew that Carlisle was not going to quit. The man was too damn stubborn.

"So, shall we get on with it?"

Winters

There was still an hour to go before Proverb was due to arrive, and the crowd was already causing traffic problems in the surrounding streets. Astor Place was completely closed off, but the mob that had turned out to see Arlen Proverb had filled the square and was spilling out onto Broadway and Third Avenue. Winters could not imagine where they had all come from. Was Proverb's machine really that good? He would have thought that after the beating they took outside the Garden, Proverb's followers would have been content to lie low and lick their wounds. Like most of the junior deacons, Winters blamed it all on Washington. It was as if they were afraid of Proverb. As far as he and his colleagues were concerned, it was childishly simple. The

STG had made the first move outside the Garden. All that had been needed was to follow it up with mass arrests. It had been done before, and there was no real question that Proverb was anything but a subversive. If Washington had not lost its nerve, the whole business would have been cleared up in a couple of weeks. As it was, Winters and the other disgruntled deacons had to content themselves with mixing in with the TV crews and taping the faces of the crowd for future analysis. All they could tell themselves was that the day would come when they would be turned loose to round up Proverb's heretics, and they intended to be ready.

Winters's mood did not improve when he spotted Harry Carlisle in the middle of a group of plainclothes PDs. He had hoped that the man would be dead by now. Over a week had gone by, and he had heard nothing from the Magicians. He had wanted to say something to Rogers, but he had realized that any word would violate the oath that he had taken in the basement of the whorehouse. All he could do was wait and fume. It angered him to see Carlisle walking around safe and sound.

Winters raised the minicam to his eyes and ran tape on a bunch of Elvi who were holding a banner that read "We Love You Arlen." The camera had the letters KGOD on its side. He was supposed to be a cameraman for the satellite feed, although everyone knew that KGOD was largely a deacon front. He was annoyed at the degree to which Proverb's arrival was being treated as some big-deal event. The four major networks had camera trucks there, as well as the local stations and two satellite news feeds. The PD was covering things as if it were the president arriving. He knew that there had to be Proverb sympathizers among the top brass who would have to be winkled out in the end. Uniforms in full helmets and armor stood three deep around the entrance to the CCC complex, and more manned the barricades blocking the roads that ran into and out of the square. Others were held in reserve, sitting in Pharaohs and armored buses parked at strategic points around the outside of the area. A podium and banks of speakers had been set up on the sidewalk in front of the main entrance to the building. It seemed that Proverb was going to be allowed to make some kind of speech—another example of how the people around the president were behaving like a bunch of gutless wimps, Winters thought.

There were fifteen minutes to go. Some teenagers in Arlen Proverb sweatshirts and bowling jackets were climbing on the statue of John Wayne in the middle of the square. Winters pushed his way into the crowd to record them for posterity. They spotted the camera and the KGOD logo and started waving. Yeah, wave, you morons, you'll get yours in the end. He wished he were shooting a machine pistol and not a camcorder.

Noon came and went and there was no sign of Proverb. The bastard was going to milk the situation for all it was worth by showing up late. At twelve-thirteen, Winters's tracy started flashing.

"Winters."

"This is to all officers. The Proverb motorcade will be entering the square in three minutes."

"Winters, ten four."

At the briefing, he had been told that Proverb was going to be coming up along Eighth Street. Winters started moving in that direction, intending to get pictures of the crazies who actually mobbed the car. The other cameramen had also received the word and were going the same way. That, in turn, tipped off the crowd. A bottleneck was created at the entrance to Eighth Street, and the PD uniforms started pushing back the crowd. Despite all the hands-off warnings, the police were none too gentle in their treatment. Arms linked and batons held in front of them, they cleared a path by cutting the mass of people in half with a flying wedge that then opened out to push everyone back onto the sidewalk. There was scrabbling and shoving, and a sudden surge pushed a half-dozen bystanders through the plate-glass window of the diner on the corner. Even that incident, however, did not seem to spoil the general euphoria.

Winters's tracy was flashing again.

"This is to all officers. The Proverb motorcade is entering the area. You are now on full alert."

Four NYPD motorcyclists came first on big Harley Davidson Powerglides, gunning their engines and looking around warily for any sign of trouble. They were followed by a Jeep Seminole with four armed rentacops riding in it and a rack gun quad-mounted on the roll bar. Behind the Jeep was Proverb's white limousine, a custom armored stretch Cadillac, with more security walking beside it and riding on the running boards. A second Jeep with a full complement of rentacops brought up the rear.

The motorcade eased its way around the square at slightly less than walking pace. Winters found himself in the middle of the scrimmage in front of the car. The police gave no special treatment to the camera crews, and Winters found himself jostled and shoved around just like the ordinary spectators. A couple of cops seemed to take a particular delight in manhandling him, and he suspected that they knew he was a deacon by the KGOD logo on his camera. He looked for their badge numbers and cursed when he found that they had been covered up by electrical tape, common practice on crowd control details that were expected to turn hairy.

The parade finally came to a stop in front of the CCC building. The limo pulled up directly in front of the podium. The sidewalk had been cleared for ten yards in either direction; only cameramen, reporters, and a lot of men in dark suits who were either deacons or NYPD remained. The car door opened. The big cowboy bodyguard got out first and scanned the crowd. There was a roar of almost hysterical applause, and the uniforms had trouble holding back the struggling front rows of the mob. Seemingly satisfied that the situation was under control, the cowboy leaned into the car and beckoned. The big Muslim also got out, and uniformed cops moved in to surround them, struggling with the media who also wanted to get as close to their man as possible. A small figure in a white suit emerged from the car. Flanked by his bodyguards and the surrounding press of police and media, he moved quickly to the steps of the podium and the safety of its Plexiglas deflector screens. Then, at the foot of the steps, there was some sort of disturbance, followed by the sound of shots.

Kline

The TV in the C86 computer section was tuned to the precensor satellite feed for the arrival of Proverb in the square out front. Cynthia had quickly discovered that a posting to C86 was supposed to be something of a privilege. All the women there were exceedingly pretty and very free in their interpretations of the standard uniform. They also did very little except work on their nails and talk on the phone. C86 was a data access pool for a group of senior deacons, particularly senior deacons who liked to stop by, chat with pretty girls, and invite them to dinner. It was considered diplomatic to accept at least some of the invitations. Cynthia had decided to play that part by ear.

There was a ripple of interest as the motorcade made its way slowly through the crowd in front of the building. One of her colleagues, a petite blonde called Toni, with soap-opera hair and perfect makeup, looked up from her bootleg copy of *Elle*.

"They're really making a production out of all this."

Her friend Laura was well informed but tended to chew gum. She was reputed to be the mistress of Senior Deacon Spencer. She snapped her gum and looked up at the TV screen. "Proverb's got to work it for all he's worth. He's got his ass in a vise. It's only the president that's keeping him out of Joshua."

Cynthia was aware that Harry Carlisle was down in the crowd somewhere. He had called her a number of times and twice stopped by her apartment late at night. She knew that she was running an unreasonable risk by involving herself with someone, particularly someone with such a dubious political reputation, but she just could not bring herself to turn him away.

Proverb was getting out of the car. The camera was jostled by a uniformed cop, and the feed cut to a long shot from a helicopter. It came back to show a closeup of Proverb preparing to mount the steps to the podium that had been set up. Suddenly there was some sort of commotion and the sound of shots on the audio. The women's attention was riveted to the screen.

"My God, have they shot him?"

Carlisle

As the man lunged, there was a slow-motion moment of chaos. Confused hands reached out for him. The two bodyguards were the fastest to react. Rashid Murjeen dived to the floor, taking Proverb down with him. There were three shots. The crowd was screaming. The attacker was instantly buried under a pack of bodies. Everyone's gun was out, and an explosion of panicked firing threatened.

Carlisle was yelling as loud as he could, trying to cut through the confusion of voices. "Stay cool! Hold your fire! Hold your fire!"

Cops were already clearing the area. Carlisle pulled out his lieutenant's shield and pushed his way through. Someone was shouting for paramedics.

"There's a man down here!"

At first he thought the victim was Proverb. But, though blood covered the preacher's white suit, Proverb was being helped to his feet by Joe Don Cutler. Rashid Murjeen was stretched out on the sidewalk. A uniform was bending over him, gloves off, feeling for his pulse.

"He's dead," the man announced.

Carlisle looked quickly around. Two uniforms and two plain-clothes men had the gunman pinned to the ground; a cameraman was down on his knees shooting into the killer's face. A half-dozen more officers stood around him with their guns out. Carlisle hurried over to the group.

"Don't hurt him! We want him alive!" he ordered.

"Do we move him?"

"Take him to one of our holding cells. Do everything you can to keep the deacons away from him."

The assassin was picked up and taken into the building at a run.

Carlisle shouted to Reeves. "Go in with them and do your best to head off the deacons."

He turned his attention to Proverb. With Cutler standing protectively over him, the preacher was kneeling on the sidewalk in an attitude of prayer. The cameras were working overtime. Carlisle could not believe that the man could be that cool. He held out his badge.

"Lieutenant Harry Carlisle, Reverend Proverb. I think we should get you inside."

"I think it's more important that I talk to the people and calm their fears. There must not be another riot."

Carlisle had to admit that Proverb was right. He just could not believe that the man could be so composed so soon after an assassination attempt and with one of his bodyguards dead on the ground. He glanced at Cutler.

"So, shall we get him onto the podium?"

Cutler looked worried. "Are you sure you want to do this, chief? There might be other shooters out there."

Proverb nodded. "We have to do it. There must be no more trouble."

"If you're certain."

Carlisle rounded up a small squad of PD detectives and started for the stage. They formed a worried, watchful knot around Proverb as he stepped up to the microphone. There were shouts from the crowd as they saw the blood on his clothes. He quickly held up a hand.

"There's no need to panic. I'm okay. There was an attempt

on my life but it wasn't successful. The man has been arrested. The police have him.''

Carlisle had to admit that even without the special effects, the preacher had immediate control of the crowd. He talked to them, and they listened. It was a simple but powerful rapport.

''I guess I should be thanking the good Lord for my deliverance from the assassin's bullet, but my heart is heavy. Rashid Murjeen, my good friend and loyal employee, is dead. He was killed by the bullet that was meant for me.''

A hush spread through the crowd. They seemed unsure about how to react. Proverb was safe, but there was still death in the air.

''These are terrible times, my friends. Terrible times. My heart is full, and I can hardly talk.''

Carlisle observed that Proverb had no visible difficulty in talking. The cops around him had started to relax a little now that no second gunman had appeared. Carlisle wondered how long the man intended to speak. He would be a lot happier when the whole thing was over.

''Remember one thing, though. No matter how dark the clouds may seem, do not lose heart. The Lord is with us. He has not forsaken us. The forces of evil sorely try us, but we must have courage and we must have faith. We know that we will triumph in the end and come to our promised reward.''

There were shouts of ''amen'' from the crowd. Proverb had certainly calmed them down. It was little wonder that the deacons and the hierarchy were frightened of him. He seemed to be able to do anything with a mass of people, no matter what the circumstances.

Proverb pointed to the CCC building behind him. ''I have to enter this place and talk with the people inside.'' He made it sound as if he were about to brave the portals of hell. ''Before I go, however, let us share a moment of silent prayer. Let us pray for the soul of Rashid Murjeen.''

Proverb clasped his hands and bowed his head. The crowd followed suit. Some of the cops did the same, while others maintained their watchful vigil. After about a minute, Proverb raised his head and blessed the crowd. Carlisle could imagine the TV images: Proverb in his bloodstained suit surrounded by praying cops in full armor. There was even enough of a breeze to ruffle his hair. The footage was going to be classic.

''May the Lord be with you and keep you from harm.''

Proverb turned to Joe Don Cutler, instantly businesslike. "Shall we get moving?"

Cutler nodded, and they started toward the steps. Carlisle was part of the immediate escort that followed them down. At the foot of the steps, Rashid Murjeen's body was being loaded into the morgue wagon. Proverb glanced back at Carlisle.

"Do we have a name on the gunman?"

"We don't, but they should have run something on him inside by now."

"Do the deacons have him?"

Carlisle shook his head. "I certainly hope not. Officially, it's still a police department case, and I gave orders that the deacons should not be allowed to question him. The deacons, unfortunately, have ways of overriding PD orders."

Proverb looked grim. "I want to know all about the man as soon as possible."

"Where will you be?"

Proverb gave him a hard look. "That remains to be seen."

Carlisle realized that Proverb was frightened. Although perfectly understandable, it came as a complete surprise. Up to that point, the man had seemed so totally in control.

They entered the building. The big hall was a scene of tension and confusion. The steel shutters were down on all but one pair of doors, and the covers were off the concealed gun emplacements from which robot ultralight machine guns could sweep the entire area. Squads of guards, both police and deacon, looked as if they were expecting the mob to storm the citadel at any moment. Carlisle had not noticed them around when the shooting had gone down. Steel boots clattered on the marble floor and echoed around the high white dome of the ceiling that was supposed to symbolize judicial purity. Other officers simply milled about.

A loud argument was taking place in front of the main bank of elevators. Reeves and a solid block of stone-faced uniforms were refusing to let a gang of deacons, led by a senior deacon called Spencer, into the elevator that went directly to the basement holding cells. Carlisle was glad to see that his boys were holding their own.

As soon as Spencer spotted Proverb, he pulled his team away from the potential Mexican standoff with Reeves and his uniforms and hurried to intercept. He waved excitedly to the men around him, pointing at Proverb. "Arrest that man! Arrest him!"

Carlisle and Cutler moved as one. Both had their hands on their guns.

"Nobody arrests anybody!" Carlisle dragged out the old .357 and waved it at the nearest deacon. "This man is under my protection, and I'll shoot anyone who lays a hand on him."

That produced a much-needed pause. Spencer was glaring at him with the outrage of a shark that had just been deprived of lunch.

"Have you gone insane, Carlisle?"

"Maybe."

"I order you to turn that man over to me and then instruct your men to let me interview the assassin you have in custody."

Carlisle gave the senior deacon a long hard look and slowly shook his head. Reeves and his men were there providing backup. Carlisle had the edge if any of the deacons wanted to go the distance.

"I was given the responsibility of keeping this man alive, and until I'm told otherwise by someone a good deal more convincing than you, I intend to go on doing exactly that. As for the assassin, he's the suspect in my investigation, and nobody gets him until I'm through. There's going to be no coverup on this business. That's the official stance. Unofficially, I don't trust you bastards farther than I can spit."

"Very well put, Lieutenant, although I don't think it'll make you many friends."

Carlisle knew that voice. He turned. Deacon Matthew Dreisler, with his inevitable entourage, had made another of his entrances. Carlisle's eyes were cold. "You're not having him, either."

Dreisler laughed. "You're good, Carlisle. You're really good. You're like something out of the twentieth century."

"You're not getting him."

Dreisler lowered his dark glasses and peered at Carlisle over the black rims. "I suggest you ask the Reverend Proverb about that."

Carlisle looked at Proverb. "What's he talking about?"

Proverb hesitated before he answered. "I think I should probably go with Deacon Dreisler."

Carlisle's jaw dropped. "With him? Do you know who he is? He's the top deacon headhunter."

"I think, in this situation, Deacon Dreisler could provide me with a certain . . . how shall I put it . . . a neutral corner?"

Carlisle smelled a rat. "What's going on here?"

Dreisler quickly glanced at Spencer. "I don't think we need detain you any further, Deacon Spencer."

Spencer was not ready to be summarily dismissed just like that. He was so angry that he seemed to have forgotten with whom he was dealing. "If you think I'm letting Carlisle—"

"I'll deal with Lieutenant Carlisle." Dreisler's voice was as smooth as silk.

Again Spencer missed the point. "He threatened me with a gun, damn it."

"I said that I'd deal with Lieutenant Carlisle."

The hint of steel in Dreisler's voice was not wasted on Spencer. He stiffened and his voice became clipped and curt. "I'll take my men back to the twenty-third floor."

Dreisler smiled. "That's a good idea. I'll stop by your office later and we'll talk."

Spencer looked as if that was the last thing he wanted. He contented himself with barking at his men as they passed Reeves and his squad on their way to the elevators. Once they were gone, Dreisler turned his attention to Carlisle.

"What are we going to do with you, Harry? You seem to be a born troublemaker."

"I try to avoid it."

"Some of my brother officers were ready to nail you a few days ago."

"Fortunately they didn't."

"They'll try again."

"I'll face that when the time comes."

"You shouldn't fight with me, Harry. I could be a valuable ally."

Carlisle's face was blank. He was growing more and more certain that Dreisler was up to something exceedingly devious. He had had that feeling when they had met in the house on Fifteenth Street, and now it was stronger than ever. For some bizarre and probably unwholesome reason, Dreisler seemed to be trying to befriend him.

"I'll remember that," he told the deacon.

It was Carlisle's turn to be treated to the Dreisler smile. "Please do that."

With that, Dreisler seemed to have finished with Carlisle. He directed a half bow to Proverb. "Perhaps we should be going."

Proverb offered his hand to Carlisle. His grip was firm and assured. The professional TV smile came on.

"I really am grateful for all the care you've taken of me, Lieutenant Carlisle, but I do think it would solve a lot of problems if I went with Deacon Dreisler."

Carlisle could not figure what the two of them were up to, and he was deeply suspicious. "What is this? Protective custody?"

"I think I'll merely be Deacon Dreisler's guest."

"Are you sure you know what you're doing?"

"Lieutenant, I know what I'm doing."

Carlisle sighed. "I'll still need to talk to you about the murder of Rashid Murjeen."

"That can be arranged through my office."

Carlisle faced Dreisler. "And do you want the hit man as your guest, as well?"

Dreisler laughed. "No, I'd rather you conducted the interrogation. My people can get a little impatient. Torture gets confessions; I think *you* might get the truth."

Carlisle stood and watched them go. Was there really an alliance between Proverb and Dreisler? It hardly seemed possible. Was Dreisler really so sure of his power that he would embrace a man that most of the other deacons would be happy to hang?

Reeves stepped up beside him. "What was that all about?"

Carlisle shook his head. "I'm damned if I know."

"So what do you want me to do?"

It was time to get on with business.

"Stick with me. We'll go and talk to our assassin."

Kline

What the hell was going on down there? After the shooting, the unedited TV pictures became a confused jumble of fleeting images. There were the panicking spectators, the running police, the big Muslim bodyguard stretched out on the sidewalk, a mass of men wrestling someone to the ground, and Arlen Proverb being helped to his feet with blood all over his clothes. The camera work was jerky, unsteady, and fragmented as the crews, completely taken by surprise, desperately tried to focus on what was really happening. Suddenly, for almost a minute, the screen went dead, as if the satellite feed had been killed. During that time all the women in C86 talked at once. It seemed that everyone knew someone who was on duty down there. How many shots had there been? Was it only the bodyguard that had been hit? Was Harry all right?

Then the picture came back. Arlen Proverb was speaking from the podium, still in his bloody white suit, calming the crowd. Cynthia spotted Harry standing right behind him. At least Harry was not hurt. Proverb seemed to have a calming effect even on the women in C86. They watched the screen, looking for any last snippet of information.

"Seems like only the black was killed."

"There were a lot of shots."

"Surely he'd say if anyone else was hit."

"I don't trust that Proverb."

There was a full closeup of Harry as the party was coming down from the podium. Despite telling herself that it was insane for a woman in her situation to act girlish about a man, Cynthia felt a distinct thrill seeing him on the screen.

"They're coming back into the building."

Some of the women left to see what was going on. Cynthia sat tight. She would wait for ten minutes and then try to get Harry on the phone. Then Senior Deacon Spencer stormed into the section. He seemed furious. He whispered angrily to Laura. In the middle of the conversation, he looked up and spotted Cynthia. He glared at her.

"Are you Kline?"

"Yes, sir. I'm Kline."

"The one who shot those rioters awhile back and got on television?"

"That's right, sir."

"You've been seeing that bastard Carlisle, right?"

Cynthia did not like this at all. "I dated him a couple of times. It was nothing serious."

"If you see him again, tell him something from me, will you?"

"If I see him, sir."

"Tell him he's dead meat. I mean it. Tell him he's history."

"I . . ."

"Just tell him."

After he left, Cynthia sat looking at the phone. This was

starting to get dangerous. She had to distance herself from Harry Carlisle. Finally she picked up the phone and entered Harry's code. First it rang his office. There was no answer. It beeped and went on autosearch. She hung up. If he was in the building, his tracy would tell him to call her.

It took seven minutes for the phone to ring. She answered it with a neutral, official voice. "CA Kline."

"This is Harry. You wanted me to call you."

The idea of distance quickly melted. "Are you okay?"

"I'm fine, although things have started to turn decidedly weird."

"What happened down there?"

"This guy tried to kill Proverb. We're questioning him now. He missed Proverb, but he wasted one of the bodyguards."

"We saw some of it on TV."

"Then you probably know as much as I do."

"Harry, there was this senior deacon here. Spencer. He was very angry."

"I had a run-in with him just now."

"He's really mad at you."

"I can imagine."

"I mean really mad."

There were voices in the background at his end.

"Listen, Cynthia, let me call you at home later. I'm really up to my ass in it right now."

"Harry?"

"Yeah."

"Be careful, will you?"

"I'll be careful."

He hung up. She put down the handset.

"Damn."

He would call her later, then he would probably come over, and she would not do anything to stop him.

Carlisle

"Goddamn it to hell! I don't believe this. Are you telling me we've got an Oswald here?"

Reeves looked extremely unhappy. "He checks out as the most perfect lone gunman you could imagine."

"It's not right," Carlisle said. "It's too convenient. It's too perfect. I hate the whole thing. It's like the Reichstag fire or the Ortega assassination. This guy's timing is too perfect for a lone nut.''

''You can't build a conspiracy on nothing.''

''That's exactly what a perfect conspiracy leaves behind. It's watertight.'' Carlisle stared angrily through the one-way glass. ''Wallace Jay Burns. A ten-year history of mental problems but never previously violent. Hospitalized on four occasions. Dropped out of sight fourteen months ago. Told doctors he was going to hermit out in the wilderness to prepare for the coming of the Apocalypse. Shows up today showered and shaved, in a brand-new suit from Barney's and nothing in his pockets but a plastic .50 Sterling. Does that about sum it up?''

''The *Reader's Digest* version.''

''It's like he was newly delivered.''

''With a cannon like that, it was lucky that the slug didn't go right through the bodyguard and take out Proverb, as well.''

''He had the right piece.''

Reeves suddenly grinned. ''There was one thing that wasn't perfect.''

''Yeah, that's true. He didn't get his man.''

On the other side of the one-way glass, Wallace Jay Burns faced the wall with a Norman Bates stare. When he had first been brought in, he had been howling and screaming, holy-rolling stuff about how Proverb was the Antichrist and how killing him would break the Master Lock and free the Motion of the Universe so the Rapture could begin. He had been yelling over and over.

''I am the designated of the Lord, the slayer of the Antichrist. I come with vengeance and a sword.''

''Can somebody shut him up before we all go nuts?'' someone had asked.

After the serious questioning had started, however, he not only shut up but suddenly came to a cosmic full stop. His eyeballs rolled up, and the lights went out. From that point on, no one was home in the mind of Wallace Jay Burns.

Reeves peered through the glass at Burns. There were blackening bruises down one side of the assassin's face, and his right eye was closing up. The men who had disarmed him had not been particularly gentle.

''Maybe we should play the tapes of him raving again.''

"We've heard it all," Carlisle said. "That Damien stuff gives me the creeps."

"We could get Dr. Feelgood down here to try to wake him up chemically."

Carlisle shook his head. "I don't want to load any drugs into him yet. It could well be drugs that put him where he is now."

"Nothing showed on the bloodscan."

"Microdelics wouldn't show on a bloodscan. They could have used a binary or maybe some three-tier, precision time-release deal. First layer makes him calm and lucid so he can make the hit. The second, maybe triggered by his own natural adrenaline, starts him raving."

"And the third turns him into an eggplant."

"Can you think of a better scenario?"

Reeves shook his head. "I think you'd be better off if you stopped thinking of a mysterious 'them.' "

Carlisle rubbed his eyes. "Maybe. It just bugs me. It's too pat."

He knew that he was approaching exhaustion. He needed food, coffee, cigarettes, and most of all sleep. He stood up and stretched. "I don't know. Maybe I'm not thinking straight. Did we get anything on the gun yet?"

"It's clean as a whistle. It was part of a batch shipped to a Dallas gun store eighteen months ago. There's no record of the purchase."

"There wouldn't be in Texas. Guns come from God down there."

"So where do we go from here? We can't keep the deacons at bay forever."

"I suppose we can run some routine stuff on him. Hook him up to a polygraph and run the Schultz-Dixon Image Test on him, see if we get a response. After that, there's nothing left but to start with the drugs."

Reeves picked up the phone. "Get an S-D kit down here, will you?" He glanced at Carlisle. "I gotta tell you, Lieutenant, I think we've lost this one."

Carlisle leaned against the one-way glass. "I hate to admit it, but you're probably right."

The door opened and a technician wheeled in a steel trolley with the Schultz-Dixon polygraph kit on it.

"You want me to wire him?" the technician asked.

Reeves opened the connecting door that led to Burns's observation cell. "Yeah, go right ahead."

The technician went to work on Burns while Reeves and Carlisle watched from behind the glass. Burns did not react in any way as his shirt was pulled off and contact points stuck to his torso.

Carlisle turned away as if not expecting to get any results. Suddenly he clapped a hand to his forehead. "Goddamn it, I'm getting stupid."

"You thought of something."

"Not exactly. I've just been forgetting one of the first things I was taught. Deal with reality, not supposition."

Reeves blinked. "Say what?"

"So far we've been treating this as an attempted hit on Arlen Proverb."

"What else could it be? You're not saying that Burns had a beef with the bodyguard?"

"No, I'm not. I'm just saying that we ought to look at what we have. First question in any crime. Has anyone benefited by what happened?"

Reeves was starting to look concerned, as if he were worried that Carlisle was finally losing it.

"The bodyguard's dead and the shooter's a veggie. What benefit?"

The tech stuck his head around the connecting door. "I've run the preliminary. This Burns is a full-scale what-me-worry. It's just like something wiped his synapses. I ran the first set of shock images, sex, violence, religious symbols. Nothing but background motor functions. No response to concept that I can find. Do you want me to go on?"

Carlisle looked down at Burns. The man was festooned with wires attached to his head and body by contact clamps.

"Yeah, run the whole deal, if only for the record." He turned back to Reeves. "Did it occur to you that, as things stand, Arlen Proverb has had a very good day? Most of the TV images from today will get through, and he looks like the man they couldn't silence. Now he's the center of attention again."

Reeves put a hand on Carlisle's shoulder. "Listen to me, Lieutenant. If you're thinking in the deeply weird direction I think you're thinking, they are going to kill you. This is now, boss. They're not going to let you crack the world open with this case. They're just going to take you out and hang you."

NINE

Winters

WINTERS WAS COMING BACK FROM THE SHOWERS. THE marks on his body had not completely faded, but after being buffeted around in front of the building all day, he needed to wash the smell of the mob off him. He had decided to drape a towel over himself and take the chance that no one would notice the welts. The new prudery had dictated individual shower stalls when the center had been designed, but a lot of the men were inclined to share a naked, towel-snapping camaraderie. Winters had never appreciated that kind of horseplay and tended to keep to himself. If anyone had noticed, they had not reacted. He had washed quickly, dried himself and dressed in his sweat suit with the logo of the Twenty-first Street Gun Club on the back and his English Reeboks and started out for a cup of coffee and something to eat. After his shower, he was in a considerably better mood and he was even looking forward to checking out the CAs in the commissary.

The particular section of corridor was deserted. It was still as brightly lit as any other part of the complex, but the emptiness was eerie. So when the figure came around the corner like something supernatural, Winters was startled. For a fleeting instant, he thought he was confronting the Black Knight. The man was built like a defensive end and wore full assault armor and a command helmet with the neck ring computer. His visor was down, and not a single insignia or identifying symbol could be seen anywhere on his uniform or equipment. He was carrying a large and very elaborate hand weapon down by his side. As he came closer, Winters saw that it was one of the legendary, state-of-the-art Taidos, calibrated for heatseekers. Its plastic shielding gleamed as the figure walked by. It was in mint condition. Winter had not thought there was a piece like that outside the Japanese military.

He had walked about three paces when a voice called out from behind him.

"Hey, you!"

Winters froze. The voice was coming through one of the same distortion devices that had been used in the basement of the whorehouse. Winters slowly turned.

"Me?"

"You dropped this."

The figure was holding a small folded slip of paper in one of his thick armored gloves. Winters blinked.

"I did?"

The figure held out the slip of paper. "Take it, it's yours."

Winters took the paper. The figure turned on its steelshod heel and walked away. Winters stared after it. It made no more sense than a visitation from Mars. Without thinking, he unfolded the paper.

3333 2374 19886
Call from a pay phone.

Winters could feel the hairs on the back of his neck rise. It was the signal. The Magicians wanted him. He was not sure why it had been delivered with such a splendid show of force, but he was completely impressed and not a little scared. He quickly refolded the paper and, concealing it in his hand, hurried for the locker room and his street clothes.

He walked three blocks from Astor Place before he started looking for a pay phone. Somehow calling from right outside the CCC complex did not seem appropriate.

The first phone he came across was broken. It had been smashed by vandals. The slogan *"There will be a cleansing of the temple"* had been scrawled across the coin box. He walked on and found a pair that looked as if they were in working order by the entrance to the subway on Lafayette. A couple of drug-addict types were lurking by the phones. They seemed to be waiting for one or both of them to ring. As Winters walked up, they looked at him suspiciously, held a fast, muttered conversation, and moved off. Winters quickly keyed in the number. It rang four times and then a machine answered.

"Repeat this phrase for voice identification."

Winters waited for a few seconds before realizing that that was the phrase that he was supposed to repeat. He felt a little ridiculous as he mouthed the words into the mouthpiece. "Repeat this phrase for voice identification."

There were a series of pulses on the line. His voice must have passed the test, because a second tape was activated.

"Be on the corner of Broadway and Twenty-sixth Street at four forty-five A.M. tomorrow. Wear dark, serviceable clothes. You will be picked up."

The message repeated once and stopped. Winters slowly hung up. He was in. They were going to kill Carlisle, and he was to be part of the team.

Kline

It was five-fifteen in the morning and the phone was ringing. Cynthia Kline jerked awake with the reflexes of someone trained to expect trouble at all times. She snatched for the handset from inside the cocoon of blankets. Harry Carlisle muttered in his sleep.

"If it's for me, I'm not here."

"Hello." Her voice was neutral and tentative.

"Cynthia?"

"Who's this?"

"It's Laura at C86. We're having a panic here. Can you come in?"

Cynthia groaned. "Do you know what time it is?"

Laura did not sound too pleased with Cynthia's response. "I know what time it is. I've been here all night. This is important."

"Okay, okay. I'll get there as fast as I can."

She sat up in bed but hesitated before she turned on the light. She had to do something about Harry. She was not comfortable with the idea of leaving him alone in her apartment. She was confident that there was nothing glaring that would give her away in a routine search, but it was a different matter having a trained detective hanging around there. They got impressions from random patterns, things that other people did not even see. No matter what she felt about him, he was still a cop.

As she shook him gently by the shoulder to wake him she felt bad. He had looked so exhausted when he had finally showed up around one-thirty, and even now he had been asleep for less than two hours.

"Harry, wake up. The office called, and I have to go in."

Harry Carlisle blinked. He did not seem to be quite sure of where he was. "What office?"

"I just got a call from C86. They're having some sort of emergency and they want me to come in."

Harry yawned. "C86 doesn't have emergencies. It's just a bimbo pool for the deacon brass."

Cynthia glared at him. "That's a fucking sexist remark."

"That's probably the first time the phrase 'fucking sexist' has been heard south of the Canadian border in a coon's age. Besides, you told me yourself that it was a bimbo pool, or as good as. I think you were being a little more ladylike at the time."

Cynthia didn't know whether to blush or go white. She'd made a bad slip. Only someone who had recently been out of the country, where they still used phrases like that, would call something "fucking sexist." His mention of the Canadian border was too close to home. The best she could do was to give him a defiant look. "Sometimes I revert."

"I'm glad to hear it."

He did not seem to want to pursue it. She lit a cigarette.

"Listen, Harry, I guess I ought to get going."

"And you figure that I ought to get going, too?"

"I didn't say that. Really, if you—"

"Nobody wants someone else alone in their apartment."

The more he came awake, the more he seemed to grasp the situation. He started to climb wearily out of bed. Cynthia felt bad.

"You don't mind?"

"Hell, no. I need to go back and get a clean shirt."

"You want some coffee?"

Carlisle shook his head. "Just give me a cigarette. I'll go straight to bed when I get to my place and sleep until somebody demands that I get up."

He was gathering his clothes.

Winters

Winters was on the corner of Twenty-sixth and Broadway fifteen minutes before the appointed time. He was all but dressed for a commando raid in a black nylon windbreaker, a black rollneck, black sweat pants, and running shoes, not his expensive Reeboks but a pair of beat-up Converse All Stars. All he had in his pockets was a compact 9mm automatic and a hundred dollars. He had left all of his identification back in his room, just to be on the safe side.

There was a definite chill in the air, but the way that he jogged on the spot, like a fighter warming up for the ring, was more from nervous energy than cold. A helicopter—it sounded like a Cobra—rattled overhead. Winters stepped lightly back into a doorway. He did not want to be seen by any kind of authority. He looked too much as if he was on his way to commit a crime, which, in some respects, he was. As the sound of the chopper faded, he emerged onto the sidewalk again. He peered anxiously up Broadway, but the early-morning streets were deserted. There were just the cardboard boxes in which the vagrants nested. One had a small garbage fire going in front of it.

There was the tiptap of high heels behind him, coming down Twenty-sixth Street. It was a woman, walking unsteadily. At first, he could only see her in silhouette, but when she came into the glow of a lighted street lamp, her spandex pants, sequined tube top, and exaggerated shoes told him immediately that she was a prostitute, probably one of the bottom-rung street women who tried to scratch a living among the cardboard-box people. Her makeup was smeared, and she was having trouble focusing her eyes. It was obviously the end of a long evening. When she saw Winters, she increased the swing in her walk.

"You're up late."

Something really had to be done about the number of whores in the city and the shamelessness of their behavior, Winters thought. It seemed that, each time he looked, there were more of them, in more blatant states of seminudity. A serious crackdown was needed.

"What's the matter? Lost your voice?" She stopped in front of him. "Feel like a blow job to go to bed with?"

Winters eyes bugged out of his head. "I—I'm not going to bed."

It had taken him a second to gird his moral authority around him.

The prostitute shrugged. "So call it breakfast. Only cost you fifty."

There was a car coming down Broadway. Winters hissed at the woman. "Go away."

She planted her hands on her hips and looked drunkenly belligerent. There was a flower painted on her right cheek. "It don't cost nothing to be polite."

The car was close. The headlights were just two blocks away. "Will you get out of here!"

Still she did not move.

"Who in hell do you think you are?"

The car went straight past. It was the wrong one. The prostitute was on a roll, her voice rising in pitch and volume.

"Think you own the street or something? What gives you the right to tell me what to do?"

A couple of vagrants were peering from their boxes. Winters wanted to tell the whore that if she did not shut up, he would arrest her. Of course he could not do that. He considered pulling out his gun and shooting her, but that would create its own set of problems. With the Magicians due at any minute, he had to content himself with vague threats.

"If you don't get away from me, you'll regret it."

"Oh, yeah? Who's gonna make me? You some kind of big shot, or do you just have fun threatening women?"

"I'm warning you . . ."

"Don't be warning me, Jack. If you're so fucking righteous, how come you're out here at five o'clock in the morning?"

"You tell the bastard, Bernice."

Now the vagrants were joining in. Winters took a step toward the woman. At precisely that moment a black van came wheeling into Broadway out of Twenty-eighth Street, running the lights in a shriek of tires. It came straight at the corner where Winters was waiting and squealed to a stop. The side rear door slid open and an electronically distorted voice echoed from the dark interior.

"Get in."

The face of Bernice took on a look of horror. "It's fucking Dracula."

Winters scrambled inside. The door slammed, and the van accelerated away.

"What were you doing, Winters? Hiring on a little entertainment while you were waiting?"

The distorted electronic laughter was reminiscent of the sounds in an old-time video parlor. There were four other men in the back of the van, sitting on bench seats. They were dressed pretty much like him, except their heads were encased in the same visored helmets that had been worn at the first meeting. Their voices came through the same distorters. They all had .60 Mossbergs cradled in their laps. The nearest man indicated that Winters should sit down on an empty stretch of bench. Another Mossberg and a helmet were passed down to him.

"Take these, Winters."

The helmet was identical to the others except that it was a dull gray. He was clearly the novice on this job. He put on the helmet and dropped the visor.

"Test the distorter."

"One, two, test."

He sounded like the others. With the visor closed and the heavy Mossberg gripped in his fists, he experienced a sense of power greater than anything he had ever known. This was why he had joined the service. He was an anonymous and vengeful angel dispensing justice and death. These really were the final days.

There were no introductions. "Okay, Winters, listen up. I'm only going to say this once. This is your first mission, so you keep quiet and strictly run backup. You understand?"

"I understand."

He was cut down to a very junior avenging angel. The Magician went on.

"We are going to park outside an apartment building on Thirty-eighth Street. The woman Kline lives there. In ten to fifteen minutes, Carlisle will come out and we will take him. Alive. We want him alive. That is crucial."

"What about Kline?"

"We leave her alone, for the moment."

The driver was in a separate, partitioned front section. The partition was also used for racking a redscope and a heat surveillance scanner. The Magicians seemed to be able to get the best and most advanced hardware. After driving for about ten minutes, the van pulled over to the curb and stopped. The Magician in the blue helmet turned on the redscope. It showed a wide-angle view of a deserted street.

"Now we wait."

Carlisle

Harry Carlisle let himself out of the front door of Cynthia Kline's building, wondering about his chances of getting a cab so early in the morning. He had left before Cynthia, giving her a few minutes alone to get ready for work. He could not imagine what they were up to at Astor Place, calling her in at this hour. At first, he did not notice the black van. There was no reason why he should—it was just one more in the line of parked cars at the curb. It was only the sound of the rear door being wrenched open that made him turn and look at it. When the five armed men jumped out, his first thought was that it was a particularly elaborate mugging. Then he saw the visored helmets and the weapons that they carried, and he realized that it was something much more sinister and much more exclusively directed at him. He was still warm from Cynthia's bed and a little sleepy. He clawed for the .357 under his arm, but his reactions were slow. His fingers touched it, but suddenly there were five Mossbergs pointed at him. The voice was like that of a robot.

"Take your hand away from the gun, Carlisle, or we'll blast you where you stand."

The fact that they knew his name confirmed his worst suspicions. It was a deacon death squad. Pure terror clutched at his guts as he raised his hands.

They were all around him. The Magnum was removed from its holster. Hands grabbed him and threw him headfirst onto the hood of a parked car. His hands were pulled roughly behind him and a pair of old-style steel handcuffs were clamped onto his wrists. They were locked too tight, and the metal cut painfully into his wrists. With his arms immobilized, he was carried to the black van and thrown inside. He finished up on his knees on the floor of the van. The interior was loaded with high-tech snooper equipment, but he was given no time to look at it. They were far from finished with him. One of his captors grabbed the chain that linked the cuffs and pulled his arms hard up behind his back. The chain was clipped to hook into the roof of the van, and he was left hanging, knees bent and head thrust forward. The pain was excruciating. His hands were going numb, and his shoulders felt as if they were being dislocated.

The pain became even worse as the van started to move. He had no way of stopping himself from swinging from his wrists each time the van braked or made a turn. Five blank black visors looked down at him, masking the wearers' expressions. All he could see was his own reflection, made grotesque by the curve of the visor. He could not even tell from which of them the robot voice was coming.

"We're going to mess you up, Carlisle. You've caused a lot of trouble, but now we're going to mess you up. There's no one to help you, and no way that you're going to crawl out of this."

One of them pushed him with a booted foot to set him swinging even more. His arms felt as if they were on fire.

"Yes, Carlisle. We are going to mess you up very profoundly."

Winters

Since no one had told him, Winters had no idea where he was or where he was going. At one point the sound of the tires had changed briefly. He had assumed that they were going over a bridge, probably to Queens or Brooklyn. They had taken Carlisle very easily, and now Winters' hated enemy was hanging in front of them, handcuffed and helpless. There would be no more of his smart mouth and subversive attitudes. All the small humiliations that Winters had suffered at his hands would be paid for a hundred times over. The best part was that Carlisle did not have a clue as to who was doing it to him. Winters laughed silently behind his visor. I'm going to watch you die, you bastard, he thought. I'm actually going to watch you die.

They drove for just over a half hour, then made a turn and started bouncing on an uneven surface, probably a dirt road or a parking lot. Sweat stood out on Carlisle's face. The idea that the man was in pain and no doubt terrified out of his mind filled Winters with a deep satisfaction that was almost a sense of freedom. He was free to go all the way with his hate. Previously there had always been limitations. He had only been a small component in the machine that dispensed justice. Here it was an angry, face-to-face justice, a cruel ancient justice where a righteous man could relish the hurt and the death of his enemy.

There was a power growing inside him. Jesus Christ, he was looking forward to this.

The van stopped and the door was opened. They were in a parking lot, long abandoned, overgrown and full of potholes. It was empty but for the remains of a long-dead tractor trailer rusting away amid dark weeds and drifts of garbage. They seemed to have come to an industrial wasteland in the depths of God knew where. Rotting skeletons of buildings were on three sides of them, and the air stank of black water, decaying chemicals, and clogged drains. A drab, gray, overcast dawn was just breaking. Winters smiled to himself. He thought that to Carlisle it probably looked like one of the outer circles of hell—and, indeed, it might prove to be exactly that. They unclipped Carlisle from the hook and manhandled him out. One of the Magicians had walked away across the derelict parking lot. He was opening a door to one of the more substantial ruins. A light shone out, orange amid the general gray. They carried Carlisle toward it.

The interior of the ruined factory was a place of towering shadows, collapsed gantries, and loops of impossibly thick steel chains, red with rust. The first pale light of the day was creeping through the holes in the roof. Rats scuttled in the twisted falls of masonry. The massive bulks of forgotten machinery were scattered, as if by the hands of some giant child. There was a pool of bright electric light, and within that luminous circle everything had been made ready in advance. There was a single, low stool set directly under the light. On a table to one side, surgical instruments had been laid out beside a small hand-cranked generator. There were also undisguised instruments of torture: a metal and plastic reverb helmet; a length of steel cable, frayed at the end, that could be used as a whip; a number of clamps; an electric branding iron. Above the stool, there was a pulley system of ropes and chains. A large rubber sheet covered the floor of the area. A single helmeted figure presided over the ad hoc dungeon. As the men from the van entered, he greeted them with a strange finger and thumb hand signal.

Even the torturers' creature comforts had been taken care of. On a second table there was a coffee machine and a tray of plastic-wrapped sandwiches. Three robot camcorders were standing silent, waiting to be activated to record the event for posterity.

Carlisle was placed on the stool under the light. He made no sound, but his eyes were closed and his hands were an ugly mottled red. There was something strangely anticlimactic about the moment, a lull in the ceremony before the next act got under way. The Magician in the gold helmet, who once again seemed to be in control of the proceedings, nodded to the prisoner.

"Take off the handcuffs."

The Magician in the blue helmet moved forward and unlocked the manacles. Carlisle gasped as his wrists were freed. He started to massage his hands. To Winters's surprise, the Magician unfastened the straps of his gold helmet, pushed back the visor, and eased the whole thing over his head. It was Senior Deacon Spencer.

"Remember me, Carlisle?"

Carlisle said nothing. Spencer pushed his fingers through his hair. He took a pack of cigarettes from his field jacket and lit one. Very deliberately, he walked to the table and poured himself a cup of coffee.

"We have a lot of time. You're going to die very slowly, Carlisle. When they find you, I want you to be a major example to the others."

One by one, the other Magicians took off their helmets. Winters' surprise continued. There was Rogers, Gleason, Proxmire, and a man that he did not know. Their faces were smug, as if they shared a secret. Winters was the last to reveal himself. He was not sure about the way the others looked at him as he took off the plain gray helmet. He was very conscious that he was the rookie and that they were waiting to see how he would make out on his first job. They probably hoped that he would make a fool of himself, that he would break down or throw up or something.

Spencer seemed to be aware of his nervousness. "Winters."

"Yes, sir?"

"Strip the prisoner."

Winters stood rooted. The idea of taking off any other man's clothes revolted him. The fact that it was Carlisle made it ten times worse.

"Did you hear me, Winters?"

The others were starting to smirk.

"Yes, sir."

He took a deep breath and advanced on the seated Carlisle. Carlisle did not resist him, but he also did not do anything to help. As Winters was unbuttoning his shirt, his eyes opened and he muttered in a rasping voice, "Are you enjoying this, boy?"

Winters did not think. He simply lashed out in a flash of discharging tension and slapped Carlisle open handed, hard across the face. Carlisle swayed on the stool.

"I told you to strip him, not beat him up," Spencer snapped.

"Yes, sir. I'm sorry."

Spencer looked at the others. "You all better remember this. I don't want his face damaged. He has to be recognizable."

Carlisle's clothes were finally removed. Winters stepped back.

"The prisoner is naked, sir."

Spencer nodded. "So I see."

He turned to Rogers. "I think we'll put the reverb helmet on him."

"Yes, sir."

The reverb helmet in its primitive form supposedly had been invented by the Chilean secret police during the Pinochet era and had quickly spread to law enforcement agencies in South and Central America and even ones as far apart as Haiti and Iran. Originally it had been a simple steel headpiece that caused the victim's own screams to ring deafeningly in his ears. The modern version was a good deal more sophisticated, using miniature electronics to amplify the sounds way past the pain threshold.

Rogers lowered the helmet over Carlisle's head and snapped it shut. Carlisle looked like the Man in the Iron Mask. The weight of the helmet bowed his head forward.

"We'll start by suspending him from his ankles. Replace your helmets and run the cameras."

Carlisle

The amplified sound of his own breathing roared in his ears. He could see nothing, and the noise was the whole world. Harry Carlisle had never known that it was possible to be so afraid. This was it. The unthinkable was starting. The worst part was that he was angry with himself. Back there on the street, he should have pulled out the gun and forced them to blow him away. He would have been spared what was coming. But he had not pulled the gun. The immediate, moment-by-moment impulse to self-preservation was formidable, and now it was too late. Something was being looped around his ankles. His feet were jerked upward. He toppled from the stool and grunted as he hit the floor. The sound inside the headpiece was like a thunderclap. He was being pulled up by the feet until his dangling fingertips cleared the rubber sheet. He could feel himself slowly turning. He had no idea where the pain would start and from what direction it would come. His whole body cringed.

Winters

Spencer seemed to take an absolute delight in what he was doing. He selected the first man. "Proxmire, we'll start with you. Is the branding iron fired up?"

Proxmire had the look of a man who had been through it all before. He nodded. Spencer smiled and closed his visor. Winters prayed that he would never see that smile directed at him.

"Confine your work to the skin around his armpits."

"Yes, sir."

"Activate the cameras."

Proxmire seemed in no hurry. He inspected the heated tip of the iron and walked slowly to where Carlisle hung upside down and naked like a side of beef. He put a hand on Carlisle's chest to stop the slow rotation of the body. Then there was a *crack*, and Proxmire's head burst in a spray of bloody mist.

They seemed to come out of nowhere. The first Winters saw of them was the muzzle flashes of their guns. Spencer went down, and less than a second later, Rogers was hit. There were dark figures rappelling down from the rusty overhead gantries, the chatter of automatic weapons, and indistinguishable yelling. The light over Carlisle shattered, leaving only the gray dawn to see by. Maybe a dozen of them were moving in the gloom. There was an explosion and smoke. Winters, under hostile fire for the first time, could not believe it. He froze. The chaos did not apply to him. The bullets would go around him. Then bullet spurts stitched the rubber sheet at his feet. He looked desperately for cover. He attempted to sprint to safety behind a corroded megalith of a machine, but he was cut off by another seam of bullets. He swerved and then realized that he could not go back. In terror he dropped to his knees. A figure—ski mask, night goggles, flak jacket, bare arms—was running at him.

"We're the Lefthand Path, motherfuckers!"

Winters raised the Mossberg and pumped the trigger. It stuck. The godforsaken safety was still on. He had never checked. He frantically flicked it. A rifle butt was coming at his head. The world exploded and was gone.

Carlisle

The pain still did not come. How long were they going to play with him? His muscles were starting to twitch uncontrollably. He was shivering. Then something warm spattered his body.

"What?"

His exclamation was almost a shriek, deafening him. There seemed to be noise beyond the headpiece, but he could not tell because his head was ringing so hard. Still nothing happened. Then hands touched him. He shuddered. It was the roar of the surf. He was being lowered, gently lowered, to the ground. His neck muscles could not support the headpiece, and it banged on the hard floor. He was in a nuclear explosion. Someone tried to remove the helmet without first turning it off. Triple nuclear explosions. Then they did it correctly, and the howling was only in his head. The helmet was lifted off. A face in a knitted ski mask was looking into his. He could scarcely hear the words.

"Just be calm. We're getting you out of here."

A hand was holding a syrette.

"We're going to give you a little shot."

A second face in a ski mask entered his field of vision. The first ski mask questioned it.

"Did we leave a witness?"

The second ski mask nodded. "Just one. We greased the rest."

"Good. Get something to wrap this guy in. He'll be out in a second."

Carlisle sighed. He was out now. He was drowning in a warm black lake, and he didn't give a damn.

TEN

Mansard

"**P**RAISE BE TO LARRY FAITHFUL, GOVERNMENT WITHOUT end."

"You should watch your mouth, boss. We're on their turf now."

"Screw them all. They need me more than I need them."

There were ten days to go to the Day of National Reconciliation, and Charlie Mansard was chain smoking and carrying a hip flask. He was standing beside Jimmy Gadd on a drafty outer runway in the military security section of Newark Airport, watching soldiers riding walkers and driving forklifts, breaking down the cargo mass of a C87. They had watched the impossibly bulbous aircraft come in to land. It seemed like a miracle that anything so heavy could ever lumber into the air. It was finished in winter warfare camouflage. Mansard had wondered for what ambitious scheme it had been originally commissioned. Probably some wishful but eventually aborted invasion of Canada. The government no longer had the trillions that the Reagan era had had to throw around, but considering the nation's straitened circumstances, the military continued to get most of the toys it wanted and still managed to remain ineffectual. After everything that had been poured into the Southern Border War, the Mexicans and their Havana Pact allies still held their slice of Texas, including Corpus Christi and, the crowning humiliation, San Antonio. There had been mutterings about nuking the greasy papist bastards, but everyone was well aware that any use of the

218

aging nuclear arsenal would provoke immediate retaliation from Russia, Japan, and probably China. A red, white, and green Mexican tricolor with its gold eagle continued to flutter over the Alamo.

As the side panels of the C87 were removed and the containers were slid from the plane's interior framework, Mansard realized that he was actually getting his own small slice of the pie. Jimmy Gadd felt it, too.

"It's goddamn Christmas. I've never seen so much stuff. I didn't know there was this much hardware in the country."

"Our leaders move in mysterious ways."

"Half this stuff is technically illegal."

"Exactly."

A laden, olive-green forklift hooted at them, and they stepped out of the way. A walker followed with a redheaded corporal effortlessly providing the motion base for its gargantuan arms and legs.

"Those things always remind me of the old Toho monster movies. Godzilla heading out to eat Tokyo, remember? Shall we follow it into the hangar and watch the presents being unwrapped?"

Inside the big military hangar, soldiers were swarming over the containers from the C87, reducing them to their smaller components, which were then loaded onto waiting trucks for the second stage of their trip to the construction site. They would be trucked to Hoboken and transferred to pontoons, finally to be floated downriver to Liberty Island, where the enormous floating projector units were being assembled. The island had been closed to the public—not that it saw many visitors anymore. Access had been limited ever since the Daughters of Islam had tried to blow up the statue in '04. For Mansard, it had been turned into a full-scale military camp, complete with patrol boats, helicopters, and a floodlit perimeter. He had become king of his own island and he was loving every minute. His behavior had become shamelessly Napoleonic, and the military, in its turn, appeared to lap it up. Jimmy Gadd had his own explanation.

"The poor bastards probably welcome any diversion from being shot at by Zapata Legion snipers with those nasty little Cucaracha missiles."

Supply sergeants pulled cases off the line at random and checked that the contents matched the manifest and had arrived intact. Mansard and Gadd strolled toward one of those inspections. The lids had been removed from four aluminum coffins. Inside, four Sony DL-70s nestled in beds of blue foam rubber. Jimmy Gadd blinked in surprise.

"Those are DL-70Cs. We've always been lucky to get the basic model. They don't have these anywhere in South America yet."

Mansard laughed. "Are you suggesting that our holy leaders are doing covert business with the heathen japper?" A thought struck him, and he looked sharply at Gadd. "You do know how to operate these new wonders from the rising sun?"

Gadd grinned and shrugged. "I can read a manual with the best of them."

Mansard looked askance at him. "Christ, no wonder I'm an alcoholic."

"You're losing your sense of humor."

"That's hardly surprising."

Gadd was looking at his watch. "Listen, things seem to be running smoothly out here. Why don't we head back to the site and see that my guys aren't getting in any more beefs with the army?"

Mansard nodded. The downside to all the technical largess coming to them via the military was that the production had been turned into a military operation. The disrespect and loose camaraderie that held together Mansard's team and turned them into a fiercely efficient unit when they wanted to be had clashed badly with the army technicians' concepts of organization and discipline. There was yet to be a fistfight, but screaming matches were a daily occurrence, and there had been one unfortunate incident that was already being referred to as the Donut Strike. One of the roots of the friction was that Mansard's people handled quality control and invariably had the last say. The military did not take kindly to being ordered around by civilians, particularly civilians who looked like hairy subversives. They were also not used to working with women. All women had been removed from the military in the first three months of the Faithful administration while Mansard had always taken a perverse delight in doing all the equal opportunity hiring that he could get away with.

Despite all that—and to Mansard's surprise—the work was slightly ahead of schedule. Those Christian soldiers seemed to get the job done if only by sheer weight of numbers. If nothing went weird on them and open warfare did not break out between soldiers and civilians, they could ground test the power rigs in four days. Charlie Mansard, despite his glib cynicism, was filled with a mounting excitement.

As they walked back to the limousine, Mansard started quizzing Gadd about the new Sony modification.

"What will it do to the color/light density?"

"Should beef it up."

"By much?"

"I haven't looked at the specs, but I imagine by quite a bit. This is Sony. They won't put out a new model just for the sake of it."

"So we could have ourselves an almost solid image?"

"Close."

Mansard clenched his fists gleefully. "Great. I've got real plans for this show."

Gadd looked at him curiously. "Do you know something that I don't?"

Charlie Mansard laughed. "Who knows? This is going to be the biggest sky image anyone's ever seen. We might just touch off the Day of Judgment."

Gadd snorted. "Your hired help have commented on how, these days, you seemed to think you're Hitler. We didn't think that you'd progressed to God."

Mansard ignored the crack. "Nobody seems to have noticed that they're letting us play with dynamite. I mean, what happened when we put up the Four Horsemen?"

"There was a bloody great riot."

"I thought we were dead after that. I thought they'd close us down for sure and outlaw skywalkers as works of Satan. Instead, they hire us to build something four times as big. What they don't seem to realize is that we could get four times the reaction."

"The images will be out on the water. That should soften the impact a little."

"Quite the reverse. Remember, the barges will be moving. For those who are just busting a gut to believe in that kind of thing, it'll look like the Beasts of Revelations are advancing on the city. The final fall of Babylon-on-the-Hudson."

Jimmy Gadd looked at his boss suspiciously. "You're getting a little strange, Charlie. What do you think is going to come out of all this?"

For someone of his size, Mansard was almost coy. "I don't know. Maybe the fall of the government."

Gadd shook his head. "You're working too hard."

Kline

Cynthia Kline was worried. It was four days since she had heard anything from Harry Carlisle. She was aware that a police officer might be called away to some situation in which it would be impossible to make personal phone calls, but there was something about his silence that did not seem to be quite right. She told herself, over and over, that she was not simply being the kind of neurotic who needs a lover to phone her four or five times a day. It was some sixth sense, or maybe just an extension of her own instinct of self-preservation, warning her that things were taking a disturbingly odd turn. It had started with the predawn call summoning her to Astor Place. Harry had left first, and she had waited; she could not afford to be seen walking out with him. The drunken nights when she had been Longstreet's protégée had done enough to her reputation around the building. She had sat on the bed and smoked a cigarette before finally pulling on her topcoat and going out into the empty streets.

The scene at C86 had been one of near chaos. Laura, who had been appointed pro tem supervisor, explained that they were trying to contain a computer virus and sent her directly to her terminal. The monitor was flashing bizarre dialog boxes that insisted that she enter complex thirty-two symbol codes. She had never seen anything like it. She was simply some kind of interface. She had no idea what was going on. The monitors told her what to do, and she did it. She had no idea if the virus was winning or losing. For all she knew it might be the virus issuing her instructions.

It was the not knowing what she was doing that quickly killed any kind of excitement or sense of participation. There might have been an epic cyberfight going on, but since she did not understand it, she could hardly feel a part of it. Hers was but to keyboard. After an hour, she was profoundly bored and resentful at being dragged out of a warm bed and away from Harry for such nonsense. It was quite possible that the dialog boxes and her increasingly resentful responses were nothing more than computer makework, part of some demented deacon exercise.

On her first break, she had run into Laura in the rest room, and the second oddity had occurred. Laura, who had been staring at herself in the mirror as Cynthia had walked in, glanced up.

"Weird night."

"You can say that again."

"Do you even know what a computer virus is?"

Cynthia decided that the best thing would be to play it like an airhead. "I'm not sure any of them really know what a computer virus is."

There was a pause as Laura worked on her makeup. She wore a great deal by the standards of the time and place. She looked at Cynthia's reflection in the mirror. "Are you still going out with that cop?"

"Uh-huh."

"You know it's not too smart, don't you?"

"I know that. I've been thinking of breaking it off, but I do kind of like him."

Laura was preparing to leave. "I'd look after myself if I were you. That cop of yours may not be around much longer."

Cynthia's head turned sharply. "What do you mean by that?"

Laura obviously realized that she had said too much. She was already on her way to the door. "Nothing, honey. I just meant that he has a knack of getting himself into trouble."

She was through the door and gone. Cynthia wanted to go after her and shake the truth out of her, but attacking even a temporary supervisor would put her in serious trouble. What had the bitch meant by he "may not be around much longer"? Laura slept with that bastard Spencer. Had she heard something? People did, all too frequently, disappear.

Cynthia was still worrying about the remark as she went back to her terminal. In fifteen minutes, however, all thoughts of Harry were temporarily driven from her mind.

LOOK TO THE SKIES.

A cold hand clutched at her stomach. It was the signal. The green letters were pulsing right there on her primary screen. After maybe five seconds, they faded, to be replaced by a simple instruction.

PREPARE TO LOAD PROGRAM IN THIRTY SECONDS.

She had to stop herself from sneaking a glance at the security cameras. That was the most common method of giving oneself away. She had to be calm and load the diskette from the Lefthand Path as if it were the most natural thing in the world.

LOOK TO THE SKIES.

She already had the diskette concealed in her desk rack in among a lot of harmless subprograms. She removed it and placed it next to the input drive. No alarms sounded, and nobody seemed to have noticed anything.

LOAD PROGRAM NOW.

She clicked in the diskette and tapped out the code. 771-36971-2458-666. She had memorized the numbers. The screen went blank for about fifteen seconds, and then the meaningless dialog boxes came back. Everything was normal again. For a full half hour she waited for something to happen. She had half expected the whole system to crash the moment the guerrilla program was loaded, but there was not even a flicker, nor did anyone come and place a hand on her shoulder and take her away. She had done what the organization had asked, but she had no more idea of what had been achieved than she had about her work for the deacons.

The next strange occurrence was at lunchtime. The deacons came for Laura. There were four of them. It seemed less as if they were arresting her, than as if they had some very bad news and were taking her somewhere to break it to her. They were formal and awkward. They seemed frightened to touch her. Deacons were never like that when they were making a bust. Laura did not come back. All afternoon, the rest room muttered rumors. It was something to do with Spencer. He was dead. He had been arrested. He had done something terrible and was on the run. There were photographs of him and Laura. Cynthia could not find it in herself to feel pleased.

Things slackened off in the late afternoon. The screens stayed blank for minutes at a time. Cynthia took the chance to call Harry. He could not be located. She had an immediate twinge of unease. The unease carried on all evening and through the night. When she arrived at work the next day, there was a message waiting for her from a PD captain called Parnell. On the tape, he sounded profoundly uncomfortable.

"Harry Carlisle asked me to give you this message. He's hit a difficult patch in an investigation. He's had to go to ground for a few days and he won't be able to call you. He doesn't want you to worry."

He doesn't want me to worry. So pick someone to deliver your messages who can lie effectively. Where the hell are you, Harry Carlisle? He was not the kind to dump her through a third party. Something must have happened to him. She caught herself in the middle of contemplating in anguish all the grisly fates that might have befallen him and reined in her imagination. Lusting after Carlisle might well be her downfall. He was a cop, and he was in the unit working on the Lefthand Path. The other and very logical explanation for his behavior was that he was on to her.

Carlisle

Harry Carlisle found it very pleasant to drift on the black lake. Thoughts slipped through his fingers like sparkling drops of water. He could not focus; he could not form sentences or string ideas together. Nothing made any sense, but that really didn't matter. He was in a place between consciousness and sleep where nothing really mattered. He knew that he was lying on a bed, although even that was, at times, far from certain. There were moments, sometimes moments that seemed to stretch forever, when the clean white sheets stretched into Arctic snowfields or expanses of hot white sand. Always, in the end, though, they melted back into the comforting womb waters of the black lake. He knew that people came and looked at him. He was vaguely aware of the murmur of their voices. He knew that they were talking about him, maybe even talking to him, but he could not make out their words. His most frequent visitor was the figure in white. She came regularly, hovering for long periods at the edge of his vision. The word "nurse" seemed to fit, although sometimes she was a lazily gliding sea bird or a floating cloud in the blue of a summer day.

Every now and then a bubble of danger would burst from the dark depths of his lake. Phrases would crowd in on him. There was. He had to. He needed to. Move. The world outside was.

But the phrases were wrong and they soon went away. The world outside was not, and he did not have to do anything.

Speedboat

Speedboat drank beer, watched TV, and wondered what was going on in New York. He watched a lot of TV to try to stop himself thinking about his own situation, but it did not work. His own situation was so profoundly disastrous that it refused to leave him alone for any more than a few minutes at a time. Even getting drunk, something he only rarely did in the normal world, was not much of a help. He was screwed, and there was no way to avoid facing it.

He had taken the creaking DC15 to Buffalo. He had been so jangled by the clerk who had inspected his documents that he had gone through the process like a zombie. All he had wanted to do at that moment was to get the hell away from La Guardia; boarding the plane had seemed, at the time, to be the line of least resistance. Even when he had reached Buffalo, he had had no formulated plan. He had taken a cab and, on the advice of the driver, checked into a rundown motel not too far from the airport. The manager had taken one look at him and doubled the normal room rate. Later he was to find out that the manager was paid off to ensure that guests like him did not have their documentation looked at too closely.

He had left it for two days before he had called the number the clerk had written on the hundred-dollar bill, the number of the organization that supposedly might get him across the border. As always, he was looking out for a possible setup. Not that his caution seemed to have helped him so far. The woman who had answered had been noncommittal. She had asked him where he was, and when he had mentioned the name of the motel, she had laughed.

"We have a lot of clients who stay there."

She had told him that he would be contacted.

He had made a couple of forays into downtown Buffalo, but mostly he stayed in the motel. He had forgotten how things had become outside of New York City. There were women on the street in white linen caps and long black dresses down to their ankles, and men in baggy black suits and flat, broad-brimmed hats. They looked like the audience at a witch burning. Maybe that was what they did for fun on a Saturday night. He had copped ten greenies in the toilet of a beat-up, bad-neighborhood bar that looked as if it had once been a topless joint, but they had not even made a dent in his nerves. He had also inspected the border, from a healthy distance. It had looked even more formidable in reality, with its minefields, its wire, watchtowers, and steel wall, than it had looked on TV or in magazines. It required no effort to remember that the Herod gunships swinging low over the wide, bulldozed scar of no-man's-land would shoot at anything that moved. It seemed impossible that anyone could cross such a barrier of instant and automated death. When the Canadian border had first been closed and fortified, the White House PR people had tried to sell the country on a name for it: the Line of Truth. But that ridiculous name had refused to stick. A deacon car had come slowly up the road that overlooked the frontier. They appeared to be taking photographs of anyone who paused to look at it for too long. Speedboat had quickly made himself scarce.

Now he watched TV and waited for the phone to ring. He could get beer, booze, and pizza delivered, so he had no reason to leave his room. From all he had seen, he wanted as little as possible to do with the citizens of Buffalo. Apart from anything else, they might decide that he would be a fit subject for a Saturday night barbecue. He certainly did not see himself asking around if anyone knew somebody who would get him into Canada. If smuggling people across the border was an industry in the city, there were no signs of it. From a couple of conversations with the manager and the boy who brought his beer, he started to form the impression that the real underground industry was ripping off fugitives who were waiting in vain. The woman from the hundred-dollar bill had called after six days. The message had not been encouraging.

"The canuks seem to be running some kind of military exercise on their side of the falls. The army has responded by beefing up the defenses here."

"So I wait?"

"These things don't happen overnight."

Speedboat's concern over what was going on in New York was not a matter of either boredom or nostalgia. He was going to run out of money in approximately two weeks, and getting back to the city was his only failsafe option. If he could not get out of the country, Manhattan was about the only place he could survive.

The TV was hardly informative, but, reading between the lines, it was pretty obvious that some strange shit was going down. First there had been the freakout and hoopla over the attempt on Arlen Proverb's life. Speedboat was amazed that it got on TV at all. They had blanked out the entire riot outside the Garden as if it had never happened. After the Proverb incident, the wall went up again with a vengeance. The networks were smothered in a barage of happyvision, puppies, kittens, old folks, miracle cures, and just plain miracles. Jesus was everywhere. He even smote the enemy. There was footage of a large squad of Mexican and Cuban prisoners who had surrendered after a fierce firefight forty miles south of Austin. Speedboat was certain that he had seen that footage before.

The big news was the latest Faithful propaganda fest. The president going to take over Liberty Island for something that was being trumpeted as a Day of National Reconciliation. It was being pitched as a very big deal. There was an item about it, or at least a reference to it, on practically every show. That, in itself, was a definite indication that something was slipping out of sync in the world of the true believers. National reconciliation was quite a mouthful for a regime that never admitted there was the slightest dissent in the ranks. They would not be pissing away some millions on a TV special from right in the heart of New York, a town never loved by Fundamentalist Christians, unless there was a potential major problem and it was centered right there. A thought struck him. Maybe that was why the Canadians were massing troops on the other side of the border. It was not uncommon for the Canadians to know more about what was going on inside the United States than the country's own population knew. Indeed, there were times when it was hard to know less.

Speedboat's beer was all gone. He had a sudden urge to hurl the bottle through the TV screen. He was bored with all the madness. He restrained himself with difficulty. He told himself firmly that it was no time to get stir crazy. Time might move slowly holed up in this cruddy motel, but it did not move half as slowly as time moved in Joshua.

Winters

Winters woke to a deacon's worst nightmare. Dreisler and what looked like half of Internal Affairs was at the foot of his bed. Short of Satan on the bedpost, that was as bad as it got. He had a blinding headache, and his mind was still fuzzy from whatever they had used to sedate him. He struggled to sit up in bed.

Dreisler seemed amused. "Good afternoon, Deacon Winters."

"Good afternoon, sir."

Winters did not know whether it was day or night. The hospital room he was in—if, in fact, it was a hospital—was a windowless white cubical. A neodevotional print of Lazarus being raised from the dead hung in a cheap plastic frame on the wall beside him.

"Where am I?"

Dreisler ignored him. "You've been very careless, Winters."

Physical pain aside, Winters was very frightened. He had heard all the horror stories of what happened to erring deacons who fell into the hands of Dreisler's IA headhunters.

"Careless?" he asked.

"It's one thing to go out and engage in illegal torture and executions. In some parts of the service, they look on that kind of behavior as the mark of a healthy enthusiasm on the part of an up-and-coming deacon. To lose your whole team, however, on your very first mission is just plain careless."

"I . . ."

Dreisler sat down on the bed, fastidiously adjusting the knife-edge creases in his pants. There was something almost friendly in the move, a vague suggestion of the desire to confide. "You'd probably like to talk to me."

"I don't know. I'm confused."

"Of course you're confused. You're also in a bit of a double bind. You'd like to tell me all about what happened, but you're well aware that that would violate your mortal oath to the Secret Order of Holy Magicians. I have this problem, Winters. My reputation tends to precede me, and people seem to be very anxious, as a rule, to tell me things. In your case, though, you also have to consider the reputation of the Magicians. They can get very creative with oathbreakers."

"I wasn't—"

"No, I know you weren't. It was Spencer who was in charge. He should have made sure that the building was secure. Unfortunately, Spencer's dead, as are all the others."

Winters knew that he would blurt out everything in the end. What would happen to him then?

"It was the Lefthand Path," he said.

"How do you know that?"

"The one who hit me with the gun butt, he yelled it out. "Lefthand Path, mother—" He could not say it in front of Dreisler.

Dreisler laughed. "You only have his word for it."

"What are you going to do with me?"

Dreisler stood up. "Normally there would be disciplinary action in a case like this. Fortunately these are troubled times, and I need all the men I can trust. I can't spare you."

Winters was surprised. "You trust me?"

"Yes, Winters, I trust you."

Winters could not read his expression.

"In fact, I trust you so much that I need you to be in a key position on the Day of National Reconciliation. It's possible that the heretics will use the occasion to cause trouble."

"What position will that be?"

Dreisler shook his head. "Get your head fixed first. You have a skull fracture. You'll get your orders when you're up on your feet again."

"Thank you, sir."

Dreisler threw his coat over his shoulders. "Don't thank me yet, boy. You may not like these orders."

He walked around the bed, then hesitated as if he had just remembered something.

"By the way, do you have any idea what happened to Carlisle?"

Winters shook his head. The motion hurt. "I didn't see him after the attack started, and then I was out cold."

Dreisler nodded. "It doesn't matter."

Carlisle

The black lake was gone. There was spring sunlight streaming in through a window that was secured by three serviceable steel bars. The drugs had worn off, leaving Harry Carlisle with a queasy hunger in his stomach and a gritty feeling under his eyelids. The old-fashioned sash window was open about five inches at the bottom, and a breeze was blowing in. That felt good. Each deep breath helped clear the narcotic residue from his brain. Goddamn, but if there was ever a time that he needed his brain functioning to the max, it was right then. Where the hell was he? And, even more important, what was his status? The last time he had looked, he had been dead meat. Then, in what had seemed to be the nick of time, a bunch of guys, shooting off guns and yelling that they were the Lefthand Path, had rushed in and rescued him. Why they had rescued him was another matter. In the best of all possible worlds, they would have saved him simply because he was an unfortunate victim of deacon oppression. Unfortunately, it was not the best of all possible worlds, and he feared that his saviors, whoever they were, also had a use for him. He could only pray that it would not be as a mutilated corpse.

He took stock of his situation. He was lying on a metal-framed, hospital-style bed. It had been set up in the corner of a large institutional room. There were three barred windows, dirty green walls, and a wide expanse of dusty floor. Except for the one near his bed, the half-dozen light fittings had no bulbs. They came with the kind of cheap metal shades that were used in schools and government offices. He decided to get out of bed and explore a little more. Someone had dressed him in a white cotton hospital smock. He stood a little gingerly but experienced no difficulty. His legs felt weak, but they were able to support him, and he did not suddenly become nauseous or dizzy. So far, so good.

He recognized nothing in the view from the window; all he could see was the dirty wall of a factory building across a vacant lot. He could have been in any industrial neighborhood, anywhere. As far as he could estimate, he was on the third or fourth floor. The door at the far end of the room proved to be locked, as he had expected. A quick scan turned up no cameras, sensors, or microphones. Foiled for the moment, he went back and sat on the bed.

Half an hour later, when he was starting to wonder if someone was trying to bore him to death, he heard the sound of footsteps outside the door, followed immediately by the beeping of the lock. Carlisle tensed. Now what?

It turned out to be a nurse—the figure in white from his

drugged haze. She wore a starched white uniform in the demure style of the times and had a scrubbed, no-nonsense face. She carried a tray containing scrambled eggs, toast, and tea.

"So we're up and around, are we?"

Carlisle nodded. "So it would seem."

She put the tray down on the bed.

"You're probably feeling a little queasy, so eat this. It'll help." She straightened up again. "I know you must have a hundred questions, but I'm not authorized to answer any of them. You're going to have to wait until someone more important comes to see you."

"There is maybe one thing."

"What's that?" She looked a little impatient. She clearly had not been hired for her bedside manner.

"It's kind of boring sitting here. Could I get a newspaper or magazine or something?"

The nurse looked at him coldly. "Perhaps you'd like a TV brought in?"

"I just asked."

She relented a little. "I'll see what I can do."

"Also . . ."

"What?"

"Where do I go to the bathroom?"

"Look under the bed."

The magazine or newspaper did not appear, and Carlisle spent a long time looking out of the window. A pigeon had attempted to land on the windowsill, but flew off in a panic when it saw him. Eventually there were more footsteps beyond the door and another sequence of beeps. He turned, expecting to see the nurse—carrying, he hoped, a copy of *People* or *Timeweek*—and instead saw something in the doorway that made him wonder if he was having a drug flashback.

"What the hell?"

Matthew Dreisler smiled like the Devil himself. "Surprised to see me?"

"You're not quite what I expected."

"Didn't you know that I'm everywhere?"

Carlisle scowled. Obviously the game was continuing. "All hearing and all seeing?"

"You're getting the idea."

"I suppose you run the Lefthand Path, too?"

"In a manner of speaking, I do."

Carlisle slowly nodded. "Ooookay."

Dreisler stood smiling. Carlisle sat on the bed feeling like a very helpless rat in a very complex maze. He could easily believe that Dreisler was behind everything that had happened to him. It was some twisted behavioral experiment that was pushing him through each horrible stage of some monstrous Kafka-esque nightmare.

"I expect you'd like to know what's going on."

The words were said with such bright lack of concern that Carlisle suddenly wanted to start screaming. Okay, I give up. You've driven me mad. Unfortunately, they had not. He could still keep himself under control. With an effort, he formed his face into an expression of caution.

"Are you going to tell me?"

"That's exactly why I'm here."

The story was nothing short of incredible. Harry Carlisle had heard some incredible stories in his time, but this one was head and shoulders above the rest.

"I'm organizing a little revolution."

"You are? When?"

Dreisler walked slowly over to the window. He was using the large empty space almost as a set, going for the full dramatic effect. He was the debonair secret policeman, master of intrigue, Carlisle was the bleary political prisoner. The bare, dusty room was their enclosed universe, an area of nothing after the claustrophobic horror of the Magicians and their factory.

"If everything goes according to plan, it will come to fruition on Larry Faithful's Day of National Reconciliation."

"That's only slightly over two weeks away."

"Less actually. You've been out for five days."

That was another shock. "I have?"

"We thought it was best."

Dreisler turned and looked out of the window. Carlisle sat on the bed in his hospital smock, head bowed, watching him. What did Dreisler think he was? Every part of his image was so carefully contrived, the fashion-plate clothes, the fop's gestures and bantering manner, the black glasses, the overlong blond hair, and the leather coat over the shoulders. He was like a twentieth-century movie star. No, that was not quite right—he was more like one of the old grand-manner rock stars. Like them, he seemed to live by illusions—and the bulk of his illusions came from the darkside.

"Aren't you biting off rather a mouthful, running your own revolution?"

"It's a dirty job, but somebody has to do it."

"Are you serious about this?"

Dreisler turned and faced Carlisle. "I'm deadly serious, Harry."

It only took one look at his face to convince Harry Carlisle that Dreisler meant every word he was saying.

"In actual fact, the preparations have been going on for some time. This isn't some half-assed uprising, Harry. This is the real thing, the full-scale overthrow of the theocracy." Dreisler made a scything gesture with a flattened hand. "The theocracy is not functioning, and it has to go. I like power, Harry, and power can become very limited in a bankrupt and backward country."

"Just like that?"

"The times they are a-changin'."

"You're very optimistic."

"I've done my work very well."

"What are these preparations?"

"Mainly computer viruses."

"Viruses?"

"When, as under this administration, you have your computers confused with the Almighty, you tend to become very dependent on them. You also believe everything that they tell you. Why not? The theocrat treats his computer monitor like God's own porthole." Dreisler was warming to his subject. "Over the last six months, I've had various shaped viruses loaded into the computers of all branches of the administration. Some were getgo active and have been doing deep data corruption; others are dormant, waiting for either a binary or a situational trigger. There are already whole sections of the deacons operating according to total fantasy data."

Carlisle did not think that Dreisler was insane, but he still did not know what to think of the man. He was not too sure about himself, either. Despite all his doubts, Harry Carlisle was being drawn into Dreisler's mad tale of conspiracy.

"You designed these viruses?"

Dreisler laughed and shook his head. "No, of course not. I never do anything that specific. I'm a Renaissance man."

"Machiavelli?"

"Exactly. I'm a master of the overview."

"So who wrote the viruses?"

"Most came from the Canadians; some were Japanese."

In a sentence, the conspiracy fantasy had become high treason.

"You're dealing with the Canadians?"

"Of course I'm dealing with the Canadians. We can't off the Fundamentalists without Canadian help."

"Do you know what you're doing?"

"My dear boy, on the Day of National Reconciliation, Canadian troops will cross the border at a dozen different points, immediately after I've arrested Larry Faithful."

"You've sold us out to the canuks?"

Harry had no more doubts that Dreisler was telling him the absolute truth. The most powerful deacon on the Eastern Seaboard was plotting a coup with the help of the Canadian government. The real question was why he felt the need to tell all to a mere police lieutenant. Carlisle was not sure he wanted to know the answer.

"Omelets and eggs, Harry. It can't be done without them. It's really too late for a display of irrational patriotism."

Carlisle shook his head. "I don't know about any of this. How can you be talking to the Canadians?"

"I've also been talking to the Mexicans and the British. Don't underestimate me. Policing the deacons and also what's left of the FBI/CIA has given me the chance to build what may be the biggest personal intelligence network in the world. You have to remember that I've got agents out in the field who don't have a clue who they're really working for. Once you reach that level, it's possible to talk to anyone about anything."

"What are you talking to the Mexicans about? You giving them the rest of Texas?"

"You're going to have to get over this attitude problem, Harry. I'd always believed that you were a pragmatist. For your information, the Mexicans are going to do nothing. They've agreed to hold their position until the coup has established itself."

"And you trust them?"

Dreisler shook his head. "Of course I don't trust them, but I think we have a working understanding."

Carlisle cradled his head in his hands. "I don't know about any of this."

"Believe me, Harry. This is going to work."

Harry Carlisle needed space to digest some of Dreisler's tale. "Let me get this straight. You're telling me that you've used your position as head of the deacon IA to thoroughly contaminate the government computer system. In two Sundays from now, total chaos is going to break out, and you're going to arrest Larry Faithful, Canadian tanks are going to come steaming over the border, and we're all going to live happily ever after. Is that correct?''

''Crude, but those are the basics. There are a number of other details, but that's the general intention.''

''Are you crazy?''

Dreisler smiled blandly. ''Never felt better in my life.''

''This just isn't possible. One man, no matter who he is, can't topple a government.''

''I have associates. Look at it more as the generals' plot against Hitler.''

''They ended up hanging from piano wire.''

''But we're not going to. You have to remember that none of this would be possible if the present government wasn't as corrupt, inefficient, and out of touch with reality as it is.''

''I don't know.''

'I'm not trying to convince you, Harry. I'm just telling you what is.''

''So what are these other details?''

''Over the years, we've infiltrated a large number of subversive and heretic groups. Some we've busted, but others we've used—fed them disinformation, used them for setups, kind of like the FBI and the old Communist Party. They'll be causing their own bits of trouble on the day. More confusion.''

''And the Lefthand Path? Are they part of this?''

''Heavens, no. They're much more sophisticated than that. I'm very proud of the Lefthand Path. It really is my own creation. The truth is that the Lefthand Path doesn't actually exist. That's why they were so hard to catch. We had a few fanatics in a classic cell structure to take a fall if ever we needed one, but as for the rest, it was a bunch of pros from the Canadian Secret Service. Mostly expatriate Americans.''

''I spent fourteen months chasing your creation.''

''We watched you. That's how I discovered that you were good. By the way, you're sleeping with one.''

Carlisle was confused. ''Sleeping with one what?''

''A pro from the Canadian Secret Service. Cynthia Kline is a Canadian plant. She's thinks she's doing deep cover for the Lefthand Path.''

Carlisle was up from the bed and on his feet. "Cynthia?"

"Yes, Cynthia. But don't worry. It's not part of the plot. She just took a liking to you."

Carlisle sat down again. "Christ."

"She's also not doing anything particularly dangerous."

"Christ."

Dreisler gave him time to digest that piece of news. He had been sleeping with a woman who was part of what he had thought of as the enemy. Now he did not know who the enemy was or, by the same token, who his friends were.

"What is this, Dreisler? Some kind of psych workout? Tear me down and then rebuild me?"

"If you want to think of it that way."

"But Cynthia . . ."

"Will you forget about Cynthia Kline? You're not a teenager."

Carlisle suddenly became angry. "Okay, let's look at this lunacy from another direction. How in hell do you expect to arrest Faithful? He's always surrounded by a whole platoon of bodyguards."

"Actually it's comparatively simple. You may have noticed that over the last few weeks, I've arrested a number of senior deacons pending investigation. Over the next week or so, a lot more will be brought in. It's very easy once you start. Nudge one and the rest go down like dominoes. They're all locked into their petty conspiracies. By the time he sets foot on Liberty Island, the deacon chain of command will have been broken into its individual links. Any group that I don't command directly will have been neutralized by putting an idiot in charge. God knows there's no shortage of them. When Faithful arrives for the ceremony, his primary protection will be my people. He'll have only a handful of his regular guards. There will also be military present, but they won't interfere. Their colonel and I have an understanding that centers around some grossly compromising tapes."

The whole thing was starting to sound more and more plausible. Carlisle hated to admit it, but it just might work.

"Okay, so let's say, for the sake of argument, that you've got Faithful under lock and key. What happens then? You become president-for-life or something?"

Dreisler looked genuinely shocked. "You really have misread me. I wouldn't dream of becoming president or anything like it.

I don't want to be on television all the time. I'm happy to remain in the shadows, just as I am now.''

"The power behind the throne."

"What else?"

"And who'll get the throne?"

"Arlen Proverb will be offered an interim presidency. He'd head a committee of national reconstruction.''

So that was the deal between Dreisler and Proverb.

'I thought you wanted to off the theocracy.''

"It'll be a period of transition.''

"And at the end of that?''

"Who knows? It's still very much a matter of playing it by ear. We'll certainly restore parts of the Constitution. Maybe even hold limited elections.''

"Don't go hog wild.''

"Don't worry, I won't.''

"I take it that the only reason you're baring your soul to me is that you have some role planned for me in all this,'' Carlisle said, wishing he were wearing something more suitable to historic conspiracy than a hospital smock.

"It is rather obvious, isn't it?''

"And I have little choice about whether I accept it or not.''

"That should also be self-evident.''

Carlisle sighed. "So what's the role?''

Dreisler chuckled. "I want you to walk point for me.''

"What's that supposed to mean?''

"I estimate that there's up to a hundred men in the PD who'd follow you without question.''

Carlisle shrugged. "Maybe.''

"I want you to assemble a team that, on the day, can take control of the Astor Place complex. That's where we'll be bringing Faithful.''

"My bosses might have something to say about that, from Parnell all the way up to the commissioner.''

"I think you'll find you'll have no trouble from that direction.''

ELEVEN

Mansard

THE DAY OF NATIONAL RECONCILIATION ARRIVED IN A shroud of yellow, pollution-heavy, morning fog. The Statue of Liberty stood aloof and silent, torch high, head and shoulders above the ground mist that obscured the island and hid the water clear out to where the ocean started. The fog brought with it an intense Sunday-morning silence that was broken only by the moaning of the horns on the Staten Island ferry and the desolate cry of seabirds above the hypnotic lapping of the waves. There was no rumble of traffic and no sound of human voices. In the mist, time seemed to be suspended, and it was possible to imagine sea-change ghosts lingering in ancient mariner loneliness.

Charlie Mansard shivered. He was up early. He had spent the night on the yacht that they had rented as a location headquarters for the production, but he had slept very little—partly because of the motion, and partly because he had Lynette with him, but mainly because of the preshow nerves that were now building to their final peak. Charlie sat in the welldeck behind the wheelhouse, wrapped in a yellow slicker and nursing a cup of hot, black coffee and a large brandy. Lynette, wearing a thick, navy-blue fisherman's sweater thrown on over her skimpy black bikini, was up by the bow, leaning on the rail and staring into the mist.

"It's like the whole city just went away."

Mansard grunted. "I wish to hell it would."

Lynette grinned. "And leave you all alone to play with your toys? Come on, Charlie, you know you love an audience."

Charlie scowled. "Sure, I love them to death."

"Are you going to behave like a bastard right up until show-time?"

"Probably."

"You want to go back to bed?"

Somewhere in the mist there was the slap of a helicopter. Mansard looked up. "It's too late now."

"That's not what you said last night."

Despite himself, Mansard grinned. "Last night was okay, wasn't it?"

"You always do get it up the night before a production."

By midday, the fog had thinned out to a dirty gray haze. On Liberty Island, the last preparations were in full swing. Cargo helicopters came and went in constant rotation, and gunships circled overhead. TV crews laid cable and positioned cameras while deacons, some with bomb sniffers, prowled the area. Caterers had started laying out the aftershow buffet for the president and his guests. The musicians were about to begin the sound check, and the two-hundred-piece live choir would start being ferried in by chopper. The whole process was being conducted under the hard, watchful eyes of soldiers toting M-25s and demanding passes from everyone who moved.

Charlie Mansard was greatly relieved that his part of the event was off the island and onto the water. The projector banks were installed on the four big bridging rafts, each of which was quite capable of carrying a tank. They were moored some two hundred yards out from Liberty Island, bobbing on a gentle swell as the riggers crawled over them making last-minute connections. The tugs that were going to tow the rafts to the starting point would arrive at two-thirty. In the hours between dawn and noon, the yacht had been transformed from Mansard's love nest to his flagship. The decks were full of his people, and there was a constant shuttle of small boats between it and the rafts.

Compared to the show they had put on inside the Garden for Arlen Proverb, the four skywalkers that would go up the Hudson were fairly simple in terms of hands-on control. They were big, but they were in no way as complex as, for instance, the red mist and multiple apparitions that had been done for Proverb. Like the original Four Horsemen, the new figures were preprogrammed and, once started, pretty much ran themselves.

Human intervention would be necessary only in the case of serious malfunction. That took a major weight off the teams who normally ran the manual and DNI controls, and the atmosphere on the boat was close to that of a party. Champagne was being served, and a number of the men had brought their girlfriends. Mansard had taken a very liberal attitude toward the project's government expense account. Nobody had complained about the receipts he was turning in by the truckload, so he just went on spending. "We may never pass this way again, so let's get as much as we can," he said.

Mansard had managed to exclude from the boat anyone who was not part of his own team. There were no military personnel and no one from the White House. That arrangement did even more than the champagne to enhance the sense of it being a day out. There was even some barely covert drug use. By the early afternoon, it was warm enough to sunbathe. Nobody was too particular about the size and modesty of their swimwear, and at one point a deacon gunship had hovered overhead, complaining by radio about the naked and near-naked people on the deck of the yacht. Mansard had instucted the communications operator to ignore it.

"What are they going to do? Blow us out of the water? They can't deprive Faithful of his show."

At around two-fifteen, Jimmy Gadd, who had not joined in the party but remained on the raft to supervise the checks and last-minute adjustments, called over.

"We've got the tugs on the radar. You should be able to see them in a couple of minutes."

Mansard moved to the rail and peered into the haze. He could not see the tugs, but it was good to know they were out there and on time. He turned his attention to the rafts. There was very little movement. Things were practically ready. The party noise behind him was forgotten. As soon as the sun went down, his crowning creation would blaze into life. He slowly rubbed his hands together.

"Just you wait, New York. Just wait until dark."

Carlisle stepped out of the car and looked around. The fog still clung between the buildings. It was so heavy and sluggish that he did not want to think about what it was made of. Reeves and Donahue were waiting for him, but he hesitated before walking into the building. Whatever happened, this was the last day. When he walked out again, the world would be different— if, indeed, he walked out at all. By the end of that day he could well be dead or a prisoner in the subbasement. There might be a new regime, or he could end up in the middle of some uniquely weird product of Dreisler's warped imagination.

A gunship rattled overhead and Carlisle looked up, watching until it vanished beyond the skyline to the west. Vultures gathering? During his drive down to Astor Place, the city had looked as if it were in a state of siege. The streets were empty, even for Sunday morning. It was as if the people of New York, at least, put no trust in Larry Faithful's Day of National Reconciliation and its promise of sweetness and light. New Yorkers expected trouble, and they could not have been reassured by the massive show of official strength. NYPD, deacons, and the army were all out in force. Pharaohs and Patton vehicles rumbled through the echoing streets. Police cruisers and the deacons' Continentals sped across intersections with their sirens screaming, ignoring the stop lights. Large knots of riot police were gathered at strategic points, like Columbus Circle and Herald and Union Squares. With so much manpower on the streets, only a skeleton crew could have been left at Astor Place.

Harry Carlisle squared his shoulders and walked into the main entrance of the CCC complex. Reeves and Donahue fell into step beside him. At least the day would see the end of that particular nonsense. For the last week, they had been guarding him as if he were a celebrity or a politician. As the three of them walked in, Reeves carefully scanned the interior of the entrance hall. There were only the routine guards and receptionists.

"So this is the day?"

Carlisle nodded. "That's what they told me."

"What do you expect to happen?"

"Anything could happen. Just remember one thing: Be ready to duck. Don't get so far into anything that you won't be able to duck back out again."

"We'll be looking to you."

"That's the part I love."

Carlisle had been held incommunicado by Dreisler for another four days, supposedly for his own protection, but Harry
Carlisle had given up trying to guess what Dreisler was up to.
On the fifth day he had made a carefully choreographed return
to work. From that point on, he had been guarded night and day
in case the deacons took another crack at him. He had even been
stashed in an Upper West Side apartment. He thought it unlikely
that the Magicians would try again so quickly after their last
failure, but it seemed as if not much was working according to
logic anymore.

The situation between Carlisle and the deacons was a strange
standoff. Probably every deacon in the city knew unofficially
about the attempt to disappear him and the resulting deaths of
Spencer and the others. Officially, however, the incident had
never happened. Winters, the only survivor, could not file any
kind of report without violating the Magicians' damn-fool blood
oaths. Deacons shot him murderous looks when they passed him
in the corridors of justice, but looks could not kill. They were
enough, though, to make him glad of his bodyguard and to
ensure that he spent most of his time in parts of the building that
were solid PD turf.

When Carlisle, Reeves, and Donahue reached Carlisle's office, the two detectives faced their lieutenant, standing in front
of his desk like men who wanted answers. For their own protection, he had told them nothing about Dreisler's plans. All
they knew was that they were to assemble a clandestine force of
trusted PD men and have them at Astor Place on that particular
Sunday afternoon.

Before they could say anything, Carlisle held up a hand. "All
in good time."

He had been carrying a brand-new, gray Samsonite brief-
case. He placed it on the desk, keyed in the lock combination,
and opened it. The case had an up-to-date and fully comprehensive set of bugblockers built into it. When Reeves and Donahue
saw it, their eyebrows shot up. He touched all of a row of six
red buttons. A galaxy of leds came on as all the blocking systems
activated. If the deacons had his office bugged, as they undoubtedly did, they would no longer be able to hear a thing. They
would know that he was using some kind of jamming device,
but their only real option was to come down and bust into his

office. He was counting on the fact that they would be too busy with Day of National Reconciliation business to bother.

Reeves and Donahue exchanged glances, as if each was waiting for the other to start. Finally Reeves took the initiative.

"So what's the story, Lieutenant?"

"You mean, if I ask you to put a small secret army together for me, you want to know why?" Carlisle asked, sitting down. The levity was a crock—but he did not want to communicate his fear to the others. He was scared enough for all three of them.

Reeves shrugged. "It's human nature."

"So, do I have my army?"

Donahue nodded. "They're coming, just like you said, one at a time and in small groups. They'll all be in the building and ready for orders by three."

The two detectives waited. Carlisle leaned forward.

"Okay, here's the story. We've received information that a group of disgruntled, middle-echelon deacons is going to use today's extravaganza as cover to stage a coup."

Carlisle did not like lying to his men, but it was the only way to protect them. If everything came unraveled and they were all arrested, or if Dreisler pulled something unexpected, they would at least be able to say that they were only following orders. There was one other consideration. He may have reluctantly thrown in his lot with Dreisler, but he was in no position to explain the complex conspiracy to anyone else. He did not know it all himself. He really was walking point.

"They are going to use the expected disturbances after today's telecast as an excuse to arrest Faithful and declare a deacon junta. Only the PD, a handful of deacons, and some sections of the military can stop the deacons from seizing power."

"Where do we figure in all this?"

"If the deacons have control of this complex, they essentially control the city. We have to stop that. Now, it's in our favor that there's hardly anyone on duty in the building. On a prearranged signal, we will seal the entrances, take over the communication center, and arrest any deacons who want to make trouble. We have one other advantage in this apart from the fact that almost everybody is on the street. You may have noticed that Dreisler's people have arrested a large number of senior deacons in the last few weeks. Their chain of command is screwed, and the ones who are left will be without too much high-level direction.''

"Is Dreisler involved in all this?"

Carlisle shook his head. "We have to assume that Dreisler's on our side."

The two detectives looked dubious. "You're not telling us everything."

Carlisle looked down at his hands. "No, I'm not. I don't know everything. I couldn't tell you if I wanted to."

Donahue was thoughtful. "Where does the brass stand in all this?"

Carlisle paused before answering. "They'll be one hundred percent if everything comes up roses. If it doesn't, it'll almost certainly be every man for himself."

That was actually very close to the truth. Even before Dreisler had let him go, he had been permitted to talk to Parnell. During a very stilted conversation, Parnell had intimated that the higher-ups in the PD knew of Dreisler's plan and would do nothing to stop or hinder them. They would throw in with his Committee of National Reconstruction if he was successful, but if he failed, they would put so much distance between him and themselves that it would seem as if he had the plague.

Reeves and Donahue looked at each other.

"So it's all down to us?" Reeves said. "If we win, we're heroes, and if we lose, we're dogmeat."

Carlisle nodded. "Dogmeat would look good in comparison." He leaned back in his chair. "You can bail out now."

There was a long silence. In the end, it was Reeves who again spoke for both of them. "What the hell, we'll go for it. If something isn't done about the deacons, they'll get us all soon enough."

Carlisle placed four diskettes on the desk. "These are the detailed orders for the individual squad leaders. On a more general level there are three things to remember. Make sure that the roof helipad is kept open and is under our control. That's vital. You should ignore the computers. There will be all manner of weird stuff coming up. The whole system will be virused to hell by the end of today. Don't trust the computers, and don't trust anyone you don't know."

"What levels of force do we use?" Reeves asked.

Carlisle looked him straight in the eye. "Whatever it takes."

Both Reeves and Donahue nodded. "Is that all?"

"I wish I had some encouraging speech to make. I don't. All I can tell you is that, one way or the other, it will all be over in a matter of hours. I pray that things will be better."

The two men seemed to sense his doubts. "Don't worry, Lieutenant, we're with you."

After they left, he sat for a long time in silence. Somewhere over the last few days he had lost some kind of innocence—or maybe it was his integrity. The last of it had finally banished during the conversation with Reeves and Donahue. He had deceived his own men, and he could no longer shelter behind the spotless shield of the honest cop. He was a conspirator just like the rest of them. Maybe not as tainted as Dreisler, but it was only a matter of degree.

He sighed and picked up the phone.

"Code 8971A Dragonfly," he said.

It had started.

Winters

Winters had never felt so alone. All his life he had been part of a team—in school, at college, and now in the service. There had always been people around him, comradeship and shared ambition. Since he had survived the attack of the Lefthand Path, he had become an outcast. Nobody spoke to him except in the course of duty, and his duties had dwindled to routine data shuffling. There was no point in telling the others that it was not his fault that he had been knocked unconscious instead of killed outright. They already knew that it was only his vows to the Magicians that kept him from reporting the incident, and they suspected that Carlisle was associated with the terrorists, but none of that seemed to make any difference. He had returned neither victorious nor on his shield. That was enough to make him a pariah. His recent hopes, encouraged by his summons to the Magicians and the implication that he was going to be asked to join their numbers, had been cruelly dashed. He could not see how he would ever recover from the disgrace. He had thought about trying to redeem himself by killing Carlisle, but the lieutenant seemed to be constantly guarded, ever since his mysterious return.

The only individual who showed any sign of being aware of Winters's situation was Senior Deacon Dreisler, and even he had

not come through with the orders that he had talked about in the
hospital. All he had heard from Dreisler was a cryptic message
that he should be present at the Astor Place complex that Sunday
and ready for any orders. Now it was Sunday, and he sat at his
workstation, staring at a blank screen and waiting for a silent
phone to ring. It occurred to him that it was probably just as
well that he was not publicly linked with Dreisler. The senior
deacon might well be the kiss of death to any plans Winters may
have had to reinstate himself with his comrades. The purges that
Dreisler had been conducting had made him the most feared and
hated man in the service. Anyone connected with him and his
department was looked on as an informer and a traitor.

The junior deacons' squad room was all but deserted. Almost
everybody was on the streets. A few deacons came and went,
but they had the air of men passing through on more important
business. There were no greetings or reports of what was going
on outside. They treated him as if he were invisible. At one
point, Thomas had come in, looking as if he were about to speak;
but then his face had stiffened and he walked out without a word.

The hours dragged by. One o'clock, two o'clock. His monitors
remained strangely blank. He ran a function check, which told
him that everything was working normally. There was just no
data being fed in. Was there some sort of security blanket that
no one had bothered to tell him about? When, at about three-
thirty, the primary screen suddenly flashed into life, he almost
started in his seat. There were just two words on the screen.

EMERGENCY OVERRIDE.

Winters leaned forward eagerly. The words remained on the
screen for thirty seconds, and then they were replaced by a
specific instruction.

ACTIVATE SCRAMBLER CODE 42.

He keyed in the code. The screen disintegrated into colored
moiré patterns for about fifteen seconds and then it cleared.

REPORT IMMEDIATELY TO THE BASEMENT ARMORY.

Winters's heart leapt. They did have a job for him after all.
Perhaps he was not a total outcast. He was on his feet, buttoning
his jacket.

As he was waiting for the elevator, five men in windbreakers and blue jeans turned into the corridor. They had machine pistols slung over their shoulders and they looked like PD detectives. What the hell were armed cops doing up here?

One of them called out to him. "Hey, you! Where do you think you're going?"

Winters looked around angrily. Who did they think they were? "Who wants to know?"

At that moment, the elevator door slid open. The PD men, if that was indeed what they were, quickened their pace. He swiftly stepped into the elevator car and thumbed the "door close" button. The doors hissed shut and began to descend.

When he arrived at the armory, there were some twenty junior deacons assembled there, surly and more than a little confused. Winters received a few hostile glances, but nobody said anything. Thomas appeared to have taken charge.

"I've called you all down here because there seem to be some strange things going on in this building."

There were murmurs of agreement.

"Something is disrupting internal communication, and a number of channels to the outside are not responding. In addition to that, some of the surveillance cameras are down, but the ones that are left are showing armed groups of PD detectives patrolling the building, and there's no record of any authorization for this. Being of a curious disposition, I ran a check on the office of our friend Lieutenant Carlisle."

The name was greeted with catcalls.

"There's a bugscrambler being used down there."

The catcalls turned to angry muttering.

Thomas ignored the noise. "Accordingly, I suggest that we draw heavy weapons, divide into small groups, and conduct a systematic reconnaisance of the building."

A deacon called Erhardt raised his hand. "What do we do if we come across one of these groups of PD?"

"We order them to return to their own areas pending a full investigation."

"And if they refuse?"

"That's why we're drawing heavy weapons."

Mansard

"Will you look at that? It's like something out of an old news-tape of Vietnam or Honduras. They ought to be playing 'Ride of the Valkyries.' "

The presidential aerocade was coming down the river, led by a pair of King David light attack helicopters, flicking from side to side across the width of the Hudson, close to the water, like giant mosquitoes. Behind them there were four old, solid Hueys, running straight ahead, line abreast. The president's big Nehemiah—*Air Force Four*—came next, flanked by a pair of Herod gunships. Four more Hueys brought up the rear. The official formation was also surrounded and followed by a dozen or more police helicopters and news choppers, which stood off at a respectful distance. The slap of their massed rotors was like the low rumble of distant thunder.

"Behold, the Lord cometh."

"Old Larry sure does like to make an entrance."

Charlie Mansard looked at his watch. It was four fifty-five. "Old Larry's ten minutes late."

Mansard was very conscious of time. The show was due to start at six. There was an hour of intro filler, the choir, the massed flagwavers and baton twirlers, the dancers, and the celebrity walk-ons. Faithful himself went on at seven. He would do an hour, and at exactly seven fifty, just as he was running up to the final climax, Mansard's people would light up the four skywalkers, and the tugs would slowly move the barges upriver.

"Let's hope they haven't started screwing up the schedule."

Carlisle

Carlisle looked from the phone to the digital clock on his desk. It was two minutes before four. He had been doing the same thing for the last thirteen minutes. The signal should have come already. There was a icy liquid feeling in his stomach, and his shoulder muscles were threatening to cramp with tension. Was the whole thing going bad before it had even started? He was all too well aware that he did not stand a chance if Dreisler failed. He was doing his best to keep his imagination tamped down. The reverb helmet was all too vivid and recent in his memory.

"Come on, damn it."

The phone warbled, and he grabbed for it like a starving man grabbing for a crust. "Carlisle."

There was a synthivoice at the other end, only barely cutting through the hiss created by multiple scrambling. "The Vulture has landed."

That was it. The signal was clear. Larry Faithful was down on Liberty Island. The Dreisler plot was going ahead, and from that moment on there was absolutely no turning back. It was win—or lose everything. He broke the connection and keyed in a fresh code. The phone on the other end rang only once.

"Reeves." The detective sounded tense. He clearly had a good idea how far out on a limb they were, even if he did not know the real reasons.

"It's me, Carlisle. I just received the signal that I've been waiting for. It's time to go. Are you still in a position to seal all the entrances to the building?"

"Shield controls are right in front of me."

"So seal us in."

Still cradling the phone under his chin, Carlisle tapped a code into his computer. An image of the exterior of the main entrance came up on the primary screen while the smaller ones showed split screens of the other entrances. The two deacon guards outside the main doors spun around in amazement as the heavy steel shutters started to roll down. One of them drew his pistol. Carlisle wondered what the man intended to do. The shutters could stop a rocket attack. Neither of the men seemed to have the presence of mind to duck back inside before the shutters closed completely.

"Damn fools," Carlisle grunted.

Reeves was back on the line. "The shop's shut, Lieutenant."

"Okay. So send the one squad up to the roof and the other to the communications center. We need to secure them both as quickly as possible."

"Where will you be?"

"I'm coming down to communications with you. Meet me at the elevators."

Kline

It was four o'clock—time for Cynthia to load the final stage of the program. After that, her work would be done. Her instructions were to leave the building as quickly as possible and go to the Eastside Heliport where she would be contacted and, presumably, taken either to a safe house or out of the country altogether. She fed in the diskette. The primary screen flickered and a message appeared.

THIS PROGRAM HAS TO BE FED INTO THE MAIN ACCESS GRID IN SECTION C70. GO THERE IMMEDIATELY.
THE SURVEILLANCE CAMERAS ARE DOWN SO YOU WILL NOT BE DETECTED.

She thought about the gun in her handbag. Nobody had told her to come armed, but there had been such a strange atmosphere around the CCC complex for the last few days that she had decided to bring a token of personal insurance. She had felt a little trepidation about bringing the little palm gun through the weapon detectors in the lobby, but if anything was going to get past, it was the lightweight, plastic Browning. If she had really reached the end of her assignment, she had to be extremely careful. Since she had been kept so much in the dark, she had no way of telling what might be coming to a head in some other part of the operation. There was also the chance that one of her superiors had decided that she was expendable. It had happened before and would certainly happen again. When she had first volunteered for service in the United States, she had known that there was a chance she might be killed. If nothing else, the suicide cap in one of her back molars was a constant reminder. She did not intend to go without a struggle, however. As far as she was concerned, there were not many fates worse than death, and passive acceptance was a betrayal of the principles for which she was fighting.

She stood up and slipped the diskette into her pocket. There was only one other person in the section: Toni, who had also pulled duty for that crucial Sunday, was watching soap opera reruns on her primary screen. Most of the girls had wangled invitations to see the president. A number had also been transferred out to God knew where after their deacon boyfriends had been arrested by Internal Affairs. Cynthia concealed the Browning in the palm of her hand. In training camp, they had called it the princess pistol.

"I'm going to the little girls' room," she announced.

Toni did not even bother to look up from *Tender Time*. Cynthia left the work area and hurried down the corridor in the direction of the seventy section where the unfiltered landline link to Virginia Beach was housed. She wondered if Harry Carlisle was in the building. He had been acting so strange since he had come back from his week-long disappearance. They had talked on the phone, but he had been so tense and distant that she had become half convinced that he knew what she was.

She reached the entrance to C70. The empty corridors were very spooky. The complex was sinister enough when the corridors were bustling with the business of God and justice. Now, without the hurrying people, an aura of dread pervaded, as if something evil and threatening was lurking around every brightly lit corner.

C70 was a closed white door. As she walked up to it, a synthivoice made clear just how closed it was.

"This is a class A security area. Identify yourself and produce authority for access."

That seemed to be the end of her mission. Somebody somewhere had screwed up. There was no way that she could get into C70. She turned to go. The synthivoice stopped her dead.

"Your authority is accepted. Proceed."

The door slid open. Cynthia walked in. She had expected it to close behind her, but it did not. Feeling a little uncomfortable, she surveyed the room. It was large and white, bare except for the terminal against the far wall. Only twice in her life had she seen anything quite so complex. It had three tiers of keyboards, eight monitors, and even provision for DNI leads. Large letters were flashing on the central monitor.

READY TO LOAD—FEED ME.

She sat down in the workstation's large white leather chair, wondering who routinely used the thing. It had certainly not been designed for underlings. She fed in the disk. The screens all lit up. A large cartoon vulture appeared on the primary screen. It lazily flapped it wings.

WAITING

The vulture flapped its wings once more, and then the screen cleared.

THE PROGRAM IS LOADED—THANK YOU FOR YOUR SUBMIS-SION.

She removed the diskette. It was time to get the hell out of there. She looked up from the monitor and, to her horror, saw Deacon Winters standing in the open doorway with a big Mossberg pointed at her. The expression on his face was an unpleasant leer.

"So what do you think you're doing in here?"

Winters

Winters had been paired with a deacon called Gresler—John Wayne Gresler. He was a hard, pious, and, Winters suspected, brutal man. Promotion had passed him by, and he seemed content to remain a solid foot soldier in the battle against the forces of evil. Closed and silent, he had a face as yielding as a granite mountainside. Along with Winters, he had been assigned to C section. Everyone expected it to be a milk run. Although the surveillance cameras were out, a number of deacons had reported that there was only a handful of women up there. Winters and Gresler were to go up there and, as fast as possible, make certain that such was still the case, then use the override channel to get fresh orders. No one saw any reason to send a backup with them.

When they reached the floor, the two of them split up to check through the numbered work sections. It hardly seemed worth bothering. As predicted, the place was like a high-tech morgue. Winters was working his way down through the high seventies when he spotted something that was not quite as it should have been. The class A, ID only, security door to area C70 was jammed in the open position, and a red warning light was flashing on the wall above it. A class A door never remained open.

Winters got a good grip of his Mossberg. Thomas had handed out the heaviest weapons in the armory; he seemed to be taking the strange behavior of the electronics and the unusual prowling of the PD very seriously. Winters was not quite as convinced. What could the PD do to them? Without calling out to Gresler, he moved almost cockily toward the door, sure that there could be nothing life-threatening beyond it. It was probably another symptom of the electronic chaos that seemed to be breaking out all over. Raising the Mossberg to the ready position was little more than bravado.

He turned into the open doorway. To his surprise, he saw that there was a woman sitting in the control seat of the room's single terminal. She suddenly turned and faced him, as if she had sensed him standing there. His eyebrows lifted in surprise. It was Cynthia Kline, the whore who had been sleeping with the traitor Carlisle. Something unpleasant uncurled in his mind. He had a fleeting vision of Kline and himself, alone in one of the chambers in the subbasement. She was naked and strapped down to a vaulting horse frame. Her expression was one of pure, silent-scream terror. As the vision faded, his own face twisted into an unpleasant grin.

"So what do you think you're doing in here?"

Kline

She fired without thinking. The plastic Browning was in front of her on the terminal. She scooped it up in one smooth movement and aimed by instinct. The Browning made a series of quiet pops. The flat, lozenge-shaped slugs were tiny when they left the gun's rectangular barrel, but on impact they sprang open to form ripping, tearing stars of hardened plastic. The first took Winters in the chest. The second hit him in the throat. The third and fourth were close together in his forehead. Her instructors would have been proud of her. For a few seconds Winters stood absolutely still, blood flowing down his face and neck and staining his shirt. He looked surprised. Then his eyes rolled up, and he toppled and fell. His blood spread in a widening pool, across the white tiles of the floor. Cynthia let out a harsh bark of grim laughter.

"That'll teach you to go up against a professional. Think you were taking on a bimbo, did you?"

There was a shout from somewhere nearby.

"Winters? What's happening?"

Cynthia screamed loudly and knelt down by Winters's body. The Browning was concealed in her palm. She heard the sound of running feet. A second deacon, also carrying a Mossberg, swung through the open doorway to C70. He took in the scene in one stony glance and formed the understandable conclusion that Cynthia was nothing more than an innocent bystander.

"What happened?"

Cynthia had no trouble with sounding choked by terror. "PDs—they shot him."

"Where did they go?"

"Down the corridor."

As he turned his back on her to look out of the door, she calmly shot him. He staggered, and she fired again. Some spasm caused his fingers to close around the trigger of his weapon. The gun went off with a deafening roar, the blast chewing a large bite out of the door frame. Cynthia knew that she had to get out of there right away, before anyone else showed up. She could not turn the same trick twice. She was on her feet and moving. She stepped over the body of the second deacon, ran through the door, and hurried down the corridor, making for the elevators. Just as she turned the corner that led to the elevator banks, the doors were opening. She was in luck. She was about to step into the car when figures suddenly appeared around a corner on the opposite side of the elevator banks. They were running men in windbreakers and blue jeans. From the way that they brandished machine pistols and riot guns, they had to be plainclothes PD.

"Hold it right there, lady!"

There were too many of them, and they had too much firepower. If she simply jumped into the elevator, they could easily blast through the doors. She let the Browning drop into her shoulder bag, hoping that they were too far away to notice the move. They would not expect a woman to be armed. She raised her hands.

"Don't shoot!"

They were all around her barking questions. There were five of them, young and tightly wrapped.

"We heard shots."

Cynthia nodded. "There are two deacons back in C70. They're dead. They've been shot."

One of the five detached himself; a second followed.

"We'll go take a look."

They hurried back the way Cynthia had come.

"Did you see who shot them?"

"It was me. I shot them."

The remaining three looked at her disbelievingly as she took the Browning from her bag and held it out to them.

"You shot them?"

"What did you do that for?"

Cynthia had always had the gift of instant tears on demand. She began to cry. "They were going to kill me. It was some kind of revenge on Harry."

"Harry?"

One of the others looked at the speaker impatiently. "Don't you recognize her, dummy? It's Kline. It's the lieutenant's girl-friend."

"Of course it is."

The other two were coming back. The one who had recognized her first called out to them. "We got Carlisle's girl, and she says she shot them."

"We definitely got two stiffs back there, with expander slugs in them, bleeding all over the place. One of them is that little prick Winters."

Cynthia made her play before they could ask too many more questions. "Can you take me to Harry? Do you know where he is?"

The PDs looked at each other.

"So what do you think? Do we take her down to the lieutenant or what?"

The agreement was fast.

"Yeah, take her to him. Then it's out of our hands."

Carlisle

The clatter of gunfire was amplified over the communications center audio system. The audio override on their tracys was the only contact they could trust. Everything else was going crazy as the multiple and constantly mutating viruses took over.

"They've got us pinned down in the entrance to the roof." Donahue sounded desperate. "There's a bunch of them. All got Mossbergs. We're safe in the stairwell for the moment but we need help up here."

Carlisle spoke in the bead mike of his headset. "I'll get more people up there."

"We need a grenade launcher or a couple of small AP missiles."

257

Carlisle looked around. "Can we get anything like that?"

"Not while the deacons are holding the arsenal."

A detective called Murphy spoke up. "There's a Cucaracha locked up in evidence. We took it off those greasers, the ones that were calling themselves the Screaming Fist. It hasn't gone to weapons disposal yet."

"Get it and go."

Another man pushed his way through to the front. "I got a Parsons and a clip of grenades in my locker."

Carlisle looked at him in amazement. "You keep a grenade launcher in your locker?"

The man shrugged. "You never know when it might come in handy. I got it back when—"

Carlisle cut off the explanation. "I don't give a damn right now. Just get it and get up there. I want the helipad secured."

He spoke into the bead mike. "Donahue, did you hear all that?"

"I heard it. Just tell them to hurry."

Taking the communications center had been easy. Running it was a great deal more difficult. When Carlisle and his men had stormed in there, the deacon operators had already been confused by the increasingly erratic behavior of their equipment. Only two had tried to put up a fight, and they had been shot out of hand. At the sight of the bodies bleeding on the floor, the others had become immediately cooperative—not that there was much with which they could cooperate. The communications center was the brain of the CCC complex, and that brain seemed to be going into some electronic grand mal seizure as the final wave of Dreisler's viruses took hold. In normal times the com center was, for all practical purposes, the Astor Place war room, the mission control for all law enforcement in the city of New York. Banks of monitors displayed the ongoing status of various operations and investigations; they showed manpower figures and deployment reports. The computers answered, channeled, filed, and recorded the thousands of calls that came into the complex during each twenty-four-hour period. They coordinated vehicle dispatch and all the mobile message systems available to the officers. They oversaw the massive electronic eavesdropping network, maintained the links with Virginia Beach, and even integrated the internal surveillance system.

The centerpiece of the large, circular, and dimly lit room was the complex situation board that gave visual breakdowns of what was happening in various parts of the area. On any other day its cold electronic glow, moving lights, and the mathematical tracery of its grids were the products of a cold logic. A signal was sent, a car was dispatched, and every detail appeared on the situation board. A visitor could easily be convinced that it was the graphic representation of the implacable majesty of the law in action.

On that day, however, it would have been hard to convince a visitor that the entire communications center was anything but an extention of some insane pinball machine that was about to hit tilt. Some monitors simply rolled and strobed, while others exploded into riots of color. Whole banks remained stubbornly down, their screens blank, like dead, catatonic eyes. Every now and then, a cartoon vulture would appear at random on a monitor and flap its wings. Carlisle knew that the vulture had to be a product of Dreisler's warped sense of humor. The situation board itself danced with lights like a hyperkinetic Christmas tree. Even the sections that appeared to be responding normally could not be trusted. Much of the displayed data that, at first glance seemed plausible and organized, turned out, on closer examination, to be total nonsense. Even when logic was theoretically holding up, there was no guarantee that the information bore any relationship to reality. The deacon operators, under the watchful eyes of armed PD officers, sat and stared dumbly at the induced lunacy. They had the look of men in the grip of a nightmare.

Even amid the chaos, there was hard data still coming in. The TV satellite feeds still came through, apparently intact, and it was clear from the pictures that large crowds were massing all along the Hudson from Fourteenth Street on down. It was also obvious that the computers themselves were still running the operations on the street according to some diseased, corrupted master plan. The deacon in charge of operations in the Times Square area had suddenly appeared on what had previously been a blank screen and requested permission to shuttle a party of prisoners down to the Astor Place lockups. A synthivoice calmly diverted him to an uptown precinct. Nothing, though, was telling Carlisle what he really wanted to know. He had no idea what was going on on Liberty Island. Had Faithful been arrested, or had the plot collapsed? He half expected deacon reinforcements to come through the door shooting, bent on retaking the com center. Each time the door opened he had to stop himself from twitching for the Uzi that was slung over his shoulder.

There was so much to do that Cynthia Kline was the very last person on his mind. When the group of detectives brought her into the center, his heart sank. Not now. He did not need it. He had enough to worry about. Ever since he had found out that she was a Canadian agent, he had tried to blank out all thoughts of the woman. Unfortunately she seemed bent on talking to him.

"Harry, I need to talk to you."

He tried to duck her. "I'm really busy."

"I've shot two deacons. What's going to happened to me?"

Harry Carlisle groaned inwardly. He looked at the detectives who had brought her in. "Is this true?"

"There's two stiffs up in C section."

"Christ." He faced Cynthia. He could hardly believe that only a couple of weeks ago they had laughed in each other's arms. "I don't have time for this right now."

"But . . ."

"I don't know what you've been up to, but I know what you are. By some weird set of circumstances, we're on the same side for the moment. You can stay down here, but keep quiet and don't get in the way. Okay?"

"Listen, Harry . . ."

"Either you keep quiet, or I have one of my men take you out and shoot you. Things are that bad, so you better make up your mind fast. Okay?"

Cynthia was very pale, but she went silently to a empty seat and sat down. Carlisle glanced at one of the men who had brought her in'. "Keep an eye on her."

Donahue's voice was on the audio again. "We've secured the roof."

"Casualties?"

"It was rough, but it's done."

"So hold on to it until you hear from me."

Kline

How in hell did he know what she was, and what did he mean they were on the same side? Questions rampaged through her brain, fueled by the adrenaline of fear, but she knew she was not going to get any answers. She did her best to remain calm and sit quietly, but it was not easy. The communications center seemed to have gone crazy. She could only suppose that the program she had loaded was partly responsible. The only consolation was that everybody else seemed to be waiting for something, too. She had never seen Harry look so tense. Part of her wanted to go and do something to comfort him, but another, much colder part told her to sit where she was and shut up. When he had said that he would have her shot, she had known instantly that it was no empty threat. She had seen the bodies covered by plastic sheets and the guns pointed at the heads of the deacon operators. Carlisle had apparently hijacked the communications center, and she wished she knew why. A war had obviously broken out between the deacons and the police department. Things were coming to a head.

The clock, if the clock could be trusted, crawled toward six. The bank of satellite feed monitors, the only ones that consistently did the same thing, was showing the opening credits of the presidential special; a tattered Old Glory, with the superimposed cross of the Christian United States, fluttered bravely against a storm-cloud sky, and then an aerial shot zoomed across the sunset city and closed on the Statue of Liberty. They were not getting the audio in the com center, but she guessed that the show was being accompanied by suitably patriotic music. The credits gave way to a pause where the affiliates could jack in their own commercials. On the screens, the choir was moving into position in preparation to going on the air with the opening. They were arranged on a huge apron stage at the base of the statue, in front of giant twin pictures of Larry Faithful and Jesus Christ. As far as Cynthia was concerned, it was the same old predictable—but still dangerous—hokum, and it was a mercy that no one had to listen to the audio. A digital countdown was displayed in the corners of the screens. The moment it hit zero, the choir's heavenly smiles glowed and their mouths started moving.

One monitor showed a different scene: a corridor and the door of what had to be Faithful's dressing room. Deacons and soldiers stood around, and technicians in nylon crew jackets walked back and forth. The camera, probably a robot, was feeding but not in use. It was there to catch a fast cutaway of Faithful coming out of his dressing room. Suddenly something weird happened over at the side of the screen. Two deacons seemed to be scuffling. Guns were out. Technicians also seemed to be involved.

It was hard to see exactly what was happening. The robot, without programming, did not pan to the action. Rushing bodies obscured its field of vision. The fact that there was no sound did not help. A machine pistol silently spurted smoke and muzzle flash. Every eye in the com center was fixed on the one small screen. The confusion continued for some thirty seconds. Then a yellow censor blanket washed over it.

"Can you get rid of that thing?" Carlisle snapped at the deacon operator.

"In theory. The way things are, who knows?"

"Will you try?"

The PD man behind that particular operator leaned forward with his machine pistol. The operator shrugged.

"That's all I can do."

"So do it."

The operator entered a ten-figure code. The yellow rolled back, but it was too late. The corridor was empty. The camera had been moved to show a different angle, straight up the corridor, where three bodies were sprawled on the ground. At the same moment, all the other TV pictures were suddenly blocked by a feed interrupt sign.

"What in hell is going on out there?" someone asked.

Some of the PD men were on their feet as if expecting a physical attack. What came next was almost as bad. A talking head of Matthew Dreisler appeared on all the TV feed monitors.

"This is to all units," Dreisler announced. "The vulture has been caged."

Kline looked around in bewilderment. Everyone in the room was equally confused—all except Harry Carlisle. He simply looked bleakly alone. He held up his hands for quiet.

"I think it's time that I explained what's really going on here. The signal that was just received indicates that the president has been arrested and forces favorable to restoration of democracy have taken over key government installations all across the country."

Cynthia Kline could not believe her ears. Was that really Harry Carlisle she was hearing? While she had been kept in the dark, a mere cog loading programs and keeping her questions to herself, he had been right at the heart of the conspiracy?

"I haven't been able to give you the real picture up until now in case everything went wrong, but it looks as if the Faithful administration is at an end, and maybe this country has a chance to get back its national sanity. If anyone has a problem with this, I suggest that he speak now.''

His words left a stunned silence. Carlisle gave them very little time to digest what they had heard before he went on.

''The situation as it applies to us is that we of the police department are currently in control of this complex. The president is being brought here by helicopter.''

Reeves was one of the first to recover. ''Who arrested him? Who's bringing him here?''

''Deacon Dreisler and some of his IA people.''

Reeves face was a picture of contempt. ''Dreisler. Dreisler and his headhunters.''

Carlisle looked really unhappy. ''There are some strange alliances in this business.''

''So it would seem.''

It took Murphy to voice the question that was in every PD man's mind. ''Why couldn't we be told about this from the start, Carlisle?''

''I wanted to give you men the excuse that you were only following my orders.''

Murphy's face was reddening. ''So you took it on yourself?''

''That's my job.''

''Men have died today without knowing what they were dying for.''

Carlisle's face was harder than Cynthia had ever seen it. ''That's nothing new.''

''I'm not sure I like the way you do things, Lieutenant.''

One of the deacons was on his feet. He looked around at the other men and waved a fist at Carlisle. ''This is treason. The man's a traitor. We should simply arrest him.''

He started moving toward Carlisle, but Murphy felled him with a gun butt. The man crumpled, and Murphy stood over him. The other PDs had their guns trained on the remaining deacons.

Murphy stared at Carlisle. ''We're with you, Lieutenant, but we still think you should have let us make our own decisions.''

Carlisle's shoulders sagged a little, but he quickly recovered and turned to Reeves. ''I'm going to the roof. I want you to hold the fort here.''

Reeves nodded stiffly.

Carlisle glanced at Cynthia. ''Keep an eye on her.''

"The TV feed's down!"

"What?"

"There's nothing coming through, just a malfunction signal."

Mansard jerked away from what he was doing. "What are those idiots playing at?"

"There's no one responding from the island."

"How can that be? There's a half-dozen TV units on that island, plus deacons and the army."

"Don't ask me. It's like they were all blanked out, just like that."

"Are our people still on the line?"

The PA at the radio nodded. "Loud and clear. It's just the island that's communications dead."

"That's ridiculous."

Someone was shouting from the stern of the yacht. "There are choppers coming up from the island. One of them's the president's."

Two paces took Charlie Mansard to the rail. It was true— there were three helicopters rising from the island. One was *Air Force Four*; the other two were Herods from the escort. What he was seeing was insane. Was the president leaving in the middle of the show, before he had done his act? Mansard shuddered to think what power might be dragging Faithful away from the TV cameras. Maybe the country was at war.

The PA was beckoning. "There's this weird message coming in. They want us to power down and go back to the island."

Mansard held out his hand for the headset. "Give me that." He held it to his ear. "Who is this?"

A synthivoice was repeating the message. Mansard angrily shook his head. "No fucking robot is going to tell me to cancel the show. Get me Jimmy."

Jimmy Gadd was in the headphones. "What's going on, chief? Are we really calling it off?"

"The hell we are. Power up. People have come for a show, and we're going to proceed as normal."

"Are you sure?"

"Do it! We go right now!" A thought struck him. "Forget about the figure of Christ. We'll go with the other three. We'll give them the monsters. The world seems to be going nuts, so let's go with it." He suddenly laughed. "Maybe we can help it along."

Carlisle

He could still feel their eyes on him as he rode up in the elevator. He knew that he had lost a certain absolute trust, a trust that he would never get back. The men were following him out of pragmatism. He was no longer one of them, just another manipulating leader. The elevator stopped at the top floor, and Carlisle climbed the flight of concrete and steel steps that led to the roof. The wall around the door that opened on the helipad was chewed up by gunfire, and the door had been blown off its hinges. The body of one of his men, a rookie called Kaufman, was half buried in a pile of rubble. He stepped over more rubble to get to the outside. The sun was well below the horizon, and the sky was almost dark. The helipad was a mess. A third of the landing lights had been shot out, but the ones that were left were more than enough to show the other bodies and the debris on the flat landing apron and the way the concentric yellow rings that marked the pad were blackened by grenade bursts.

Donahue was waiting with his squad. They had the covers off the batteries of small Slingshot surface-to-air missiles that were mounted at the four corners of the roof. From the distrust and disappointment on their faces, they had clearly heard from the com center.

"So the president's coming, is he?"

Carlisle nodded. "They should be here any minute."

"And it's going to be a brand-new day is it, Lieutenant?"

Carlisle sighed. He did not know if he could handle an infinity of being treated like Judas. "I sure hope so."

"So do we."

The slap of rotors came from the southwest, and navigation lights twinkled by the black silhouettes of the Trade Center. The lights of the downtown towers had been extinguished for the skywalkers.

"I think this is them now."

The chopper sound came closer, and the men on the roof peered into the darkness. Soon it was possible to see that there were three of them, one large aircraft and two smaller ones—the presidential helicopter and a pair of escort gunships. The pitch of their engines indicated that they were coming fast, then, as they hit the final approach, they slowed. Whoever was in command, presumably Dreisler, was being ultracautious. They hovered a way off from the pad, and sunguns flared in the noses of the escort ships, sweeping the pad with blinding white light. Carlisle shaded his eyes with his hand, thinking that it looked as if UFOs were coming in for a landing. Finally they seemed satisfied and came on in. Only *Air Force Four* descended to the pad, whipping up a vortex of dust and light debris. The gunships stayed protectively overhead.

Before the big ship with the presidential seal on the side even touched, four men swung down from the open passenger door. They wore protective helmets and body armor over dark conservative business suits. Their weapons were at the ready. They had to be Dreisler's crack team. Next out was a cameraman, hair blowing in the prop wash—the event was being recorded for posterity. The helicopter settled on its landing gear, and more deacons clambered from the door. Some of Donahue's men were looking nervous. Maybe it was a Trojan horse? The deacons formed a protective semicircle. Larry Faithful stepped down, with Dreisler right behind him. They walked quickly to where Carlisle was standing. The cameraman was working overtime. This was the stuff of history: the landing pad on the top of the high tower, the long black shadows cast by the lights of the helicopter, the slowly turning rotors. This was the Fall of Larry Faithful.

Dreisler shouted over the roar of the engines. "You did a good job, Carlisle."

Carlisle did not want Dreisler's commendation. He nodded and mumbled, "Thank you."

"Lieutenant Carlisle, I want you to meet President Faithful."

Even at a moment of such gravity, Dreisler could still muster the sardonic smile. After the magazine pictures, the posters and billboards, the thousands of television hours, the president looked like an alien. Nothing about him seemed real. The features—the prissy rosebud mouth, the phony compassion around his eyes—were all parodies of the image. He was small, not more than five foot three, a bantam rooster who walked on the balls of his feet. His face was covered in thick television makeup that was streaked by rivulets of sweat. The flesh beneath it had the inhuman regularity of expensive plastic surgery. How was it possible for someone who looked so fabricated to have caused so much trouble?

Carlisle inclined his head slightly. What could one say to a president whom one had just deposed? Faithful's eyes gleamed briefly and locked on Carlisle's. The lines were still there, but the compassion had vanished. His voice was too soft to hear, but even by lip reading, the power of the venom was obvious. It was a flash of black ice anger.

"May you rot in hell, Lieutenant."

Carlisle was still blinking when the shouts came. One of Dreisler's men was quickly beside him.

"Sir, you'd better take a look at this."

Dreisler stabbed a finger at Faithful. "Guard him with your lives."

Carlisle hurried after Dreisler as the deacon strode to the edge of the roof. Out on the water, well beyond the tip of Manhattan, three huge figures of pure light, basking in their massive vapor columns, were advancing out of the night, bearing down on the city. Dreisler looked at the nearest aide.

"I thought we'd canceled Mansard's show."

"He seems to have uncanceled himself, sir. We could send in helicopters to break up the images."

"And we'd look ridiculous. It'd be a remake of *King Kong*. No, let him run. Arrest him when he's finished. If Charlie Mansard wants to put on the Day of Judgment, let him."

Mansard

Charlie Mansard gazed in awe at his own creation. The new projectors were a quantum advance on the ones they had used at the Garden. The image density was magnificent. His towering figures were no longer ghostly; the light seemed almost solid. He stood brace-legged on the yacht's gently rocking deck, hands clasped behind his back. The yacht was steering a course some distance out from the barges, so Charlie could see the full effect. All around him the party had stopped. An anxious silence had settled. Nobody seemed to want to stand next to him. Even Lynette was keeping her distance. He held his breath for a long time. Finally he let it out with a sigh.

"Yes, I think these are pretty much okay."

The relief among the crew was like a lifted weight. Charlie

had given his seal of approval. They gathered around, slapping his back, hugging him, and pumping his hand. Champagne corks popped.

The Beast came first. It was a roughly humanoid demon with hunched shoulders and spindly, angular, almost insectlike legs—a cross between man and mantis. Mansard had borrowed heavily from mid-twentieth-century monster movies for that one. It stalked up river with a menacing shamble. The scales on its body were a deep bottle green and they gleamed with highlights of midnight blue and acid yellow. Its eyes were upswept emerald slits that glared balefully as it swung its head from side to side as if seeking its prey. Mansard had chuckled the first time he had seen the animated motion.

"Checking out who's been naughty or nice?"

Two spiky projections that could have been either antlers or antennae rose from the top of its elongated skull. Steaming saliva dripped from its fanged mouth, and its talons constantly flexed. Every few paces it halted, and its nostrils flared as if it were sniffing the air. The finishing touch was the numerals "666," the number of the beast, which pulsed hellfire red on the scales between the towering horns that were the approximation of a forehead.

The second figure also had its roots in the pop culture of the twentieth century. Mansard had used the movie goddess Elizabeth Taylor as the basis for the Whore of Babylon. She reclined on a shell-like litter that was born on the back of a roiling, multiheaded, serpentine thing. Mansard would never have admitted it, but when they came to the dragon they had been a little short on memory for the complex image and had been forced to disguise the fact by making it look as if it were half underwater. Although the thing that carried the shell was something of a half measure, every care had been taken in creating the figure that was riding in it. Mansard had not spared a byte in lovingly fashioning the Whore exactly as he had imagined her. She lolled in her litter, lascivious, leering, and drunk. Her gaping peignoir was the same scarlet and gold as the scales of the thing, and it shimmered with its own internal light. Her hair was a cloud of curls, black as the void, that seemed to ripple with a life of their own. Her lips were dancing flames begging the moths to come to them, while Cleopatra eyes made sultry promises, a menu of original sins. She raised a huge gold goblet, encrusted with evilly glowing gems, in a toast to the city that

268

was still called Babylon on the Hudson. Wine, the color of dark blood, splashed over her all but totally exposed breasts. What did the Bible say the wine represented? The "abominations and filthiness of her fornications." In his newest creations, Mansard had pushed the moral envelope as hard as he could. From the start, he had roared at his design team.

"Go for it! There's no point in covering up her tits. The bitch is supposed to be bad, goddamn it! As bad as it gets!"

He did not want to think that the final group of figures, his original Four Horsemen, were in any way eclipsed by the new ones. They had been greatly improved since the Garden. In addition to the greater density and realism, improved computer capacity had given them a more comprehensive range of movement and gesture. The horses reared and pranced, and their riders looked from side to side as if surveying their domain. War pointed with his lance, and Death swung his scythe out over the river as if taking in all of New York in a single sweep. The sleeves of the robe of Pestilence flapped like giant wings as he broadcast his contagion, while the new levels of contrast made the black hollows of Famine's eyes look like the pits of hell.

Mansard noticed that there was a strange sound coming from across the water. It was not cheering; it was more like the confused shouting of a mob.

A PA moved up beside him, holding out a radio headset. "It's Jimmy, chief. He wants to speak to you."

Mansard held it to his ear.

Jimmy sounded jubilant. "Looking good, huh?"

"Not too bad."

"Can you hear that weird sound?"

Mansard nodded. "Yeah, what is it?"

"I think it's the sound of thousands of people going nuts. Maybe we touched a nerve."

1346408 Stone

All through the day, things had become progressively more strange. The usual mind-numbing routine of a Sunday in the camp first slowed and then ground to an inexplicable halt. In a place like Joshua, the first reaction was always one of fear. Any unexpected glitch in the normal discipline was viewed as a possible harbinger of some awful event. First, breakfast was more than two hours late, and when they were finally marched to the mess hall, the bosses were oddly quiet and preoccupied. There was none of the usual abuse and victimization. The billyclubs were still, and the hectoring voices were impossibly subdued. If anything, the guards seemed worried, almost frightened. Something was happening, but the prisoners had no idea what it was. One of the earliest theories was that there had been a breakout in some other section of the camp, but considering the wholly atypical behavior of the bosses, that idea hardly held up. After previous breakouts, the guards had actually stepped up the brutality. When the escapees had eventually been recaptured, the guards had taken a positive delight in parading their charges past the gibbet where the hanged and beaten bodies were put on display as a deterrent to the others.

The kitchens were the camp's clearing house for rumors and tidbits of information. They were one of the few places where inmates from different sections intermixed and, under cover of the steam and the clatter, were able to exchange furtive, muttered sentences. The first story to come out of the kitchens was attributed to a group on the women's side who had a clandestine radio. Supposedly, there were reports coming out of Canada that there was about to be major shakeup in the Faithful administration. Another, from G block, claimed that black deacon cars had been going in and out of the camp all through the night. There were also the usual doomsayers, who muttered that there were mass executions coming as the authorities intended to drastically reduce the size of the camp population.

In the middle of breakfast, there was an announcement over the PA. All religious services were canceled. That was unprecedented. Even the TV was shut down. The inmates spent the rest of the afternoon locked up in their barracks rooms quietly speculating what might happen next. At six, the TV came on again. The inmates were expected to watch the presidential special. They sat in silence through the opening filler, through the choir and the celebrities' pleas for peace and harmony. There were a few wry smiles among the inmates as soap opera star Charity Masterpiece exhorted the viewing audience to work together in Jesus. Then, to everyone's slack-jawed amazement, just before Faithful was due to begin his address, the transmission started to come unglued. There was a fleeting shot of running soldiers, then an interruption sign came on, only to be replaced ten minutes later by an equally confusing shot from the set of the Faithful special, showing performers and people who looked like deacons milling aimlessly about. Obviously something had completely disrupted the show. There was a kind of guarded excitement in the barracks—something was really radically wrong in the outside world. The TV signal went off again, in a flash of snow and horizontal lines.

The next TV picture was the most bizarre of all. Three enormous skywalkers were moving up a river. The Manhattan skyline identified the river as the Hudson.

1334680 Montague let out a low whistle. "The Beasts of Revelations." Montague had been a Rastafarian in the real world.

1346809 Pitlik looked at him in surprise. "They're just big holograms."

"Armageddon time. Jah know." His eyes had taken on a glaze and the whites had turned yellow. "Armageddon time. Jah know."

"He's flipped."

Montague kept repeating his words over and over like a mantra. "Armageddon time. Jah know."

Later they would come for him with a straitjacket.

The first pictures of the monsters came from circling helicopters, but in a few minutes there was one from ground level, somewhere on the lower Manhattan waterfront. The camera crew was being jostled and buffeted by a crowd of struggling people; the roar of mass hysteria poured from the speakers. Near the mike, someone was babbling about the end of the world. Hands were clutching at the lens. The world had gone insane. From within the brutal order of the camp, it was a vision of the impossible. More than one inmate of D block wondered if 1334680 Montague was right. The cameraman must have staggered forward. After a series of lurches, the vantage point was directly over the river. People were actually jumping into the water.

"Armageddon time."

The picture died completely. There was no power. The bosses had pulled the plug. There was a deathly silence, broken only by 1334680 Montague droning on. "Armageddon time. Jah know."

The PA cut in. "All prisoners will remain in their barracks blocks until further notice. Food will be brought."

In an hour, food was brought and Montague was taken away. The food was slopped out by two kapos from A block. It was an unpleasant soup. A scrap of paper was attached to the bottom of one of the pails. There was a message on it: "Faithful has been arrested! There's going to be a new government!"

It might have been a cruel joke, but if it was true, what would a new government mean? One that opened the camps, or one that would set up gas ovens? The note was passed from one man to the next in aching silence. They scarcely dared to hope. Freedom? Maybe even revenge? It was almost inconceivable.

Carlisle

"You know what this is? This is like that Orson Welles Martian freakout back in the radio days."

"Except that it's to the hundredth power."

"I don't understand this. It's mass mania."

"Do they really believe it's the Apocalypse?"

"It's like these figures of Mansard's have hit some nerve and flipped everyone out."

Carlisle looked coldly at the man who had spoken. "If you're already half out of your mind on propaganda, poverty, and A-waves, flipping all the way might not look like so bad a deal."

That brought him some sharp looks. He glanced back at Dreisler. "This is the revolution, isn't it? We've got free speech now, right?"

Dreisler was sitting behind everyone, apparently watching their reactions; he seemed almost languid. The only sign that he might also be feeling the strain was the way he chain-smoked unfiltered cigarettes, holding them between thumb and forefinger, FDR style.

"As long as you're breathing, Harry, your mouth will keep flapping."

Carlisle's mouth did indeed keep flapping. The day's events were building a reckless go-for-broke anger inside him. "You don't seem very surprised by all this. Were you expecting it? Maybe like the Proverb shooting?"

Dreisler's eyes flashed cold. "Watch it, Harry."

Carlisle ignored the warning. "Seriously, what do you think is going on out there?"

Dreisler's expression was impossible to read. "I think Johansen's right. Mansard has hit a nerve. He may even have lanced a large boil on the national psyche. Maybe it's the emotional end of the Faithful era. America wants one last, massive psychodelusion.''

Carlisle slumped down in an empty operator's chair. "People are getting hurt out there.''

Dreisler dragged on his cigarette. "People always get hurt. Omelets and eggs, remember?''

Carlisle thought of the dead cop on the stairs to the roof.

In the Astor Place com center they were watching the chaos growing outside. As soon as Faithful had been secured in the basement lockup under heavy guard, Dreisler, with the swagger of a magician, had produced a living, breathing Japanese cowboy called Hama who had jacked into the acres of corrupted software and laced in a temporary vaccine program. That, at least, had provided a narrow logic path through the virus-filled, psychedelic, random jungles that had once been the CCC base software. Dreisler had immediately used it to consolidate his position and start infiltrating his men into places that might be potential contra strongholds.

"As with revolution,'' he said, "the best time to fight counterrevolution is before it gets started.''

It was not too long, though, before he was hampered in his efforts by the growing madness in the outside world and the reports of it that began to choke every communication channel.

Later it would be called the Armageddon Crazy, and it would go into the textbooks as one of the most extreme cases of riptide mass hysteria in a supposedly developed country. The appearance of Mansard's skywalkers had convinced vast numbers of people that Judgment Day was really at hand, and those vast numbers of people began to act accordingly. They went nuts. Initially it was confined to the crowds lining the Manhattan and Jersey sides of the river. People hurled themselves into the river in ever growing numbers. There were points during the night, even after the skywalkers were long gone, when the margins of the Hudson looked like a lemming fest, with bobbing heads and the thrashings of nonswimmers who had decided that they did not want to die after all. Unfortunately, the mania did not stay confined to the river for long. It rapidly spread across the city. By midnight, it was estimated that over two million people were raging through New York City, weeping, wailing, talking in tongues, and doing their best to damage themselves. At first the police had attempted to employ normal crowd-control measures, but after a while they were forced to admit defeat and simply step aside. The Armageddon Crazy was too highly charged to be kept in check. Also peace officers were not necessarily immune. The entire crew of a Pharaoh flipped out together and ran their armored carrier off the Fifty-ninth Street Bridge. Many of those affected took it into their heads to go to graveyards and search for resurrected relatives. The hysteria was compounded by hundreds of people stumbling around among the headstones.

It was quickly discovered that the insanity could be transmitted electronically. With the TV censorship system burned out by virus, the images from New York—the giant skywalkers and the madness they had caused—went out unchecked, all over the country. As soon as the footage hit the screens in another city the same thing happened. Chicago, St. Louis, and Atlanta were infected immediately. New Orleans, Baltimore, and Detroit lasted an hour. Los Angeles held out for almost four hours, but when the Crazy got going, that city suffered one of the most spectacular outbreaks in the country. Hymn-singing arsonists burned huge tracts of the bone-dry Hollywood Hills, and naked millionaires ran down Rodeo Drive trying to give away their money. The gay underground took it as the signal to rise. Armed drag queens battled deacons to a standstill in a firefight that ran for twenty blocks down Santa Monica Boulevard.

The original plan had intended that Arlen Proverb go on TV the moment Faithful was in custody and pitch the idea of a brave new world to the country. That crucial move quickly fell victim to the Crazy. Dreisler had Proverb stashed in a safe house on the Upper East Side. When the signal was given, Proverb was supposed to get to a small basement studio and give his address, to those who still thought there might be a tomorrow, through a remote feed. The signal was sent, but nothing came back. It was discovered that the landline from the uptown studio had been put out of commission by an overzealous virus. The backup plan called for Proverb to go across the park to another studio located at Seventy-ninth and Amsterdam. According to a garbled phone message, Proverb had set off with an escort but had not been heard from since. There were reports that thousands had gathered in Central Park to pray for the end. It was all too possible that the sight of a white limo trying to bull its way through might have driven them into a kill frenzy.

In the com center, a single screen was flashing regular blue and yellow pulses. An operator pointed to it. "That could be someone trying to get a visual signal in and it's being blocked."

Dreisler glanced at Hama. "Can you jack in and create a channel for it to get through?"

The Japanese bowed. "Of course."

He quickly connected his DNI leads. Under flaps of skin that resembled gills, the cowboy had rows of receptors on each side of his head that ran from ear to collarbone. There was nothing remotely like him anywhere in the U.S.A. If America decided to rejoin the rest of the world, they might find it an alien place.

Within seconds, an image of Proverb replaced the blue and yellow pulsing. His hair was messed and there was a cut over his left eye, but otherwise he seemed okay. At first, he was mouthing soundlessly, like a fish in an aquarium, but then the audio cut in with an amplified crackle.

". . . hear me? Is there anybody out there?"

Dreisler was on his feet. "Proverb, can you hear me?"

Proverb nodded. "I can hear you, but I can't see you."

Dreisler turned to Hama again. "Can we patch him to the satellite send?"

"No problem."

"Okay, Arlen, can you go on the air?"

Proverb pushed his hair back out of his eyes. "Now?"

"Right now."

"I'm a bit of a mess, but I guess so."

Dreisler looked around the room. "Get ready to transmit this on all available channels. I don't want any mistakes." His attention switched to Proverb. "Are you ready, Arlen?"

Carlisle supposed that Dreisler was what had once been called a natural leader. He had his doubts about where the deacon might be leading them, though.

Proverb nodded. The professional communicator was coming through. "On your cue."

"I'll give you a ten-second count."

Proverb had appeared on all the TV monitor screens. A digital display counted off the time. Cynthia Kline slipped into the seat next to Harry Carlisle. She quickly squeezed his arm.

"Is it going to be possible for us to be friends when all this is over?" she asked quietly.

Carlisle raised a helpless hand. "Let's find out when all this is all over."

"Are we through? Are you that angry with me?"

Carlisle shook his head. "Not angry. It's just hard dealing with the idea that all the time we were sleeping together, we were actually on opposite sides."

"I couldn't tell you who I really was. You must realize that."

"I realize it all on a logical level. It's the emotional acceptance that I'm having trouble with. Hell, it was my job to catch you people and put you in jail, maybe see you hang. It's not an easy turnaround."

"We're on the same side now."

Carlisle sighed. "That is true."

Cynthia looked at him anxiously. "So?"

He took hold of her hand and squeezed it. "So let's see this thing through and then have a long talk about what we're going to do next."

Over on the other side of the room, Dreisler gestured with a flourish. "On the air."

A synthivoice provided the program interrupt. "We are taking you to New York City for a message from the Provisional Government of National Reconstruction."

Proverb betrayed one flash of uncertainty, and then the pro was in business. He had the expression of a man who had seen some hard times but knew he was going to win out in the end. Carlisle realized that another piece of history was being made.

"My friends, there's some of you out there who know me and some who don't. For those of you who don't, my name is Arlen Proverb. This morning I was a preacher and pretty sure of myself. Tonight, after everything that has happened, I'm just an American, and there's only one thing that I'm still certain about. I want to see this country regain its self-respect."

Speedboat

". . . I want to see this country regain its self-respect. It seems that some of us have forgotten that when you come down to it, that's all any of us are—just Americans."

Speedboat reached for his beer. "What are they high on down there?"

He lay flat on his chest on the bed in the beat-up Buffalo motel room. For once he was glued to the TV instead of using it to merely ease the interminable waiting. It came and it went. It was yanked off the air and then restored minutes later. For a while, Canadian programming had leaked through the jamming, but that had abruptly stopped. Regular programs would start only to be interrupted by wild, insane footage of the monsters attacking New York and the population going into screaming panic. Even he could see that the monsters were holograms, but the panic was absolutely real. New York had gone crazy, and the rest of the country appeared to be following suit.

Arlen Proverb was going on about a country divided and a country reborn. Speedboat switched channels to see if he could get any more live coverage of the craziness. To his dismay he found that Arlen Proverb was on every channel. He abruptly killed the volume. Then he thought he heard noises outside the room. He heard them again. He rolled over.

"That sounds like . . ."

He sat bolt upright.

"That sounds like gunfire."

There was sweat on his palms as he got off the bed and moved cautiously toward the window. He separated the slats of the dusty blind. Some large vehicle with red lights flashing on top of it sat in the parking lot. One word sprang into his mind. Raid! He looked around the room. There was no back way out. He heard more gunfire, but it was some distance away. There were voices in the parking lot. He caught a snatch of conversation.

". . . so I told him, eh, fuck with me again and I'll be taking your fucking blood pressure the hard way."

A loudhailer barked.

"You in the motel, come out of there! Everybody outside in the parking lot! Right now!"

Speedboat stood in the middle of the room. His stomach knotted as he fought off panic. There was no way that he was going to avoid the camp. He went slowly to the door and opened it. He looked out and could not believe his eyes. A massive, dark-green, amphibious tank was parked in the motel parking lot. A tank? Why the hell would the deacons be using a tank? None of the miserable refugees sheltering in the motel was that dangerous. The tank did not even look right. It had the heavy, slab-sided look that was the hallmark of the Russians, or, at least something based on a Russian design. It was then that he saw the large, red, Canadian maple leaf on the side of the turret. Speedboat could not believe his eyes. The Canadians had crossed the border. One of the tank crew was walking toward him. The collar of his tank suit was unfastened, and his visor was pushed back. He was grinning.

"Don't look so goddamn miserable, pal. You're getting liberated."

EPILOGUES AND EPITAPHS

IT WAS FIVE DAYS BEFORE THE ARMAGEDDON CRAZY FINALLY faded. America woke to the worst national hangover in history. The sense of guilt and shame that came with any hangover was buried in a furious binge of what became known as National Reconstruction. Arlen Proverb's "I'm just an American" speech seemed to have provoked a solid response, and the country appeared to have a genuine desire to let go of the Fundamentalist security blanket and really attempt to regain its self-respect. The speech was broadcast over forty times in the week following the Sunday Revolution. Unfortunately national reconstruction did not go as far as many would have hoped. Although some basic civil liberties were restored and thousands of political prisoners were released, the apparatus of repression created by the deacons was largely left in place. The economy continued to founder, and after three years there still had been no elections.

Proverb

Arlen Proverb was declared interim president and retained the title until he was shot to death by John Manly Walker during a public address in Council Bluffs, Iowa. The assassination gave Matthew Dreisler the excuse he needed to declare the infamous State of Emergency.

278

Dreisler

Matthew Dreisler became the absolute overlord of both domestic and foreign security. Although Proverb was president, Dreisler became de facto commander in chief. At first, the Canadians kept him somewhat in check, but after the pullout, he felt free to start constructing the perfect police state. His design was so self-sustaining that even after he himself was killed in the bomb attack on his private jet, the machine that he had created continued to function.

Carlisle

One month after the Sunday Revolution, Harry Carlisle applied for leave and a passport. He said he was going for two weeks of sun in Rio De Janeiro. He was never seen again. Some claimed that he had changed his name and vanished. Others believed that Dreisler had arranged his murder.

Kline

Around about the same time that Harry Carlisle supposedly left for his Rio vacation, Cynthia Kline also disappeared. Most who had known her assumed that as an operative of the Canadian Secret Service she had merely been given a new identity and transferred to a fresh theater of operations. As with Carlisle, however, there were those who subscribed to a more sinister theory: She and Harry Carlisle had both been killed at Dreisler's instigation.

Mansard

It took the new administration a full six weeks to decide whether Charlie Mansard was a hero or a criminal for having triggered the Armageddon Crazy. Finally they opted for the former, and Charlie went on to become world famous for his theatrical productions using skywalker holograms. He received special Tony awards for his presentations of Wagner's *Ring Cycle* and the musical *The Last Words of Dutch Schultz*.

1346408 Stone

Eli Stone got out of Joshua in the first wave of releases. He never, however, really readjusted to life in the outside world. After some months of being unable to hold down a job and treatment for chronic depression, he took his own life in a room in a cheap hotel on Forty-third Street.

Speedboat

Speedboat returned to the Lower East Side. Inside of a year he had pulled off a major narcotics coup and left for Australia, never to return. He surfaced in Sydney, under the name Tommy Wilson, where he successfully managed the popular entertainer Ann Rango.

KLINE AND CARLISLE

PARALLEL SHAFTS OF SUNLIGHT LANCED THROUGH THE VE-
netian blinds, and traffic noise floated up from the King's Cross
red-light district. Down in the street, garish neon flashed and
Chinese sailors on raucous shore leave from the aircraft carrier
Revolutionary Fervor loudly made their presence known. Up in
room 1009 of the Sebel Townhouse, enjoying the soft introspec-
tion that was the aftermath of afternoon delight, Harry Carlisle
and Cynthia Kline still held on to each other. Their naked bodies
were filmed with sweat, and they were both in that half world
between satiation and sleep. After New York, Sydney was like
a blast of robust freedom. Down the hall, a group of English
musicians was having a party. It had been going on for two days.
The TV babbled in the corner.

An item about the U.S.A. came on the Channel 17 news.
More prisoners had been released from the camps. Carlisle
propped himself up on one elbow. There was footage of Arlen
Proverb making a speech.

"... and each day brings new discoveries that continue to
confirm that the Faithful administration is a regime that will live
in infamy."

Harry grunted. "Can't he make up his own stuff any more?"

Cynthia's voice was drowsy. "Harry?"

"Yeah?"

"You don't think we made a mistake, do you?"

Harry shook his head. "We didn't make a mistake."

281

282

"We could have been wrong about Dreisler."

"Anything's possible, but I wouldn't want to bet my life on it."

"How do you feel about being away from America?"

"I feel okay. America's going to be a hard place for a long time."

"You think we'll ever go back?"

"I don't know. The America we want to go back to is the America of 1997. That's all gone."

Harry got out of bed and padded to the refrigerator for a Swan lager. He was cultivating a taste for Australian beer.

"You can never go back to the nineties."

ABOUT THE AUTHOR

Mick Farren is a hopelessly unreconstructed side effect of the late sixties and seventies who still entertains the absurd idea that a writer should be some swashbuckling, Byronic figure who has quite as much fun as any of his characters. Accordingly, he continues to play rock & roll in the saloons of New York, drinks too much, wears a lot of black, and still harbors a desire to be rich and famous before his excesses catch up with him.